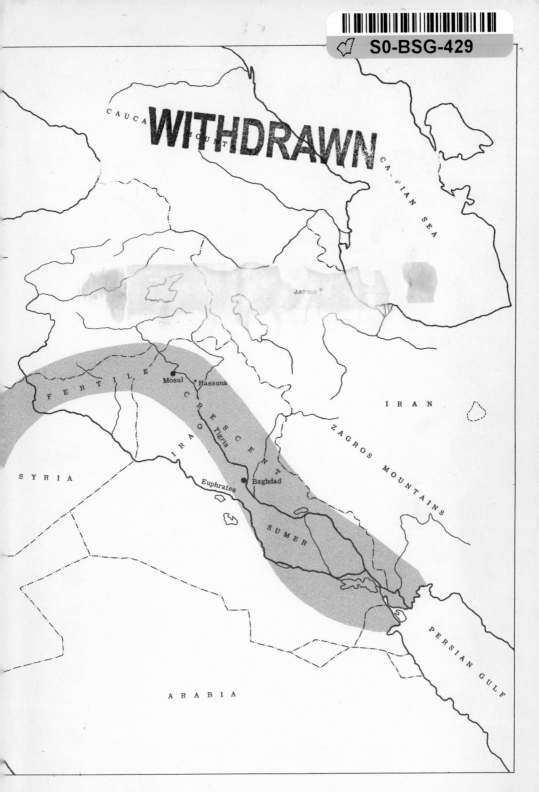

ONE IN THE NEOLITHIC AGE

F THE EARLIEST KNOWN NEOLITHIC CULTURES.

# THE SCIENCE OF MAN

# THE
# SCIENCE OF MAN

## *AN INTRODUCTION*
## *TO ANTHROPOLOGY*

By MISCHA TITIEV

*University of Michigan*

HENRY HOLT AND COMPANY

NEW YORK

COPYRIGHT 1954 BY HENRY HOLT AND COMPANY, INC.
LIBRARY OF CONGRESS CATALOG CARD NUMBER: 54-6622
PRINTED IN THE UNITED STATES OF AMERICA

28468-0114

February, 1956

This book is most affectionately dedicated
to Estelle, my wife, and our son, Bob

# Preface

. . . the present volume is an introduction to Anthropology, rather than a summary of all it teaches. . . .

While the various departments of the science of Man are extremely multifarious, ranging from body to mind, from language to music, from fire-making to morals, they are all matters to whose nature and history every well-informed person ought to give some thought. It is much, however, for any single writer to venture to deal even in the most elementary way with so immense a variety of subjects. In such a task I have the right to ask that errors and imperfections should be lightly judged.

EDWARD BURNETT TYLOR

*February 1881*

It is sometimes whispered in academic circles that a teacher writes a textbook more to impress his colleagues than to instruct his pupils. Exactly the reverse is true in this instance. The major purpose of this book is to introduce to the science of man, or anthropology, those college students and other interested readers who have had no previous experience with the subject. While trying to reach his goal, the author sought to write simply yet effectively, to integrate related facets of the topic wherever possible, and to explain and interpret his material at every step of the way.

This textbook, then, is not designed to be a more or less comprehensive encyclopedia of anthropological facts and speculations, nor will the reader be left to puzzle out for himself such inferences as may logically be drawn from the data. On the contrary, every effort will be made to derive meanings from the facts, meanings which, it is hoped, will help students to understand what anthropology is all about and also to recognize more fully the significance of many things that they say and do in their daily lives.

Anthropology entered on its modern phase under the stimulus of Darwin's teachings of evolution. His publications aroused an undying interest in man's past, and his calm reasoning led to a detached view of man's origins and his place in the animal kingdom. Not long after Darwin's time the first practitioners of modern anthropology realized that man was a unique biological creature, endowed with a special ability to create and maintain forms of culture, an ability that is never found among other animals. Ever since then some anthropological studies have dwelt on man's biology, whereas others have stressed his culture.

Partly on the basis of man's fundamental two-sidedness, there has developed in the course of the last century a marked tendency toward fragmentation, with each subdivision of the subject tending to become an independent science. Before 1900 American anthropologists joined the American Anthropological Association or the American Folklore Society, and published their findings either in the *American Anthropologist* or the *Journal of American Folklore.* Thereafter the process of segmentation may be illustrated by some of the societies and journals that came into being to further the interests of various branches of the main topic. The American Ethnological Society, specializing in ethnology or cultural anthropology, began to issue monographs in 1906; the *International Journal of American Linguistics* first appeared in 1917; the following year saw the inauguration of the *American Journal of Physical Anthropology; American Antiquity,* devoted to archeology, started in 1935; and the year 1941 witnessed the inception of *Human Organization,* a periodical dealing with applied anthropology.

Also, at different times in the past, various schools of anthropology rose to prominence. The author does not consciously belong to any one of them, although he willingly acknowledges some indebtedness to all. This book is intended not to advance the viewpoint of any school or branch of the science of man, but is written to demonstrate that all phases of man's biological and cultural behavior form an integrated theme that legitimately makes up a single discipline. Many topics are lightly touched upon, so that teachers may have ample opportunities to elaborate whatever they wish. For the benefit of those who may want to delve more deeply into some aspects of anthropology a number of selected references have been placed at the end of each chapter.

Readers will find that the bulk of the material incorporated into this volume is drawn primarily from American, and secondarily from British, sources. This is due to the circumstance that the amount of anthropological writing in English far outweighs what has been printed in other languages, and is more readily available to students in the United States. Moreover, the very definitions of basic terms, as well as the objectives and methods of our foreign colleagues, often differ markedly from American usage, and cannot fail to confuse a newcomer to the science of man. As it is, the self-imposed limitation on source materials will not prevent a reader from being served an ample feast that should be enough to satisfy his intellectual hunger.

If Tylor felt the need of apologizing in 1881 for the magnitude of the task he was undertaking, an author in our time must feel even more overwhelmed with a sense of humility. The science of man has grown so vast and diversified since Tylor's day that no one can truthfully claim to have mastered it all. Only the compelling hopes of introducing a better sense of order than is yet available into the scattered data, and of offering some fresh viewpoints and original interpretations, have led the author to undertake the audacious and arduous task of writing a new text.

He who dares to get out a general book that touches on as many topics as does anthropology must be grateful to everyone who has given him help or encouragement along the way. Above all, the writer is everlastingly thankful to his teachers and to his students. Several of his fellow anthropologists have made important suggestions, so many that it is impossible to acknowledge them all. Parts of the manuscript, pertaining to their specialties, have been critically read by my colleagues, Professors James B. Griffin, Emerson F. Greenman, and Frederick P. Thieme. To each of these many thanks are due. I am especially indebted to Professors Fred Eggan and Charles Wagley, who read the entire typescript and made a host of incisive comments. Dr. Frederick J. Dockstader and Mr. Kuei-Sheng Chang prepared original sketches and diagrams that will be found in the text.

While this book was being printed, the author had to leave for Australia in order to take up a Fulbright appointment. My colleague,

Professor Joseph K. Yamagiwa, Chairman of the Department of Far Eastern Languages and Literatures, graciously volunteered to read the page proofs and to attend to other last-minute details. I deeply appreciate his courtesy and am thankful for his friendly willingness to assume a burden which should rightly have been shouldered by me. I am also greatly indebted to Frederick P. Thieme, Albert C. Spaulding, and Elman R. Service, each of whom offered to assist Professor Yamagiwa in his own area of specialization.

It is a pleasure, also, to acknowledge the assistance of my patient wife, and to give thanks to our son, who forewent the attention of his father during the many months that this volume was being prepared.

M.T.

*Ann Arbor, Michigan*
*February 15, 1954*

# Contents

## PART TWO: THE MARCH OF CULTURE

## PART THREE: BIOCULTURAL BEHAVIOR

# Acknowledgments

For permission to reproduce illustrations, thanks are due to the individuals and agencies listed below:

Fig. 1A. Herbert Basedow, *The Australian Aboriginal,* Adelaide, F. W. Preece, 1925.

Fig. 1B. Eck Stanger, *The Ann Arbor News.*

Fig. 4. Frances B. Mason, *Creation by Evolution,* New York, The Macmillan Co., 1928.

Fig. 7. H. V. Neal and H. W. Rand, *Comparative Anatomy,* Philadelphia, The Blakiston Co., 1936.

Fig. 8 *upper.* Buffalo Museum of Science.

Fig. 8 *lower.* American Museum of Natural History.

Fig. 9. A. S. Romer, *Man and the Vertebrates,* 2d ed., Chicago, University of Chicago Press, 1937.

Fig. 10. Chicago Natural History Museum.

Fig. 11B. Zoological Society of Philadelphia.

Fig. 12. Zoological Society of Philadelphia.

Fig. 13. Earnest A. Hooton, *Up from the Ape,* rev. ed., New York, The Macmillan Co., 1946.

Fig. 14. Eck Stanger, *The Ann Arbor News.*

Fig. 15A. J. S. Rogers, T. Hubbell, and C. F. Byers, *Man and the Biological World,* 2d ed., New York, McGraw-Hill Book Co., 1952.

Fig. 15B, C, D. Eck Stanger, *The Ann Arbor News.*

Fig. 16. New York Zoological Society.

Fig. 18. New York Zoological Society.

Fig. 19. McGraw-Hill Publishing Co.

Fig. 20. Adolph H. Schultz, "Man as a Primate," *The Scientific Monthly* (1931).

Fig. 21. New York Zoological Society.

Fig. 23. New York Zoological Society.

Fig. 24. After W. K. Gregory.

Fig. 25A. New York Zoological Society.

Fig. 25B. Zoological Society of Philadelphia.

Fig. 26. Zoological Society of Philadelphia.

Fig. 27A. New York Zoological Society.

Fig. 27B. Peabody Museum, Harvard University.

Fig. 28A. New York Zoological Society.

Fig. 28B. Newton W. Hartman, Courtesy of the Zoological Society of Philadelphia.

Fig. 29. M. F. Ashley Montagu, *Introduction to Physical Anthropology,* 2d ed., Springfield, Ill., Charles E. Thomas, 1951.

Fig. 30. Wm. L. Straus, Jr., "The Riddle of Man's Ancestry," *The Quarterly Review of Biology* (Vol. 24, 1949).

Fig. 31. L. Clendening, *The Human Body,* New York, Alfred A. Knopf, 1927, 1930, 1937, 1945.

Fig. 32. Dudley J. Morton, *The Human Foot,* New York, Columbia University, 1935.

Fig. 33. E. P. Stibbe, *Introduction to Physical Anthropology,* London, Edward Arnold, 1930.

Fig. 34. W. W. Howells, *Mankind So Far,* New York, Doubleday & Co., 1944.

Fig. 35. W. W. Howells, *Mankind So Far,* New York, Doubleday & Co., 1944.

Fig. 36. Earnest A. Hooton, *Up from the Ape,* rev. ed., New York, The Macmillan Co., 1946.

Fig. 37. Earnest A. Hooton, *Up from the Ape,* rev. ed., New York, The Macmillan Co., 1946; A. Keith, *Antiquity of Man,* 2d ed., Philadelphia, J. B. Lippincott, 1928.

Fig. 38. F. Weidenreich, *Apes, Giants, and Man,* Chicago, University of Chicago Press, 1946.

Fig. 40. M. F. Ashley Montagu, *Introduction to Physical Anthropology,* 2d ed., Springfield, Ill., Charles E. Thomas, 1951.

Fig. 41. W. W. Howells, *Mankind So Far,* New York, Doubleday & Co., 1944.

Fig. 42. M. F. Ashley Montagu, *Introduction to Physical Anthropology,* 2d ed., Springfield, Ill., Charles E. Thomas, 1951.

Fig. 43. Earnest A. Hooton, *Up from the Ape*, rev. ed., New York, The Macmillan Co., 1946.

Fig. 44. George Grant MacCurdy, *Human Origins*, New York, D. Appleton, 1926.

Fig. 45. F. C. Howell, "The Place of Neanderthal Man in Human Evolution," *American Journal of Physical Anthropology* (Vol. 9, 1951).

Fig. 46. M. F. Ashley Montagu, *Introduction to Physical Anthropology*, 2d ed., Springfield, Ill., Charles E. Thomas, 1951.

Fig. 47. M. F. Ashley Montagu, *Introduction to Physical Anthropology*, 2d ed., Springfield, Ill., Charles E. Thomas, 1951.

Fig. 48. F. Boas, ed., *General Anthropology*, Boston, D. C. Heath and Co., 1938.

Fig. 49. Earnest A. Hooton, *Up from the Ape*, rev. ed., New York, The Macmillan Co., 1946.

Fig. 50. Earnest A. Hooton, *Up from the Ape*, rev. ed., New York, The Macmillan Co., 1946.

Fig. 51A. Peabody Museum, Harvard University.

Fig. 51B, C, D. Chicago Natural History Museum.

Fig. 51E. Carleton S. Coon.

Fig. 52A, C, D, E. Chicago Natural History Museum.

Fig. 53A. C. S. Coon, S. M. Garn, and J. B. Birdsell, *Races*, Springfield, Ill., Charles E. Thomas, 1950.

Fig. 53B. American Museum of Natural History.

Fig. 53C. Peabody Museum, Harvard University.

Fig. 53D, E. Chicago Natural History Museum.

Fig. 54. S. L. Washburn, "The New Physical Anthropology," *Transactions* of the New York Academy of Sciences (May 1951).

Fig. 55. W. H. Sheldon, S. S. Stevens, and W. B. Tucker, *The Varieties of Human Physique*, New York, Harper & Bros., 1940.

Fig. 57. Acme Special Services.

Fig. 58A. Kathleen M. Kenyon, *Beginning in Archaeology*, London, Phoenix House, 1952; Society of Antiquaries, London.

Fig. 59. Chicago Natural History Museum.

Fig. 60A, B. W. Köhler, *The Mentality of Apes*, 2d ed., New York, Harcourt, Brace, 1925.

Fig. 60C. H. W. Nissen and J. B. Wolfe, "Effectiveness of token rewards for Chimpanzees," *Comp. Psych. Monogr.* (Vol. 12, 1936).

Fig. 61. W. N. and L. A. Kellogg, *The Ape and the Child*, New York, McGraw-Hill Book Co., 1933.

Fig. 62. Charles P. Mountford.

Fig. 63A, B, C. F. Boas, ed., *General Anthropology*, Boston, D. C. Heath and Co., 1938.

Fig. 64. Kenneth P. Oakley, *Man, the Tool-Maker*, London, British Museum of Natural History.

Fig. 65A, B. George G. MacCurdy, *Human Origins*, New York, D. Appleton, 1926.

Fig. 65C. Kenneth P. Oakley, *Man, the Tool-Maker*, London, British Museum of Natural History.

Fig. 66. George G. MacCurdy, *Human Origins*, New York, D. Appleton, 1926.

Fig. 67. George G. MacCurdy, *Human Origins*, New York, D. Appleton, 1926.

Fig. 68A, B. Kenneth P. Oakley, *Man, the Tool-Maker*, London, British Museum of Natural History.

Fig. 68C. George G. MacCurdy, *Human Origins*, New York, D. Appleton, 1926.

Fig. 69. Chicago Natural History Museum.

Fig. 70. George G. MacCurdy, *Human Origins*, New York, D. Appleton, 1926.

Fig. 71. Chicago Natural History Museum.

Fig. 72A. Fernand Windels, *Lascaux Cave Paintings*, New York, Viking Press, 1950.

Fig. 72B, C. American Museum of Natural History.

Fig. 73. George G. MacCurdy, *Human Origins*, New York, D. Appleton, 1926.

Fig. 74A, B, C. George G. MacCurdy, *Human Origins*, New York, D. Appleton, 1926.

Fig. 74D. Robert J. Braidwood, *Prehistoric Man*, Chicago, Chicago Natural History Museum.

Fig. 75. American Museum of Natural History.

Fig. 76. George G. MacCurdy, *Human Origins*, New York, D. Appleton, 1926.

Fig. 77. J. G. D. Clark, *The Mesolithic Settlement of Northern Europe,* Cambridge, Cambridge University Press, 1936.

Fig. 78. The Danish National Museum.

Fig. 79A, B, C. F. Boas, ed., *General Anthropology*, Boston, D. C. Heath and Co., 1938.

Fig. 79D. Spencer and Gillen, *The Arunta*, London, Macmillan & Co., 1927.

Fig. 80. Chicago Natural History Museum.

Fig. 81A. V. G. Childe, *The Dawn of European Civilization*, London, Routledge and Kegan Paul, 1936.

Fig. 81B, C. *Handbook of South American Indians,* Vol. III, Washington, Bureau of American Ethnology, 1948.

Fig. 82. George G. MacCurdy, *Human Origins,* New York, D. Appleton, 1926.

Fig. 83. American Museum of Natural History.

Fig. 84. H. R. H. Hall, *The Civilization of Greece in the Bronze Age,* London, Methuen & Co., 1928.

Fig. 85. George G. MacCurdy, *Human Origins,* New York, D. Appleton, 1926.

Fig. 86. George G. MacCurdy, *Human Origins,* New York, D. Appleton, 1926.

Fig. 87. The British Museum.

Fig. 88. Edward Chiera, *They Wrote on Clay,* Chicago, University of Chicago Press, 1938.

Fig. 89. John Marshall and the Government of India by permission of A. Probsthain.

Fig. 90. George G. MacCurdy, *Human Origins,* New York, D. Appleton, 1926.

Fig. 91. George G. MacCurdy, *Human Origins,* New York, D. Appleton, 1926.

Fig. 92. The British Museum.

Fig. 93. H. M. Wormington, *Ancient Men in North America,* 3d ed., Denver, Denver Museum of Natural History, 1949.

Fig. 94. Chicago Natural History Museum.

Fig. 95. Chicago Natural History Museum.

Fig. 96A. F. M. Brown, *America's Yesterday*, Philadelphia, J. B. Lippincott Co., 1937.

Fig. 96B. Chicago Natural History Museum.

Fig. 97A, B. Chicago Natural History Museum.

Fig. 97C. J. O. Brew in *American Antiquity* (Vol. 3, 1937).

Fig. 99. B. T. A. Joyce, *Mexican Archaeology*, London, P. L. Warner, 1920.

Fig. 100. Chicago Natural History Museum.

Fig. 101. Chicago Natural History Museum.

Fig. 107. American Museum of Natural History.

Fig. 109A. Gontran de Poncins, *Kabloona*, New York, Reynal & Hitchcock, 1941.

Fig. 109B. *Handbook of South American Indians,* Vol. I, Washington, Bureau of American Ethnology, 1946.

Fig. 111. Paul Fejos; *Handbook of South American Indians,* Vol. III, Washington, Bureau of American Ethnology, 1948.

Fig. 112A. Chicago Natural History Museum.

Fig. 112D. American Museum of Natural History.

Fig. 115. F. Eggan, *Social Organization of the Western Pueblos,* Chicago, University of Chicago Press, 1950.

Fig. 118. Chicago Natural History Museum.

Fig. 119. W. H. R. Rivers, *The History of Melanesian Society,* Cambridge, Cambridge University Press, 1914.

Fig. 120. Chicago Natural History Museum.

Fig. 121A. *Handbook of South American Indians,* Vol. I, Washington, Bureau of American Ethnology, 1946.

Fig. 122A. Paul Fejos; *Handbook of South American Indians,* Vol. III, Washington, Bureau of American Ethnology, 1948.

Fig. 122C. *Twenty-seventh Annual Report,* 1905–1906, Washington, Bureau of American Ethnology, 1911.

Fig. 122D. International News Photos.

Fig. 126. D. Clifford Bond.

Fig. 129. U. S. Department of Labor: Bureau of Labor Statistics.

# THE SCIENCE OF MAN

# CHAPTER 1

# Introduction

Like Proteus, whose ability to assume a great variety of shapes made him difficult to seize and overcome, anthropology also appears in many forms and is hard to grasp and conquer. Yet, just as Proteus is regarded as a single personage, so is anthropology looked upon as a single subject of study.

It is not hard to understand the seeming diversity but underlying unity of anthropology. When, about one hundred years ago, the science of man entered on its modern phase, there was no blueprint available in advance to channel the arrangement of material into a coherent structure. Nor, we must remember, could the very earliest workers have had the advantage of studying and training under experienced teachers. The pioneers of modern anthropology had, perforce, to be amateur students of man recruited from the ranks of scholars who had already become skilled in one or another of the older established disciplines.

Thus Adolph Bastian, who became Berlin's Curator of Ethnography in 1868, and who founded the world-famous Museum für Völkerkunde in 1886, was a doctor of medicine. Trained as lawyers were Johann J. Bachofen, author of the still-debated *Das Mutterrecht* in 1861; Henry J. S. Maine, whose *Ancient Law* came out in 1861 and may be said to have inaugurated the study of comparative jurisprudence; John F. McLennan, who published his first essay on *Primitive Marriage* in 1865; and the famed Lewis H. Morgan (1818-1881), whose writings provided a great many significant contributions to our subject. The renowned Edward B. Tylor (1832 to 1912), another of anthropology's first giants, was a privately educated busi-

1

nessman who never took a university degree; while Pierre P. Broca, one of the founders of physical anthropology, who established in Paris in 1889 the first European anthropological society, was a brilliant neurosurgeon.

As to systematic anthropology in the United States, it was not until 1885 that it was introduced at Harvard; and not before 1892 was the first Ph.D. awarded at Clark University, under the direction of the late Dr. Franz Boas, himself trained as a physicist.[1]

So the pioneers of anthropology traveled along many paths, for they had no one to tell them where to go nor what to do when they got there. Some inquired into the origins and evolution of man's physical or bodily characteristics; many sought to describe and classify the living varieties of mankind; others were busy searching out and analyzing relics of human workmanship from the ancient past; and still others traveled far afield to report and interpret the customs of their primitive contemporaries. Most often the early students of man followed their special interests without recognizing or understanding the relationship of their findings to the material being made available by co-workers laboring in different branches of the same subject.

Nevertheless, whether or not they realized it, the work of the first modern anthropologists had a great deal in common. In viewpoint they practically all agreed to define man as a member of *Homo sapiens,* regardless of when or where he happened to live; in method they early came to realize that a true science of man could be achieved only if their findings were carefully and objectively made, and dispassionately analyzed; and with regard to basic aims they were convinced that man and all of his past and present activities were legitimate objects of scientific study. Within this framework each investigator was motivated to discover new and significant facts about some aspect of man's body or behavior.

Even in the present generation, when increasing numbers of young men and women are being trained from the outset to become professional anthropologists, it remains true that various workers concentrate on different specialties. Such diversity results neither from whim nor blind adherence to precedents set down in the days of

---

[1] E. W. Voegelin, "Anthropology in American Universities," *American Anthropologist,* Vol. 52, 1950, p. 350. The recipient of the first doctorate in anthropology ever granted in the United States was A. F. Chamberlin.

anthropology's uncharted period. Today the variety of divisions in
the science of man stems from a sophisticated awareness of the complexity of the subject as well as from a grasp of some cardinal principles of human structure and behavior. In some respects man is
clearly an animal whose physical body closely resembles that of many
other creatures. In other respects, as in his development of clothing,
tools, houses, language, religion, and esthetics, man is unique in
having the ability to practice a kind of extra-biological behavior that
anthropologists call cultural. On the basis of this essential distinction,
at least three broad lines of investigation are currently followed. All
who specialize in problems of the evolution, shape, structure, appearance, functioning, and variations of the human body are grouped
under the heading of **physical anthropologists,** and frequently work
as natural scientists hand in hand with doctors, dentists, primatologists, and general biologists. Anthropologists who are chiefly
concerned with culture, including the entire range of man's non-
biological, nongenetically inherited behavior, are commonly classed
as social scientists and are divided into two groups. Those who concentrate on the study of man's handiwork in times past are known as
**archeologists,** whereas they who are primarily interested in contemporary manifestations of human activity are called **ethnographers**
or **ethnologists.**

Suppose we look a bit further into the main subdivisions of cultural anthropology. By a sort of convention that has grown up
gradually, archeologists are expected to deal with human affairs in
any area of the world prior to the emergence of written documents.
As a class they start with the first recognizable remains of human
workmanship (artifacts), and carry the story of culture forward to the
development of writing, a point at which humanists, historians, and
other social scientists generally take over. In this sense archeologists
may properly be called students of pre-history. At the same time it
must be realized that archeologists usually probe so far into the past
that there are no living representatives of the cultures under investigation. It is also proper, therefore, to refer to archeologists as students
of extinct cultures.

In short, archeology provides us with much valuable information
about the origins of man's culture and the subsequent developments
that have occurred up to the threshold of recorded history. But what
of the far-flung societies which are not extinct and whose members

have never achieved the art of writing? For a long time European and American scholars labeled such nonliterate groups as primitive, and allowed them to be grossly neglected. Within the last century or so, however, there emerged among anthropologists a number of students who were eager to probe into many parts of the globe in order to discover how primitive societies were organized and how they functioned. Generally speaking, those whose chief objectives were to provide full and accurate descriptions of particular cultures came to be known as "ethnographers," in distinction to the ones whose main concerns were with laws and theories of culture in general, who were called "ethnologists." Such a division of interests has practically disappeared and to all intents and purposes modern ethnographers and ethnologists are one and the same.[2] Exponents of all branches of cultural anthropology are still set apart, though, from physical anthropologists. Nevertheless, the common concern of all anthropologists with the science of man, and the growing realization that much of human biology is closely intertwined with culture, serve to unite archeologists, ethnographers, ethnologists, and physical anthropologists as fellow-workers in one vast field.

We are now in a position to look a little more deeply into the interplay of man's biology with his culture. A great many scientists have become increasingly aware of the basic fact that practically every voluntary action [3] performed by a human being anywhere is the product of two sets of forces operating simultaneously. This is equally true whether it concerns a native Australian woman digging with a stick for witchetty grubs or a concert pianist in New York's Carnegie Hall playing a Beethoven concerto (Fig. 1). Without such necessary biological equipment as flexible fingers and wrists neither the Australian aborigine nor the concert pianist could perform his task. But without proper cultural conditioning the mere possession of adequate biological equipment is not enough to bring about the desired results. Unless she had been suitably instructed the Austral-

[2] Those whose studies emphasize the people that compose a society are sometimes known as *Social Anthropologists;* while the ones who stress the ways in which people live together are customarily called *Cultural Anthropologists.* Since no human society can exist without a way of living together (culture), the distinction between Social and Cultural Anthropologists is not easy to maintain. In this textbook they will be grouped together with *Ethnologists.*

[3] Voluntary action refers to any aspect of human behavior that requires a measure of conscious control. Involuntary actions, like breathing or the beating of the heart, may be carried on without any conscious control.

Fig. 1. Biological similarity and cultural diversity. With practically the same anatomical equipment a young Australian woman wields a digging stick (A.), and a concert pianist plays the piano (B.).

A

B

ian woman could not possibly play a Beethoven concerto, nor, for that matter would a highly skilled pianist necessarily know how to dig witchetty grubs. Yet, each has the biological prerequisites for carrying out the other's assignment.[4]

This brief discussion should suffice to make it clear that we are dealing with two separable factors, although the fact that they merge to produce a single activity frequently obscures their distinctiveness. If, however, we wish to make a scientific analysis of human behavior we must train ourselves to separate the two sets of forces, because they are fundamentally different in many respects. To begin with, as far as present knowledge goes, the biological aspect is by far the older. Scientists can trace the origin and subsequent development of human biology over a stretch of about 1,500,000,000 years; but there is no satisfactory evidence of man's cultural activities until about 500,000 years ago.

Then, again, every person inherits his biological features from his parents in only one way, through the process of sexual reproduction. This implies that at the moment of conception the human child-to-be has absolutely no choice, and that at no later stage in his life —except in rare and trivial matters—will he be able to modify his biological inheritance. The case is entirely different in respect to cultural inheritance. No one can possibly begin to acquire culture until he enters postnatal life, which means that culture can only be implanted on a pre-existing human body. Furthermore, the reception of culture does not take place at a single moment of time, nor must it be gotten only from one's parents. An individual may begin to acquire culture at an early or late age; it can be received from parents, other relatives, teachers, religious officers, playmates, and many others; and, at least in theory, a person always has the option of carrying out, modifying, giving up, or completely changing any aspect of culture that he may choose. It is certainly true that in practice people are slow to make drastic cultural changes voluntarily, yet it cannot be denied that one can change his language or religion far more readily than the color of his eyes or the length of his head.

Finally, as we shall see later on, the essential aspects of biology are much alike for all mankind, whereas the cultural manifestations of

---

[4] The question of motivation is also pertinent. Within their own cultures neither the Australian woman nor the concert artist would have any incentive for doing the other person's job. The pianist would not want witchetty grubs and a native of aboriginal Australia would have no use for a check.

different human societies are remarkable for their great diversity. Thus, all members of *Homo sapiens* have virtually identical biological mechanisms for keeping warm, but the range of houses, heating devices, and clothing that provide cultural ways of staying warm is incredibly varied. All of this leads to the inevitable conclusion that because of its greater antiquity, fixity, and universality, human biology is prior to culture. Whether one is dealing with individuals or groups it is always up to biology to provide a foundation on which culture may rest (Fig. 2).

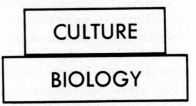

Fig. 2. Culture and biology. Although they operate according to different principles, human culture always rests on a foundation of biology.

As has already been said, man alone is capable of developing and maintaining culture, and in all times and places human societies have devised forms of culture that exert powerful modifying influences on the inherited, biological behavior of their members. So it has come about that men and women live simultaneously in two kinds of worlds, each of which has its own rules and makes its own demands. Under such conditions it is no easy matter to live like a human being, and we are led to seek the reason for man's universal willingness to pay the price of meeting the requirements of two distinct sets of forces. "Why," it may well be asked, "does not man live only biologically, as do all other animals?" We can get a clue to the answer if we contrast man's ability to cope with certain crises to that of creatures that do live exclusively by biological rules. In this way we shall soon discover that there are great rewards to be won by being human.

Perhaps the most fundamental of all animal activities, including man's, are those concerned with keeping individuals alive and giving them opportunities for reproducing their kind. To accomplish these objectives successfully, all living things must strike an adequate balance with their external environment, from which they derive at least oxygen and food. But suppose the balance is drastically upset, let us say, by an exceedingly long and severe drop of temperature. Forced to deal with such a shift, a previously well-adjusted nonhuman animal species has only one chance for survival, unless it can escape to a warmer region, i.e., by making a biological change such as growing a heavy coat of fur. If an adjustment of this sort is successfully made, it will be transmitted by sexual reproduction, so that each newborn individual of the species will automatically acquire the makings of a good fur coat as part of its biological inheritance.

If he were faced with an identical change of environment man would have two ways of responding, in addition to the possibility of escape. He might alter his biology, or he might modify his culture to include the making and wearing of heavy clothing. In the last few millenia man has almost without fail responded to different environmental conditions by changing his culture rather than his biology. It is true that this kind of adjustment has the disadvantage of forcing each human individual somehow to acquire a coat; but it also gives man the inestimable advantage of being able to take off his coat if warm weather happens to return. In the event of a reversion to warm conditions, the animal species that had biologically acquired a fur coat would stand in grave danger of becoming extinct because it could not shed its coat. It is the great flexibility of cultural mechanisms that has made it possible for mankind as a single biological species to live under the most varied environmental conditions to be found throughout the world, and to outlive many species which once seemed to be better off. To be realistic, though, we must squarely face the realization that the power of culture is like a two-edged sword. It can help to preserve man as a biological species but, in these days of hydrogen bombs, it can also serve to exterminate him.

In the normal course of our daily lives we are seldom aware of the basic distinction between human biology and culture, but every now and then, perhaps without conscious analysis, we do find ourselves distinguishing between them. Let us imagine that early on each working morning we hear someone singing, and that on one occasion we make a special effort to see and hear what is going on. If it turns out that the singer is a Negro man on his way to work, and that his song is the familiar spiritual, "Swing low, sweet chariot," we can quickly make an analysis in terms of the foregoing discussion. We know at a glance that the individual is physically a Negro because of the color of his skin, the form of his hair, the breadth of his nose, and the thickness of his lips. These features, we may be sure, could have been acquired only through biological inheritance, without reference to the man's will, and with practically no likelihood of change during his lifetime. On the other hand, we may be equally certain that the singer could not have learned the words and tune of his song until some time after he had been born, and that it is within his control to sing some other song or to refrain from singing altogether. Here, then, is a familiar and everyday illustration that shows how, at least in broad terms, one can readily distinguish between the fixity of what is biologically inherited, and the relative flexibility of cultural practices.

There is a practical side to the need for distinguishing between biology and culture. All Americans are conscious of certain difficulties that are collectively known as "race problems." If, on analysis, they turn out to be biological in nature, they will have to be corrected with biological techniques. If they prove to be cultural their solution will have to be attempted by cultural methods. Enough is already known to indicate that race problems are cultural and cannot be remedied by a biological approach.

The case of the Negro who habitually sings, "Swing low, sweet chariot," on his way to work, also affords us the opportunity to consider a third aspect of human behavior based on the interaction of biology and culture to produce a single activity. In order to sing at all a man must have an adequate anatomical (biological) mechanism with which to make vocal music. Without lungs, larynx, pharynx, mouth, tongue, teeth, and lips it is unlikely that either a tune or words could be produced. Yet, even the possessor of the best song-producing mechanism in the world could not sing the notes and lyrics of the particular spiritual, "Swing low, sweet chariot," unless through cultural training he had learned the appropriate text and melody. To sing any particular song one must learn to use his inherited biological equipment in a special way dictated by his culture. This modification of biology in conformity with the demands of culture, which runs almost the entire range of voluntary human activity, is what I propose to call "biocultural behavior."

The central thesis presented in this introduction explains the arrangement of the material to be included in the book. We shall devote the first part to the biological considerations that apply to man. The second part will deal with the origin and development of human culture in times past, and the third will treat of biocultural behavior as it may be observed wherever groups of human beings live together in societies. Taken jointly the three parts will make up our introduction to anthropology, and our contribution to a better understanding of the complex science of man.

SELECTED REFERENCES

Boas, F., *et al., General Anthropology,* Boston, 1938, Introduction.
Daniel, G. E., *A Hundred Years of Archaeology,* London, 1950.
Haddon, A. C., *History of Anthropology,* rev. ed., London, 1934.
Lowie, R. H., *The History of Ethnological Theory,* New York, 1937.
Mitra, P., *A History of American Anthropology,* Calcutta, 1933.
Montagu, M. F. Ashley, *An Introduction to Physical Anthropology,* rev. ed., Springfield, 1951, Introduction.
Penniman, T. K., *A Hundred Years of Anthropology,* New York, 1935.
Voegelin, E. W., "Anthropology in American Universities," *American Anthropologist,* Vol. 52, No. 3, 1950.

# PART ONE

# Man in the World of Biology

# CHAPTER 2

# The Earth and the First Forms of Life

## A. THE LIFELESS EARTH

To understand the physical composition of man we must go back to the very origin of the earth, for the human body is made up of chemical elements derived from the earth. There are still many unsolved problems pertaining to our globe's formation, but astronomers, geologists, physicists, and biochemists have pooled their knowledge to provide us with a plausible starting point. All clues lead back to the sun as the parent of the world we inhabit. More than two billion years ago, by one means or another, a stupendous mass of solar material became detached from the sun, and when it had cooled somewhat it became the planet that we call "Earth."[1]

For an incredibly long time, estimated at 500,000,000 years, the chemicals of which the earth was formed remained lifeless. But this is not to say that they were quiet or motionless. On the contrary, whenever temperatures fluctuated, moisture came and went, winds blew or waters flowed, and altitudes differed as hills and mountains were uplifted, numerous chemical elements underwent many changes. Subjected to the shifting pressures of various physical forces, a great number of chemicals changed shape or internal structure and some new combinations came into being. Of these, the most

[1] According to H. F. Blum, *Time's Arrow and Evolution*, Princeton, 1951, pp. 8-12, the most recent estimates put the age of the earth at three billion years. Modern studies are assigning ever greater ages to the phases of earth history, but a reasonably conservative series of dates will be used in this book.

important for our purposes was **protein,** a complex material consisting mainly of carbon, hydrogen, oxygen, and nitrogen, together with small amounts of other elements.

With the formation of protein the stage was set for the emergence of living matter, but up to this point, it must be emphasized, the highest level of structure was physical or chemical and all responses were dictated exclusively by physico-chemical laws. That is to say, the basic chemical elements on earth made changes and adjustments only when influenced by factors like heat, light, humidity, atmospheric and other pressures, gravity, radioactivity, natural electricity, and wind or water action.

At the level of physico-chemical behavior there is no emotion, no volition, and no sharp distinction between life and death. Whatever may be thought to correspond to processes of growth and reproduction must be understood to represent nothing more than mechanical responses or physico-chemical interactions. These are so fixed and standardized that a scientist thoroughly familiar with the laws of chemistry and physics can predict with mathematical accuracy how a particular element will respond under given conditions. That is why scholars who deal only with this realm are able to achieve a degree of certainty and exactness which gradually diminishes as a capacity for voluntary action increases.

## B. LIFE BEGINS

About 1,500,000,000 years ago, chemicals including minute quantities of potassium, sodium, iron, copper, chlorine, bromine, and others, somehow combined with protein to form a new substance known as **protoplasm,** which is thought to be the first material on earth to show the properties of life. Protoplasm, or living matter, is the key material out of which the bodies of all plants and animals are made. It occurs as a colloid, which means that it is a sort of thick, viscous, jelly- or glue-like substance, with small quantities of chemicals carried in suspension or solution. Since its component ingredients may differ widely in content and amount, protoplasm is a highly variable substance. Nevertheless, it exhibits without fail certain characteristics that set it apart from any known combination of nonliving elements. Under one set of conditions protoplasm acts alive but under another it becomes dead, which signifies that it has reverted to the ingredients of which it is composed and is once more responsive only to physico-chemical laws. It can stay alive only so long as it is able satisfactorily to observe a new set of regulations, conveniently labeled **Biological Imperatives.** As a minimum these require that protoplasm must be able to secure nourishment and oxygen from its physical environment. For such an accomplishment it must have at least a small potential for self-initiated or voluntary movement, a potential that is entirely lacking in lifeless chemicals. One of the most important aspects of its capacity for self-initiated motion is found in its ability to move away from a stimulus that irritates or endangers it, and to move toward anything that it somehow interprets as favorable. This points to the existence of a nervous system which, in the earliest forms of life, is thought to have been diffused throughout the entire organism.

The food elements that protoplasm takes into itself from its external surroundings undergo varied fates. Most of them are "burned" to release heat and energy, some are stored as a reserve for growth or to ward off disease, and the useless residue is excreted as waste matter. These related activities, comprising the essence of metabolism, constitute a major feature of protoplasm that helps set it clearly apart from all nonliving materials.

Closely connected with the mechanisms of growth is the process of reproduction. Whenever a unit of protoplasm reaches a given size it divides into two. At this stage, the matter of reproduction is no more than an automatic response to biological imperatives, entirely devoid of the subjective and emotional connotations that human beings associate with the choice of a mate and the begetting of children.

After the emergence of protoplasm it becomes possible to speak of a higher level of organization than had existed in the lifeless world. For the new substance had to continue to observe the laws of physics and chemistry, on top of which it had to satisfy the requirements of the biological imperatives. So we find ourselves in a realm that may be appropriately (if clumsily) designated as bio-physico-chemical. Workers in this field cannot achieve the mathematical accuracy of knowledge and prediction that is possible for chemists and physicists, because even the smallest exercise of self-initiated activity cannot be mechanically anticipated. The merest fleck of protoplasm occasionally thrusts a bit of itself away from the main body as it reacts to a stimulus or seeks nourishment, and there is no way of foretelling exactly when it will act or whether its thrust will be to left or right. All living things, including human beings, are subject to the regulations of bio-physico-chemical laws. Men, it is true, have everywhere devised systems of culture that greatly modify their responses to the biological imperatives, but even man can completely disobey the biological imperatives only at the price of death.

## C. ONE-CELLED PROTOZOA INHABIT THE EARTH

From the outset protoplasm seems to have appeared, not as great sheets or formless lumps, but organized into tiny units known as cells. As far as is known at present each cell constituted a little animal called a **protozoon,** the whole group being known collectively as **Protozoa.** An enormous number of different kinds of Protozoa must have been alive 1,500,000,000 years ago, for it is estimated that approximately 15,000 species have been described up to the present time.

Not all scientists are agreed on the environmental setting in which protozoan creatures first appeared, but a clear majority favor areas of slightly salty water, not too far from a shoreline. They point out that in a shallow part of a sea or ocean a microscopic one-celled animal, most of whose body consists of water, would avoid the dangers of being either dehydrated or crushed by excessive pressure. Salt water is also in less danger of running dry than is fresh, is less subject to extremes of temperature, has a greater buoyancy, and contains all the elements needed for building and maintaining protoplasm. Oceans and seas are constantly in motion, by means of which they continually waft sources of food and oxygen to their protozoan inhabitants, and carry away whatever wastes are excreted. Those who favor the hypothesis of salt-water origin add to the facts already given the observation that body fluids, including the famous trilogy of blood, sweat, and tears, are saline. Some scholars have even gone so far as to say that man's blood plasma is identical with archaic sea water.

Wherever or however the Protozoa came into being, it is beyond dispute that all their life processes had to be carried out by the single cell of which each was comprised. All the activities of eating, digesting, breathing, moving, growing, excreting, and reproducing, had to be performed by a cell that must have been a marvellous jack-of-all-biological-trades.

When studied under a microscope each cell that makes up a protozoon can be seen to consist of several different parts, of which the most distinctive is called the "nucleus," while the rest may be

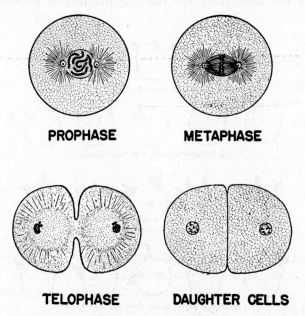

**PROPHASE**          **METAPHASE**

**TELOPHASE**          **DAUGHTER CELLS**

Fig. 3. Principal stages of cell division (after Marsland). The steps shown sum up the main stages of the reproductive process in Protozoa. Biologically, cell division is much alike in all living things.

comprised under the term "cytoplasm." Within the nucleus are tiny grains of fairly solid matter, known as **chromatin** because it can readily be colored or dyed. It is the nucleus that is most clearly concerned with reproduction. Although various Protozoa may reproduce in numerous ways, there is a general pattern of events that is consistent for almost all. The chromatin forms into a fixed number, for each species, of rodlike bodies or **chromosomes,** which cluster together exactly in the center of the surrounding cytoplasm. There the chromosomes split into two identical parts, with one full portion going to the nucleus of a daughter cell and the other remaining with the parent (Fig. 3).

Some disagreement still persists on the question of whether a chromosome is a single object or, as most experts hold, an aggregate of very tiny particles called **genes**. In either case there is universal agreement that the chromosomal stuff in the nucleus of every protozoon has always conveyed the chemical ingredients of biological inheritance from parent to child, and that the process has remained essentially the same from the time of primordial Protozoa to the present.[2]

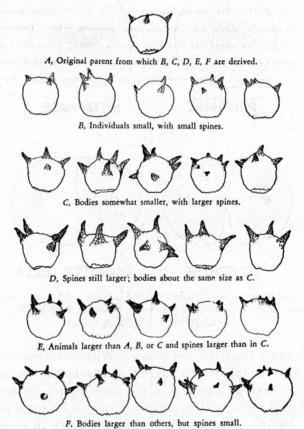

A, Original parent from which B, C, D, E, F are derived.

B, Individuals small, with small spines.

C, Bodies somewhat smaller, with larger spines.

D, Spines still larger; bodies about the same size as C.

E, Animals larger than A, B, or C and spines larger than in C.

F, Bodies larger than others, but spines small.

Fig. 4. Creation by evolution (after Mason). A single parent, in the course of a-sexual reproduction, may give rise to greatly varied offspring. When two parents join in sexual reproduction, each one's body comprising millions of cells and countless genes, the chances of creating new forms by evolutionary changes which utilize variation are infinitely greater.

[2] Those who wish further information about chromosomal or genetic transmission are advised to read R. B. Goldschmidt, *Understanding Heredity,* New York, 1952.

Somehow, in the matter of reproduction, even where only a single, one-celled parent is involved, and where offspring seem to have inherited exact duplicates of the ancestral chromosomes, descendants do not inevitably resemble their parent (Fig. 4). This factor of variability, which becomes even more noteworthy among more complex animals, provides one of the major keys to an understanding of biological evolution. By adding only one more idea to what has just been stated, the course of evolution may be shown to follow a three-branched path. Starting with a common ancestor, one branch indicates a path of extinction, which some populations of creatures inevitably took in the course of time; a second represents successive generations of descendants who never wandered far from the parental condition; and the third is the road taken by some offspring who, in later generations, came to differ so much from the original ancestor as to form a different species. (See Fig. 5.)

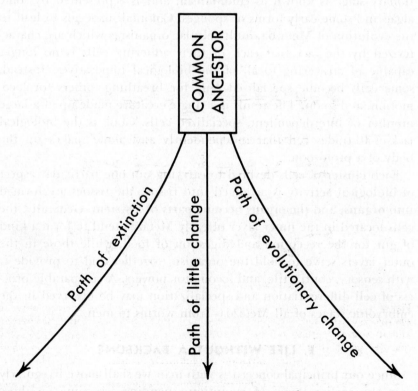

Fig. 5. The three paths of evolutionary descent.

Needless to say, although man is faced with the same biological imperatives as are the Protozoa, and although he resembles them in some details of reproduction, he is so vastly different in physical size and complexity that we must seek his immediate forebears among animals who traveled far on the path of divergence from some ancestral protozoon.

## D. MULTICELLED METAZOA APPEAR

The next major step on the road leading from Protozoa to man seems to have been taken when offspring cells adhered to their parent instead of severing all ties and going free. At first the chief difference was limited to the simple matter of cohesion, since each of the adhering cells was still capable of carrying out all the processes of life, except that independent motion became impossible because the whole mass of cells had to move or remain still together. This evolutionary stage is known as **colonialism,** and is represented by some algae and some early forms of sponges. Colonialism seems to lead to the evolution of **Metazoa,** multicellular organisms which are characterized by the fact that each of their adhering cells is no longer capable of answering to all of the biological imperatives. Instead, some cells become specialized only for breathing, others for locomotion, and so on. The result is a single creature made up of a large number of interdependent, specialized cells. Gone is the biological jack-of-all-trades cell that independently and alone makes up the body of a protozoon.

Each cluster of cells devoted to carrying out one particular aspect of biological activity is arranged into tissue; the tissues are formed into **organs;** and the organs become parts of a **system.** Generally, the cells located in the inner layer of early Metazoa tend to form a kind of gut for the reception and digestion of food, while those in the outer layers serve to hold the organism together and to provide it with sensory, contractile, and locomotor powers. A comparable process of cell differentiation and specialization may be observed in the embryonic stages of all Metazoa—from worms to men.

## E. LIFE WITHOUT A BACKBONE

Since our principal concern is with man we shall move irregularly over the earlier stages of evolution, spending less time on those organisms furthest from man's line of descent, and omitting such whole groups as plants, insects, and birds. As we come a bit closer to the ultimate emergence of human beings we are led to consider the marine Metazoa, no one of which possesses a real backbone. Together they are classed as **invertebrates,** but various groups show a tremendous diversity of forms. Worms, clamlike mollusks, sponges, jellyfish, small, lobster-shaped trilobites, squids, snails, and many others lived in the seas during the vast stretch of time that extends for over a billion years from the days of the earliest Protozoa.

Altogether the invertebrates contribute little to the later organization of man's body, except that some of them had well-developed specialized organs associated with full-fledged circulatory, respiratory, digestive, reproductive, excretory, locomotor, muscular, and nervous systems. Furthermore, there are clear indications that by a series of evolutionary steps the first vertebrates descended from invertebrate ancestors.

## F. THE EVOLUTIONARY TIMETABLE

By way of recapitulation it may be helpful to fit the record of evolution so far discussed to a more definite time sequence than has yet been offered. Information of this sort is provided by geologists specializing in the historical development of the earth, for the remains of ancient organisms are frequently found embedded in the mud and ooze of which many old rocks were formed. Geologists and their fellow scientists also furnish a chronological scale that serves as an approximate timetable of events in which students of man are keenly interested. (See Fig. 6.) The very earliest rocks known, dating back some two billion years before our era, are called **Azoic,** which means that they are literally "without life." Thereafter, the successive layers of rock are named in the order in which they are

| ERA | APPROXIMATE BEGINNING DATE | MAJOR ANIMAL GROUP |
|---|---|---|
| Azoic | 2,000,000,000 B.C. | None |
| Archeozoic | 1,500,000,000 B.C. | Protozoa |
| Proterozoic | 1,000,000,000 B.C. | Metazoan Invertebrates |
| Paleozoic | 500,000,000 B.C. | Fishes and Amphibians |
| Mesozoic | 200,000,000 B.C. | Reptiles |
| Cenozoic | 70,000,000 B.C. | Mammals |

Fig. 6. Geological record of animal evolution.

supposed to have appeared: **Archeozoic** ("ancient life"), **Proterozoic** ("former life"), **Paleozoic** ("old life"), **Mesozoic** ("middle life"), and **Cenozoic** ("recent life"). Each of these five great divisions represents an era during which animals ever closer to man's physical structure came into existence.

Protozoa appeared initially during the Archeozoic era, which is estimated to have begun 1,500,000,000 years ago and to have lasted for half a billion years. No complete remains of living organisms have been preserved in these rocks, but the indirect evidence of imprints left in what was originally soft mud, and the occurrence of minute quantities of carbon, presumably deposited by microscopic creatures, make it appear likely that Protozoa were then present. Indeed, one outstanding authority, Professor Richard S. Lull, goes so far as to call the Archeozoic era the Age of Unicellular Life.[3]

During the succeeding Proterozoic time span, which ran from about one billion to half a billion years prior to our era, considerable evolutionary progress was probably made. Only a few actual fossils, chiefly spicules of ancient sponges, have been found in Proterozoic rocks, but enough recognizable tubes and burrows have been identified to establish the existence of marine worms, and there are other indications that suggest the presence of jellyfish. Inasmuch as these are multicelled animals, the evidence strongly implies that the great advance from Protozoa to Metazoa had already been accomplished in Proterozoic times. Very likely, most of these fauna were small invertebrates, but by the next era there were such vast numbers and varieties of all kinds of spineless animals that experts believe some of them must have originated earlier. In line with such reasoning, Professor Lull refers to the latter part of the Proterozoic as the Age of Primitive Marine Invertebrates.

During the extent of the Paleozoic era that ran from about 500,000,000 to 200,000,000 years ago, the evidence of continuing evolution becomes increasingly detailed and conclusive. This is due, in part, to the circumstance that some invertebrates were secreting lime that formed hard shells or covers which resist disintegration and so provide abundant material for contemporary scholars to examine and interpret. Thanks to the great quantities of animal hard parts that have been discovered in Paleozoic rocks, it can be shown that there were then living flourishing populations of many sorts of

3 R. S. Lull, *Organic Evolution,* rev., ed., New York, 1947, p. 74.

invertebrates. By the middle of the Paleozoic, too, there is proof of the emergence of true vertebrates in the form of fishes, and with their formation a great forward stride is taken in the direction of man's body arrangement.

### SELECTED REFERENCES

Blum, H. F., *Time's Arrow and Evolution,* Princeton, 1951.

Carlson, A. J. and Johnson, V., *The Machinery of the Body,* rev. ed., Chicago, 1941.

Carter, G. S., "The Theory of Evolution and the Evolution of Man," *Anthropology Today,* A. L. Kroeber, ed., Chicago, 1953, pp. 327-342.

Goldschmidt, R. B., *Understanding Heredity,* New York and London, 1952.

Lull, R. S., *Organic Evolution,* rev. ed., New York, 1947.

Pearse, A. S., *The Emigrations of Animals from the Sea,* New York, 1950.

Raymond, P. E., *Prehistoric Life,* Cambridge, 1939.

Simpson, G. G., *The Meaning of Evolution,* New Haven, 1949.

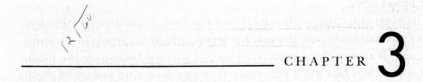

CHAPTER 3

# Variations on the Theme of Vertebrates

## A. INTRODUCING THE VERTEBRATE THEME

Far more important from the standpoint of human ancestry than any of the characteristic invertebrates were a group of aquatic forms that began to appear fairly early in the Paleozoic. These were the

**Chordates,** whose structures typically include a notochord, an elongated rod filled with a stiff jellylike substance, held together by a tough sheath of membrane, and running the length of the body. The notochord gives firmness to a body without preventing flexibility, and in adult specimens it comes to underlie a neural tube or hollow nerve center. Notochord and neural tube, it is commonly held, are two distinguishing features of all chordates, and are probably ancestral to the backbone and spinal cord of **vertebrates.** Another distinguishing trait of chordate anatomy is the occurrence of gill-slits that penetrate through the walls of the pharynx or throat cavity. They appear to have served not only as breathing mechanisms for taking oxygen from water, but also for straining particles of solid substances that were used for feeding.

Beginning with chordates and present in all succeeding lines that were to culminate in man, there is a distinctive head-end and tail-end, and forward movements led by the head-end become the rule. Still missing from chordate bodies, but of prime importance to later animals, are a true backbone, paired appendages, biting jaws, a distinct brain and bony braincase, a ventral heart, and hemoglobin in the blood cells.

Between the earliest chordates and the first of the true vertebrates it is customary to place the **ostracoderms,** a fishlike group of diminutive size, featured by a protective cover of shell or bone over the head, but sometimes lacking a real body skeleton, movable jaws, and well-developed paired fins. It used to be thought that ostracoderms were well off the main path of later evolution, but some recent scholars hold that they are the ancestors of all later Vertebrates, not excluding man.

## B. FISH SET THE VERTEBRATE THEME

Although the forms of life that were directly ancestral to **fishes** are commonly thought to have inhabited salty water, the reverse is true of the earliest bony fishes who are often supposed to have made their first appearance in fresh water streams or ponds. Only some of the later forms took up life in the sea. By mid-Paleozoic times a bewildering variety of fishes had evolved. Despite the many differences among them they possessed, as a rule, internally situated, segmented backbones, and other anatomical traits that have persisted through all later forms of vertebrates, up to man. There is more than a grain of truth in the jesting remark that man is nothing but a made-over fish.

Examination of some of the details of the general vertebrate theme should clarify the relationship of men to fish. In addition to an internal, bony, segmented, spinal column that makes possible bending movements of the trunk, virtually all vertebrates exhibit the phenomenon of bilateral symmetry, which means that each side of the body is a mirror image of the other. Thus, in man, we find right and left nostrils, eyes, ears, arms, breasts, ribs, lungs, kidneys, testes or ovaries, legs, and so forth. There is no denying our marked tendency toward bilateral symmetry, even though vital organs like the heart or liver are not duplicated on each side of the body. From the central spinal column that runs the length of each vertebrate's back and neck there extend paired ribs of cartilege or bone that give firm support to the trunk, and from which protrude two pairs of fins or limbs, one set placed near the head or neck and the other located close by the pelvis (Fig. 7).

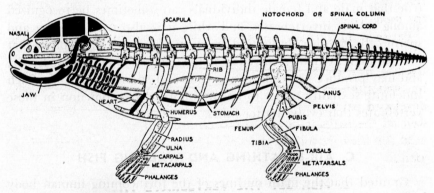

Fig. 7. A generalized vertebrate skeleton (after Neal and Rand). Many details of the typical vertebrate theme, from fish to man, are indicated.

Whereas ostracoderms are agreed to have been sluggish creatures, fishes are capable of great activity. For this they are equipped with well-developed, powerful muscles that show a high degree of nervous co-ordination. In addition, they have a number of keen senses with organs corresponding to nostrils, eyes, and ears. In fish the nostrils may be little more than a pair of pockets containing cells that are sensitive to odors, and the ears may be only a series of fluid-filled sacs or canals used for balance, but even though greatly modified these structures and their functions persist in man.

Vertebrates have bony heads that cover and protect a multi-part brain. The head is readily distinguishable from the rest of the body, contains some of its most important sense organs, and is associated with a movable mouth and jaw. So it is that the heads of vertebrates lead the way in movements that the brain directs. From this stage on all food enters at the mouth, passes into a digestive system within the main body cavity, and is excreted as waste matter at the tail end. From fish to man the excretory system is always linked to the organs of reproduction. Also present is a combined respiratory and circulatory system, by means of which oxygen is taken into the body for the use of the blood stream. A multichambered heart, through a network of enclosed vessels, pumps oxygenated blood to all parts of the organism. Fish blood is "cold" but each cell contains hemoglobin.

Lastly, there is the matter of reproduction. Among fishes the two sexes can be readily identified, and they retain feminine egg-laying or masculine sperm-producing functions permanently. While it is true that male and female individuals can sometimes be recognized among earlier invertebrates, and while it is also true that egg and sperm cells can usually be told apart, it must not be forgotten that even animals as highly evolved as oysters are indistinguishable by sex, and may produce egg cells at one time and sperm at another. Such indefinite sexuality comes to be an abnormal phenomenon in those vertebrates that evolved after fishes.

## C. AIR-BREATHING AND WALKING FISH

Granted that the main outlines of the forthcoming human body were foreshadowed in fishes, there still remain for consideration the biological distinctions that set man apart from water-dwellers. Strange as it may seem some of these factors were begun, not without a degree of success, by certain fishes.

So many varieties were in evidence during the Devonian period, about half-way through the Paleozoic era, that it is often termed the Age of Fishes. But the climate in Devonian times was not always well suited to fish life, for there were violent alternations of rainy and dry seasons. Many bodies of water probably dried out during stages of drought, leading to overcongestion of fish populations in those that remained. As a consequence the supply of available oxygen would have tended to become exhausted, a contingency that would have put the highest of biological premiums on an ability to gulp atmospheric oxygen from the air. There were two major divisions of Devonian air-breathing fishes. One, known as **dipnoi,** has a modified swim bladder that can function as a rudimentary lung. However, dipnoi use this apparatus only when there is insufficient water for gill breathing. They also have fins that are too weakly developed to be of much use on land, so that it is generally agreed that they belong on a side branch instead of on the main path that was destined to lead to human evolution.

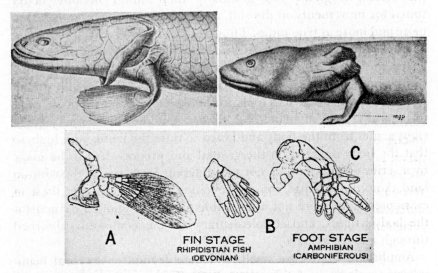

Fig. 8. Part of the evolution of land legs. (Upper series). Students should note the very close resemblance between a crossopterygian fish (left) and an early amphibian (right). (Lower series). The postulated evolution of land legs from the powerful fins of crossopterygian fishes is worthy of careful study. Particular attention should be given to the five-digit skeletal arrangement of the amphibian foot.

Closer to the direct line of man's ancestry were the lobe-finned, **crossopterygian** fishes, which combined a capacity to take atmospheric oxygen into air sacs with the possession of strong, muscular, paired fins whose firm flesh rested on a bony framework (Fig. 8). These fins were strong enough to serve as limbs whenever the animal found itself forced to progress on dry ground. Because of their distinctive features, crossopterygians were capable of living out of water for reasonably protracted lengths of time. Without question they may be considered to be ancestral to the first **tetrapods,** or four-legged, air-breathing vertebrates. So severe a change as the shift from life in water to life on land was not made in a single step, but it is believed that the crossopterygian fishes transmitted their special qualities to amphibians who, in turn, became the ancestors of the first reptiles that completely forsook water for land.

## D. AMPHIBIANS COME ASHORE

At first the **amphibians** were virtually indistinguishable from the crossopterygians, but gradually their limbs became better suited for movements on dry soil, and their air sacs came to function more and more as true lungs. Thus equipped for terrestrial existence, amphibians avoided the congestion to which fishes were being subjected and learned to sustain themselves by eating land-dwelling substances. Nevertheless, amphibians made only a partial adjustment to life on land. Their legs took on the skeletal arrangement that was to remain typical of higher vertebrates, but the limbs stuck out at right angles from the body and failed to raise the trunk very high, so that the body dragged on the ground and progress had to be made by a series of undulations not too different from trying to swim on land. Amphibian lungs, too, while somewhat advanced over those of crossopterygians were not always able to take in enough oxygen for the body's needs, and supplementary air was commonly absorbed through a moist skin.

Amphibian brains are small, and their frontal or cerebral hemispheres, as is true of fish, are principally devoted to the sense of smell. Other sense organs, though, underwent marked changes. Nostrils and eyes had to become adjusted to receiving stimuli through air rather than water, and the ear developed a membranous drum that could pick up vibrations in the form of air waves.

Above all, as may be observed from a study of modern frogs who are not, by the way, early members of the group, the amphibian life cycle remains partly dependent on a watery environment. At each spawning season the females lay a mass of small, gelatinous eggs in water; these are externally fertilized by male sperm; and the young hatch out as long-tailed, finned, limbless tadpoles, that can take oxygen from water only by means of gills. Young amphibians are really little fishes, but as they grow to maturity a metamorphosis takes place which leads to loss of the long tail, the development of limbs from fins, and a change of breathing mechanism from gills to lungs. Throughout its adult life a frog is a land dweller, but each spring the females invariably deposit fishlike eggs in water, and the tadpoles that hatch out inevitably begin their lives in a watery medium (Fig. 9).

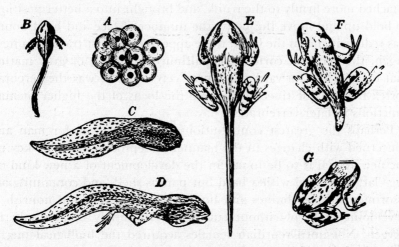

Fig. 9. An amphibian life-cycle. Each amphibian begins life in water but matures into a land dweller.

An amphibian life process can be carried out only under conditions where the females are able to find wet places for the safe deposit, fertilization, and hatching of their eggs. When severe droughts are greatly prolonged, or when amphibians wander into an arid region, a new adaptation becomes necessary whereby eggs can be laid and hatched on dry land. Such a major evolutionary change was accomplished before the close of Paleozoic times by the reptiles, who thus were the earliest tetrapods to become completely emancipated from living in water.

## E. REPTILES RULE THE EARTH

The earliest **reptiles** appeared in the closing phases of the Paleozoic era, and so nearly resembled some of the amphibians that they can be told apart only with great difficulty. As the succeeding Mesozoic era progressed reptilian forms underwent several significant changes that caused them to diverge markedly from their amphibian ancestors, and to take on characteristics that were to be retained by practically all later mammals—not excepting man. Internal organs like the heart and lungs were improved to carry out their functions more adequately; the spinal column became bonier and sturdier without losing its suppleness; the limbs were strengthened, elongated, attached more firmly to the trunk, and brought into a better position to hold up and move the body; the number of face and head bones was reduced; and in the brain there appeared the first traces of a new organ, the **cerebral cortex (neopallium),** made up of gray matter that overlies the forward portion or cerebrum. It was the cerebral cortex that was destined to become the locus of the higher mental functions in later vertebrates.

Perhaps the greatest contributions paving the way for man are concerned with changes in the manner of reproduction. The key to the new system is to be found in the development of a new kind of egg—large, covered with a hard but porous shell, and containing an assortment of membranes and liquids which protect and nourish a developing embryo without cutting off its supply of atmospheric oxygen. Not until reptilian females acquired the biological mechanism for laying this type of egg on dry land could the ties with water have been completely severed. Within the egg a membranous sac called the "amnion" encloses a fluid that surrounds the embryo and protects it from drying out or suffering mechanical injury in the event that the egg is jarred; another membrane known as the "allantois" transmits to the embryo oxygen that seeps in through the porous shell; and a supply of nourishing yolk and albumen provides enough food for growth so that a hatched-out fetus emerges fully equipped for life on land. As Professor W. W. Howells has put it, the term which larval amphibians must serve in water has been by the reptiles wrapped up in an eggshell, and while the water stage is still present in the egg reptiles, unlike amphibians, can take it with them even into deserts.[1]

If a female is to deposit a hard-shelled egg within which an embryo is to develop the egg must of necessity be fertilized before its discharge from her body. To achieve this the reptiles inaugurated copulation, the method of sexual reproduction by which the male

[1] W. W. Howells, *Mankind So Far.* New York, 1944, p. 25.

genital member must be capable of penetrating a pocket-like female organ, in order to intromit spermatozoa. No longer, as with fishes and amphibia, are tiny, gelatinous eggs laid by a female to be externally fertilized by independently discharged sperm. The basic reptilian mode of reproduction has been retained, albeit with important modifications, by man and almost all other mammals. It is scarcely necessary to call attention to the great mass of additional values and meanings that human beings have come to associate with the essential bio-physico-chemical activity of copulation.

Throughout the long, long span of about 130,000,000 years that the Mesozoic lasted the varieties and quantities of reptilian types were so great that this era is suitably named the Age of Reptiles. There is no need for an anthropologist to describe or even to summarize the diverse kinds of reptiles that flourished in the Mesozoic (Fig. 10), but as the era drew to a close an overwhelming majority

Fig. 10. Huge Mesozoic reptiles. Triceratops (left) was a monstrous dinosaur, approximately 25 feet long. It moved on all fours and ate only vegetal foods. As a contrast, Tyrannosaurus was a meat eater, which moved on its hind legs. It weighed around 10 tons and stood about 18 feet high. Many other varieties of reptiles abounded in Mesozoic times.

became extinct and those that have survived to our day shrank to a few varieties and sank into comparative insignificance. The factors that led to the rapid and dramatic extinction of countless Mesozoic reptiles, after so many millenia of dominance, are unknown to scientists, but it is postulated that changes of land forms, such as the drying out of swamps and mountain-building, coupled with lowered temperatures and an extension of winter conditions, may have played important parts.

As is well known reptiles may be provided with coverings that range from scales to plates of heavy bone, but the entire class lacks a heat-regulating mechanism and the type of hairy or furry growth that serves to retain the warmth produced by the body. All members of this class of animals are, in consequence, cold-blooded, which really means that they reflect whatever temperature prevails in their immediate surroundings. When cold weather comes they tend to freeze so literally that they become sluggish in their movements or resort to the inactivity of hibernation. Warm-blooded animals can maintain constantly high body temperatures that are much less responsive to external conditions, and so are able to remain energetic and active in all seasons. It is tempting to think that warm-blooded mammals were thus able to survive the changes of landscape and climate that carried off vast numbers of their cold-blooded contemporaries.

## F. MAMMALS TAKE OVER

Although most of the Mesozoic reptiles suffered ultimate extinction it is important to recognize that as a group they lost none of the improvements for terrestrial life that had been developed by their predecessors. Moreover, even while big hulking reptiles were the most prominent animals on earth, some of their less conspicuous relatives were already beginning to acquire **mammalian** traits. These may even have initiated the earliest known method of regulating internal body heat (warm-bloodedness), and they certainly devised a new technique for the mastication of food. Most reptiles are provided with peg-shaped teeth that are alike from front to back (homodont), continuously replaceable if lost, and utilized primarily for seizing prey and tearing food. There are no grinding teeth, so that the grinding process takes place not in the mouth but in the stomach. Unlike the more orthodox members of their class, the pro-mammalian reptiles evolved a varied assortment of teeth (heterodont) including, from the front center of the mouth to the back along each side, sharp-edged incisors for biting and shearing, pointed canines for piercing, and comparatively broad and flat pre-molars and molars for crushing and grinding. This dental arrangement is still to be found in man.

Because of the anatomical features inherited from some of their reptilian ancestors, plus many contributions of their own, the mammals that rose to prominence during the Cenozoic era beginning 70 million years ago, were well prepared to play a leading role in the animal kingdom. Thanks to their hard, bony but flexible backbones, plus ribs and shoulder and pelvic girdles, their skeletal structures were sturdy and well-knit, and their muscular systems were powerful and efficiently controlled. Their limbs were strong and properly placed to elevate their bodies above the ground, and a number of them were capable of rapid locomotion on land. The lungs, no longer feeble or rudimentary, were activated by movements of the ribs and, aided by a muscular diaphragm that separates the chest from the abdomen, they were capable of pulling in great quantities of air. A thick, four-chambered heart, through the agency of an intricate network of arteries, veins, and capillaries, systematically pumped blood to the lungs for oxygenation and out again to every part of the body. Each blood cell contained an adequate amount of hemoglobin, and the blood stream was kept at a consistently high temperature that was not readily affected by climatic conditions. This phenomenon of warm-bloodedness is maintained in mammals with the aid of a thermostatic device that is probably controlled by the thalmus region of the brain. Whenever body temperature falls dangerously below what is normal for a given species, shivering and the contraction of blood vessels attempt to provide and conserve additional heat. Conversely, sweating and dilated blood vessels make efforts to cool the body when its temperature rises too high. Much of the retention of body heat in mammals is due to insulation provided by skin covers of fur or hair. Heat and energy production are closely integrated, and it is their high metabolic rate that keeps mammals active and energetic.

Other distinguishing aspects of mammalian biological structure include, as a rule: a lower jaw that connects directly to the skull (without the intervention of a quadrate bone such as reptiles have); two occipital condyles (reptiles have only one), which are bony knobs at the base of the skull where it joins the spinal column; seven vertebral bones in the neck region of the spine, thus emphasizing the neck as a distinct portion of the body; a well-developed larynx for the production of vocal noises; an external, skin-covered ear flap designed to help catch sound waves, together with associated changes in the bony parts of the internal ear; and a marked tendency to grow assorted teeth that appear first as milk teeth meant to be shed (deciduous), and then as permanent fixtures without the capacity for self-replacement.

Smelling, seeing, tasting, and hearing abilities continue to improve as mammals become more fully evolved, and a new sensory device—a sensitive skin—sends innumerable contact impressions to the brain where judgments based on the sense of touch become highly exact and discriminating. The cerebral cortex, or neopallium, expands with an upward and backward growth of the cerebral hemispheres that it overlies, until together they make up over 80 percent of the weight of the entire brain. The human cortex alone is estimated to lodge in its intricate folds and convolutions more than nine billion cells. Coupled with its increase in size among the higher mammals is its development as an extraordinary sense combiner. Within the neopallium blended impressions sent in from various sources are formed and stored, thereby providing a basis for memory, the association of ideas, imagination, foresight, planning, judgment, and all the so-called higher mental faculties that reach their greatest peak in man.

Certainly, it is hardly to be expected that the great gap between fully evolved mammals and their reptilian forebears should have been made in one great leap. Much more probable is the likelihood that the changes occurred in a series of steps. Even if one searches only among the forms that still survive it is possible to find representatives of what are, almost without question, transitional stages. Lowest of the extant mammals, in the sense of having the least of the typical mammalian features, is the subclass called **Prototheria** (Fig. 11). At present they are found only in Australia, where they are represented by the duckbill (Platypus) and the spiny anteater (Echidna). These Prototheria have some reptilian skeletal traits and exhibit other nonmammalian characteristics in that they are toothless, and the females lay fairly large, shelled, prefertilized eggs outside their bodies. On the other hand Prototheria, like other mammals, have furry covers and warm blood, and the females have breastlike glands with which they suckle their young.

Considerably closer to full-fledged mammals is the subclass of **Metatheria,** or pouched mammals, best known from fauna living in Australia and its environs and including kangaroos, wombats, wallabies, koalas, and others, but more widely represented by the opossum. Metatherian females produce tiny eggs which are retained in the

A

B

Fig. 11. Surviving Prototherian mammals. A. The duckbill, one of the few surviving species of Monotremes. B. An echidna. Although the spiny anteater, like
the duckbill, bears little external resemblance to the higher mammals, it is believed to represent an early stage in their evolution. Both lay eggs but suckle
their young.

mother's body even after fertilization, but the eggs contain small yolks and no provision is made to feed embryos in any other way. Hence, the offspring are born after a brief pregnancy, alive but very little and immature. For shelter and nourishment they crawl up the mother's body and enter an abdominal pouch where they are kept secure, protected from the elements, and given ready access to teats from which they draw milk (Fig. 12).

The fullest expression of mammalian development occurs in the subclass of **Eutherian** or **placental** mammals, to which man belongs.

Fig. 12. A baby kangaroo, secure in its mother's pouch.

Reproduction involves the internal fertilization of a microscopic egg and its retention within the female's body for an extended length of time. During this period the embryo is provided with membranes just like the reptilian amnion, allantois, and yolk sac, which give it a fluid envelope, oxygen, and food, respectively. Soon some of these membranes combine with part of the mother's uterine lining to form the placenta. Thereafter, maternal and embryonic blood are brought close together by the placenta, although the two blood streams never merge into one. In this manner the embryo is supplied with food and oxygen, and gets rid of its waste products (Fig. 13). Pregnancy

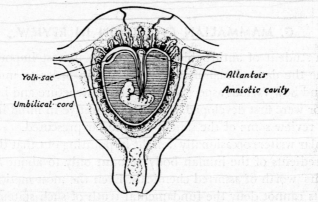

Yolk-sac

Umbilical cord

Allantois

Amniotic cavity

Fig. 13. A human placenta (after Hooton). The manner in which an embryo is nurtured and sheltered during its mother's pregnancy is very similar for all placental mammals.

terms vary in different species of Eutherian or placental mammals, but run to six months or more in large animals. Gestation is always long enough to enable the embryo to reach a far greater degree of maturity than is possible in non-placentals. Such a protracted pregnancy is to be found only among creatures whose metabolic rate is high enough to provide mother and embryo with a good supply of energy. Among the Eutheria the placenta is discharged as the afterbirth soon after a child has emerged, and a new one originates with each succeeding pregnancy. Shortly after her delivery the mother's breasts fill with milk with which a baby can be fed for many months.

Constituted as they were, the Eutherian mammals ultimately took over the dominant position formerly held by reptiles, and during the Cenozoic era they set out on a career of widespread, adaptive radiation. Most of them were four-footed and lived on the ground; but some, like the bats, developed wings and spent much of their time in the air. Others, including sea cows, whales, dolphins, and walruses, adjusted themselves to marine life; at least one, the mole, went underground; and several insect-eating types, among them the shrews, took to the trees. Those Eutheria who became adapted to life in the air, at sea, or beneath the ground, tended to become highly specialized. Others, particularly the ones who climbed into the trees, retained what may be called a generalized mammalian condition. It was from among the generalized arboreal placental mammals that the Primates are believed to have evolved.

## G. MAMMALIAN EVOLUTION IN REVIEW

To a student of anthropology it is of the utmost importance to examine the data of mammalian evolution in order to understand when and how various aspects of man's body structure and biological behavior were first developed. With this objective in mind it may be well to review some of the salient facts so far presented.

Popular writers occasionally delight in pointing out that the physical ingredients of the human body amount only to about a couple of dollars' worth of assorted chemicals. Even the most meticulous of scientists cannot deny the fundamental truth of such statements, or the additional facts that the chemicals in question are part of the earth's content and were originally derived from the sun. Whether these substances are now found in the ground, packaged in stores or laboratories, or comprised in human bodies, they unfailingly respond to the same physico-chemical laws.

When several chemical elements combined to form living matter or protoplasm, a set of biological imperatives was superimposed on the older physico-chemical laws, and had to be obeyed if life were to be sustained. Identical biological imperatives continue to apply to man. From the beginning protoplasm, like the human body, was organized into cells. At first, in the Protozoa, a single cell sufficed to carry out all the rules of life, but in the multicelled Metazoa specialized cells were grouped into tissues, organs, and systems, each of which was charged with the responsibility of satisfying only one or another of the biological imperatives. Even the most casual of observers knows that man's body also contains systems of cells that are specialized for breathing, digesting, excreting, reproducing, and so forth. Associated with the organs that make up these systems are sets of muscles which require nerve mechanisms to regulate and direct their activities. Among the invertebrates the nerve cells were dispersed in scattered units throughout the body, every unit acting almost independently to control muscular activity in its own area. Later, as may be seen in jellyfish, the disparate nerve units were merged into a co-ordinated nervous system that functioned as a central receiving and dispatching center for the entire organism. This scheme was improved upon by various Paleozoic invertebrates, many of which came to have well-developed senses—of smell, especially.

With the formation of elongated bodies among chordates and, more significantly, among truly vertebrate fishes, a pattern was devised that showed clearly marked head, body, and tail divisions; bilateral symmetry; paired appendages; and permanent distinctions of sex. Among vertebrates all of the sense organs and their associated nerve cells were connected with a brain which was lodged in a bony head that thereafter led the way while it directed the movements of an animal. Fish bodies are so specialized for speedy movement that their responses to external impressions are very quick and in the nature of automatic or reflex actions. Thoughtful behavior is something that lies beyond the capacity of fishes and they are incapable of any activity (such as first-degree murder) that requires premeditation. Above all they lack a good sense-combiner for merging sense impressions received from various sources into a composite whole. Without such an arrangement a creature cannot store up old impressions to form a backlog of experience upon which it may draw when confronted with a new or difficult situation.

Following in the footsteps, as it were, of some Devonian fish that could crawl a bit on dry soil while they gulped free air, came the ambitious amphibians who led the way to partially terrestrial life by contributing adult lungs and limbs to the vertebrate theme composed by fishes. Once their paired fins were metamorphosed to legs, the amphibians required improvements in those parts of the brain and nervous system devoted to locomotor controls. After the necessary changes were made, adult amphibians could use their legs either to walk or to swim. The senses of sight and smell likewise became adapted to air or water, in addition to which the amphibians were the earliest in the line of mammalian evolution to develop a genuine sense of hearing.

Pioneer reptiles were the first to make suitable adjustments for carrying out the vertebrate theme entirely on land. Total emancipation from life in water called for numerous changes of body, limbs, and lungs; but even more vital was a need for a new mode of reproduction. This was achieved with the development of an amniote egg and internal fertilization by copulation. Most reptiles contributed little else to the progress of evolution, with the exception of starting the cerebral cortex, a new element in the brain that was destined to play a major part in the life of man. A few reptiles converted their teeth from homodont to heterodont, and some may conceivably have begun the internal system of regulating body temperature that is conventionally termed warm-bloodedness, but these features are much better represented in the mammals.

Although mammalian evolution doubtless started over 70 million years ago, it did not reach a climax until the Cenozoic era had begun. Lowly members of the class comprise the egg-laying Prototheria, and the somewhat more advanced, pouched Metatheria, but completely mammalian body forms and behavior are restricted to the Eutheria. The females of these warm-blooded, air-breathing, hair- or fur-covered animals give birth to relatively mature living offspring. These are first nourished within the mother's body during a prolonged pregnancy by means of a deciduous placenta, and after birth they are fed on milk from the mother's breasts. As far as their anatomical structures go, the Eutherian mammals quite certainly provide the prototype for man, but there are many features of the human body that can be understood only by investigating the order of Primates, to which the next chapter is devoted.

## Selected References

Gregory, W. K., *Evolution Emerging*, New York, 1951.

———, *Our Face from Fish to Man*, New York and London, 1929.

Rogers, J. S., Hubbell, T. H., and Byers, C. F., *Man and the Biological World*, rev. ed., New York, 1952.

Romer, A. S., *Man and the Vertebrates*, rev. ed., Chicago, 1941.

———, *The vertebrate body*, Philadelphia, 1949.

Snider, L. C., *Earth History*, New York and London, 1932.
Tilney, F., *The Brain from Ape to Man*, New York, 1928.
———, *The Master of Destiny, a Biography of the Brain*, New York, 1930.

CHAPTER 4

# The Order of Primates

## A. ANATOMICAL SPECIALTIES OF THE PRIMATE GROUP

Although man's body is undeniably that of a placental mammal, it is obvious that it is also different from the general run of Eutheria. Some of man's anatomical specialties are to be found among no other animals, but several of his most typical body parts are duplicated, sometimes with startling exactness, among creatures belonging to the **Primate** order, a subdivision of Eutherian mammals that consists of lemurs, tarsiers, monkeys, apes, and men.

Take, for instance, the customary way in which a man throws a baseball or holds a tennis racquet, hammer, canoe paddle, or saw (Fig. 14). In each of these cases the same anatomical structures, shared by Primates and man, are brought into play. No tight hold, or prehensile grip, would be possible to an animal that lacked strong and flexible fingers capable of wrapping firmly about an implement. It should also be noted that in order to get a really tight grasp on something, the thumb must wrap around it in the opposite direction from the other digits. Technically, this Primate mechanism is known as the opposable thumb and is usually taken to mean that the ball of the thumb can be touched (opposed) to the tips of the other four

Fig. 14. Throwing a curve. Without a prehensile grip, made possible by an opposable thumb and flexible fingers and wrist, it would be impossible to grasp a baseball in the proper manner for pitching a curve.

fingers.[1] Flat nails rather than claws have likewise been associated with grasping functions, in the belief that they are less likely to get

---

[1] Unlike man, most other primates have prehensile feet as well as hands, and opposable great toes as well as thumbs.

in the way, and some writers have gone so far as to attribute the ridges on the insides of the fingers to the firm purchase they provide for picking up or holding things.

Then, again, the movements involved in the strenuous use of any of the objects mentioned in the preceding paragraph call for the firm attachment of fingers, hands, wrists, and arms to the shoulders. This implies the need of a sturdy shoulder girdle, in which the collar-bone (clavicle) must play an important part. Without a strong and firmly-knit clavicle, such as most Primates possess, violent motions of the arms to the sides and rear are next to impossible. So, were he not a Primate, no baseball player could swing hard enough to hit a home run and no tennis player could develop a powerful forehand.

Another distinctive bit of human and Primate behavior is made possible by the fact that the two long bones of the forearm can be rotated so that the outer one (radius) moves over the inner (ulna) (Fig. 15A). This makes it a simple matter for the hand and arm below the elbow to be turned so that the palm may face up, down, or to either side. Firm, mobile, opposable digits, a flexible wrist, and a rotating forearm attached to a strong shoulder girdle, together with their associated muscles, nerves, ligaments, and tendons, provide the biological potential for such divergent activities as digging witch-etty grubs or post holes, playing the piano or the accordion, throwing a swift forward pass, steering an automobile, knotting a necktie, rolling out bread dough, or using a screwdriver and wrenches.

Other anatomical features commonly regarded as typical of Primates include: a large, deeply convoluted brain covered with a much-wrinkled cortex; a greatly intensified increase in the sense of sight coupled with stereoscopic vision; an attendant decline of keen smell; a tendency for females to bear only one young at a time; possession, normally, of only two breasts, situated high on the chest; and a bony wall, penetrated by the optic nerve, that shuts off the eye socket at the side and rear. Not all of the body traits listed for the Primates are newly evolved acquisitions. Studies of early mammals have revealed that skeletal features like the clavicle and the rotating forearm occurred long ago, but among none of the Eutherian mammals save Primates are they still functionally important.

From time to time efforts have been made to explode the notion that there may be a cause-and-effect relationship between arboreal

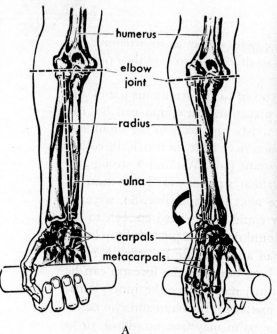

humerus

elbow joint

radius

ulna

carpals

metacarpals

A

B

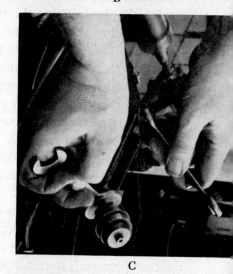

C

D

Fig. 15. Man's rotating forearm. A. (after Rogers, Hubbell and Byers.) Shows the anatomical structure that makes rotation possible. B. and C. Mechanic at work. His use of tools depends on the anatomical features pictured in A. D. It's a pass! To throw a swift forward pass a football player requires not only a strong prehensile grip and a rotating forearm, but also a sturdy clavicle and shoulder girdle.

life and Primate anatomy. Opponents object to the idea that increased reliance on the sense of sight, prehensile grip, flexible wrist, rotating forearm, and expert hand—eye co-ordination, may have arisen from their usefulness to tree-dwellers. However, since all Primates, with the exception of man, are to some extent arboreal, it is probable that a connection does exist.

Fig. 16. A Philippine tree shrew. Although this creature is very far from the hominid branch of Primates, it has five digits on each hand and foot, separable thumbs, and a differentiation of hind and fore limbs. It is generally regarded as being in the ancestral line of the Primate order.

## B. PRIMATE ORIGINS

The reader may have noticed how few specialized traits are attributed exclusively to Primates. Indeed, one may go so far as to say that the very lack of specialization is the most distinguishing aspect of the entire order. Thus, the search for Primate origins inevitably leads to highly generalized Eutherian mammals. An almost universal consensus has been reached to the effect that the parent group was most likely tree-dwelling and insect-eating, and is best represented today by the Insectivora of whom the **tree shrews** are typical (Fig. 16).

Present-day tree shrews survive only in the neighborhood between Malaya and the Philippines. They are small furry creatures, the size and shape of rats, with elongated snouts and long bushy tails. Their eyes are set on each side of the muzzle and are directed laterally, so that each eye probably registers a separate picture in the brain. They climb about in trees on all fours, grasping the branches with the soles of their feet and occasionally digging in with the sharp claws with which each digit is provided. Their brains are small and smooth, and what little cerebral cortex they have is devoted mainly to the sense of smell. Some tree shrew females give birth to small litters and are, correspondingly, provided with several pairs of teats.

From this description it is plain that tree shrews are far removed from the shape and structure of the higher Primates, but comparative anatomists have found a number of detailed resemblances to early Primate forms. Since we are now approaching so much closer to the

| ERA | PERIOD | EPOCH | APPROX. BEGINNING DATE | MAIN ANIMAL GROUP |
|---|---|---|---|---|
| Cenozoic | Tertiary | Paleocene | 70,000,000 B.C. | Insectivora |
| | | Eocene | 60,000,000 B.C. | Lemurs, Tarsiers |
| | | Oligocene | 40,000,000 B.C. | Monkeys |
| | | Miocene | 30,000,000 B.C. | Apes |
| | | Pliocene | 13,000,000 B.C. | Man-apes? |
| | Quaternary | Pleistocene | 1,000,000 B.C. | Extinct Hominids |
| | | Holocene | 20,000 B.C. | Homo sapiens |

Fig. 17. Chart of Primate evolution.

emergence of man, students of anthropology must learn thoroughly the facts that appear in Figure 17.

## C. THE LOWLY LEMURS

Although some scientists refuse to classify **lemurs** as Primates, most of them admit these creatures to the ranks but assign them to the separate suborder, **Lemuroidea**.[2] Many kinds of lemurs are still to be found in Madagascar and the vicinity, but during the Eocene epoch they were widely spread through other parts of the world, including the Western hemisphere. They are, on the whole, small animals about two feet long, with fur-covered bodies and long tails. Most varieties have pointed projecting snouts, and big round eyes that peer to the sides and fail to provide overlapping, stereoscopic vision, such as is typical of higher Primates. They live in trees and are most active at night, when they feed busily on a mixed diet of insects, bird eggs, fruits, leaves, buds, and shoots.

Lemurs are generally quadrupedal, but both the thumb and great toe are well developed and capable of being turned to touch the inner tips of the other digits. They are equipped with prehensile hands and feet and can secure a tight grasp on a branch by wrapping either organ around it. They also have rotating forearms which, in conjunction with powerful upper arms and shoulder girdles, permit them to perform such operations as grasping things at any angle, hanging or swinging by the arms, pulling the body upward or forward, pouncing and seizing on prey, conveying food to the mouth, and handling objects in a manner that anticipates the use of tools. Whenever they reach for new holds lemurs tend to use their arms and hands, temporarily throwing the weight of the body on the rear limbs (Fig. 18). These are somewhat elongated, stable, and incapable of being rotated. Such a separation of the structure and function of front from hind limbs is an important Primate characteristic that becomes increasingly marked as we run the range from lemur to man.

While Lemuroidea have enough Primate aspects to be admitted, somewhat grudgingly, to that order, they also exhibit some anatomical traits of lower evolutionary status. Their eyeballs are suspended

[2] Some physical anthropologists separate from lemurs a closely related animal called loris. See M. F. Ashley Montagu, *An Introduction to Physical Anthropology,* rev. ed., Springfield, 1951, pp. 30-39.

by membranes within rings of bone, whereas the eyeballs of higher Primates are set in bony cups with solid backwalls; their tear ducts lie on the facial surfaces outside the eye cavities, instead of being enclosed within the eye sockets; they do not have stereoscopic vision,

Fig. 18. Ring-tailed lemur. Lowly though this Primate may be, it has strong and flexible fingers and wrists, rotating forearms, prehensile hands and feet, opposable thumbs and great toes, and flat nails on the digits. The front and hind limbs are clearly distinguished.

which means that they cannot perceive depth or third dimension; and their brains are poorly developed and mostly given over to the sense of smell. This is regarded as a backward condition because tree dwellers require agility and coordination that are better served by increased visual, tactile, kinesthetic, and motor areas in the brain.

Lemurs also fall short of the more advanced Primates because they have a different number of teeth in their jaws, the lower incisors often protrude horizontally at right angles to the other teeth, the second digit of the foot may have a claw instead of a flat nail and, not infrequently, females give birth to small litters.

## D. THE SPECIALIZED TARSIERS

Somewhat more progressive than lemurs in various biological respects, but unique and overspecialized in others, is the Primate suborder of **Tarsioidea**. Today **tarsiers** are found only in a few of the islands in the Dutch East Indies and the Philippines but, like the lemurs, they had a much wider distribution in Eocene times. Their bodies average about two feet in length, but they have bare, ratlike tails that may be longer. They are covered with reddish-brown fur, and are characterized by rounded heads and short, blunt snouts. Feeding and other essential activities take place at night, and grasshoppers, small lizards, and other little fauna are eaten, but vegetable or plant foods are usually neglected.

Tarsiers are so named because of a greatly enlarged tarsus bone that in all Primates helps form the arch of the foot. To this unusual development must be added the further circumstance that the long bones of the lower leg (tibia and fibula) are merged together at their bottom. These specialties of the ankle region, coupled with the retention of very flexible toes, seem to enable tarsiers to make prodigious hops at lightning speed. When they employ this mode of progression in the trees where they habitually reside they are aided by still another specialty, for the balls of all the digits are extended into roughened, disc-like pads that are thought to prevent slipping when a fresh hold is obtained.

Other distinctive anatomical peculiarities of Tarsioidea are concerned with the visual apparatus. Being nocturnal of habit they have big round eyes, so large that only a small space separates them. The eyes are set within tremendous bony sockets whose backwalls, unlike those of lemurs, are complete. The eyes are in the frontal position, and while the fields of vision appear to overlap somewhat, it is believed that they do not have truly stereoscopic vision. Tear ducts are large, beginning within the eye cavity but extending out to the face. When it wishes to observe something above and behind it, a tarsier is said to be able to swivel its head around 180 degrees and so look directly backward without turning the rest of its body.

Despite their strange appearance and body specialties, tarsiers show various advanced Primate features (Fig. 19). The fundamental differentiation of front and hind limbs, first noted among the Lemuroidea, is more advanced. Hands and arms measure less than half as much as feet and legs, all ten digits have rather sharp and narrow nails but no claws, and there is a much greater tendency to use the hands in feeding. The teeth more nearly resemble those of higher Primates, and the incisors are vertical rather than horizontal as is true of lemurs. Tarsier brains show an increase of space devoted to sight and the olfactory area is correspondingly reduced. In general, the forward hemisphere (cerebrum) extends up and back to overlie the cerebellum at the rear. Only one off-spring is normally born at a time and female tarsiers, unlike lemurs, have monthly discharges of blood at the vagina somewhat like menstrual periods.

Fig. 19. A tarsier. Far removed from the structure and appearance of *Homo sapiens* is this lowly Primate, which is specialized for rapid hopping. Yet, its eyes are in a frontal position, and it has prehensile hands and rotating forearms. The front and hind limbs are differentiated in form and function.

A minority of highly competent primatologists led by Wood Jones,[3] hold the opinion that the line of higher evolution culminating in man branched off from a tarsioid stage of development, but the majority of biologists regard them as ancestral only to the next rank or so of the Primates.

## E. MONKEYS OF THE WESTERN WORLD

Within the forests of the more tropical parts of Central and South America there live a great many varieties of monkeys. Together they are known as **Platyrrhini,** a term that refers to the fact that all of them have broad fleshy noses within which the nostrils are widely separated and may be located at the sides so that they open outward to left and right, instead of downward. These monkeys, together with Old World monkeys, apes, and men, comprise the Primate suborder of Anthropoidea.

Platyrrhini have been in existence since Oligocene days, and are divided into two families, one of which is restricted to the little monkeys commonly called marmosets. They are somewhat squirrel-like in appearance, with bushy coats and tails, claws on all the digits except the great toes, and nonopposable thumbs. As a rule they are considered to be the least highly evolved of the New World monkeys. Except for marmosets the Platyrrhini belong to the Cebidae family, of whom the best known are the cebus (organ-grinder), howler (Fig. 20A), and spider monkeys. As a group they approximate the human body more nearly than tarsiers because they have bigger and more convoluted brains, with considerable space devoted to sight; eyes set in reduced sockets in completely frontal positions, and with bony backwalls; tear ducts entirely contained in the eye cavities; and overlapping, stereoscopic vision capable of discerning depth as well as height and width. In addition, the Cebidae representatives of the Platyrrhini have flat-nailed digits unencumbered with disc-like pads, opposable great toes and thumbs, and legs and feet well suited for climbing and jumping but not specialized for hopping. They are most active by day instead of at night, and they feed on a mixed diet of insects and vegetal materials.

Besides their broad noses and laterally directed nostrils, the Platyrrhini show two additional features that must serve to put them off

[3] F. W. Jones, *Hallmarks of Mankind,* Baltimore, 1948, p. 33.

the main line of man's evolution. They have teeth that almost resemble those of human beings in structure and numbers, except that they have one additional premolar on each side of the upper and lower jaws. More striking is the platyrrhine specialty of a prehensile tail, a tail capable of grasping a branch and holding the body securely

Fig. 20. New and Old World monkeys. A. Howler monkey. This is an American platyrrhine type, with widely spaced, laterally directed nostrils. Its swollen appearance is caused by its prodigious sound mechanism, from which it gets its name. B. A catarrhine (Macaque) monkey from the Old World. It has narrowly spaced nostrils that open downward. This configuration approaches man's much more nearly than does the platyrrhine nasal structure.

suspended while the limbs are left free for other purposes. When moving along the boughs of trees American monkeys sometimes go on all fours, but occasionally they swing from branch to branch, using their hands, arms, and shoulder girdles in the manner of gymnasts performing on rings or trapezes. This method of progression is termed "brachiating," and is best developed in the Cebidae division of the Platyrrhini by the spider monkeys (Fig. 21) who are, in spite of their few individual specialties, regarded as typifying the most highly evolved monkeys in the Western world. They have slender bodies, long and narrow heads, chests that are not rounded but flattened from front to back, arms that greatly exceed the legs in length, and well-knit collar bones and shoulder girdles. Spider monkeys have no restricted breeding season, and females menstruate regularly for 72 hours or more every 24 to 27 days.

Perhaps in conjunction with their brachiating habits, their thumbs are reduced to mere vestiges. Another spider monkey specialty is the prehensile tail. True, such tails are common among Platyrrhini, but in the spider monkeys they are extraordinary. They are nearly twice as long as the body, sturdy enough to hold the animal suspended (Fig. 21), yet so sensitive that the tail can make feeling and exploratory movements and can grasp food and bring it to the mouth.

All in all the Platyrrhini, especially the large division of Cebidae, make up the highest forms of Primates to have evolved in the Western hemisphere. It is believed that the Platyrrhini became separated in Eocene times from the main anthropoid stem. They are much

Fig. 21. American spider monkey. Use of the long, powerful, prehensile tail as an extra limb and hand is well illustrated. Spider monkeys belong to the platyrrhine subdivision.

further advanced than the tarsiers who preceded them, yet they are far removed from apes and men. For reasons that are not yet understood evolution failed to proceed beyond the Platyrrhini in the New World, and it was not until members of *Homo sapiens* penetrated this continent from Asia that higher Primates became known to any of the Americas.

## F. OLD WORLD MONKEYS

Somewhat more highly evolved than the monkeys of the New World are their Old World relatives who, together with apes and humans, are called the **Catarrhini.** This term refers to a narrow nose in which the nostrils are close together, centrally located, and pointed downward (Fig. 20B). Specialists distinguish many varieties, among the best known of which are baboons, mandrills, and macaques or rhesus monkeys, which are widely used in medical laboratories. All

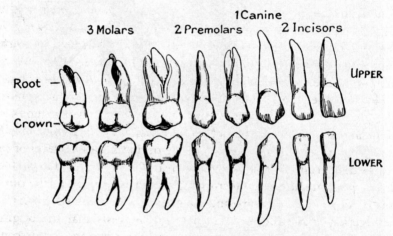

Fig. 22. Dental formula of man. The same kinds and numbers of teeth are found in the jaws of all Primates, from catarrhine monkeys to *Homo sapiens.*

of them are sufficiently alike to be grouped, for our purposes, into a single family named **Cercopithecidae.** Members of this group are the first to have the identical dental formula of man. Customarily, it is written $I\frac{2}{2}C\frac{1}{1}PM\frac{2}{2}M\frac{3}{3}$, which means that from front to back there are in each side of the upper and lower jaws 2 incisors, 1 canine, 2 premolars, and 3 molars,[4] including the wisdom teeth, making a total of 32 (Fig. 22).

Most of the Catarrhini also anticipate human characteristics because they are active by day and sleep at night and because they have relatively large brains, completely stereoscopic vision, thoroughly differentiated front and hind limbs, flat nails on all the digits, and a breeding system that very nearly approaches man's. They differ from man in that nearly all of them are arboreal; have cheek pouches for the temporary storage of food; hard, calloused areas (ischial callosities) on the buttocks; tails that may be short or long but are never prehensile; and in some species patches of skin on the buttocks that may become vividly colored, particularly during the menstrual cycles of females.

Of all the catarrhine monkeys of the Eastern hemisphere, baboons and mandrills are the most unusual because they have forsaken the trees and adapted themselves to life on the ground. Curiously enough, although they go on all fours they still have opposable great toes and thumbs, and they often sit up and use their hands when feeding (Fig. 23). Their facial areas project as snouts in a fashion that gives them a kind of doglike expression, and they have sharp, powerful canines that protrude beyond the limits of the other teeth. All the same, with the exception of a few structural peculiarities thought to be connected with their quadrupedal posture on the ground, baboons and mandrills have bodies typical of Old World monkeys.

The ancestry of the Cercopithecidae division of Catarrhini may be tentatively traced back to the Oligocene period because a level of soil of that date from the Fayum basin near Cairo, Egypt, has yielded a lower jawbone and some teeth which scientists regard as the oldest known remains of a catarrhine monkey. This fossil specimen has been named **Parapithecus.**[5] Its small size suggests that the original cercopiths were considerably smaller than their present-day descendants, but it is noteworthy that the dental formula of Parapithecus is the same as that which contemporary monkeys of the Old World share with men and apes. Even if we grant that analysis of a single, fragmentary specimen may not provide convincing evidence, the

4 Although Cercopithecidae share the dental formula of apes and men, they are apart from all other Primates because their first and second molars, at least, are bilophodont. Bilophodont means that the molars have four cusps arranged in the form of a square, with ridges connecting the front and rear pairs of cusps.

5 W. W. Howells, *op. cit.*, pp. 94-96.

discovery of Parapithecus has demonstrated the likelihood that as far back as the Oligocene the Catarrhini had already branched off from their presumed tarsioid ancestors in a direction different from that taken by the Platyrrhini.

Fig. 23. Hamadryas baboon. The raised front left leg shows the separated and opposable thumb that this animal has retained in spite of its quadrupedal posture on the ground. As in all Old World monkeys, the tail is not prehensile.

## G. INTRODUCING THE APES

Collectively the present-day apes make up the family of **Simiidae,** while the term **Pongidae** may be used for the larger varieties, exclusive of gibbons. The Simiidae are part of the same suborder of Anthropoidea that contains man's family, the **Hominidae,** and are divided into four groups, customarily known as gibbons, orangutans, chimpanzees, and gorillas. Whereas the gibbons and orangutans inhabit the southeastern portion of the Asiatic mainland and a few of the nearby islands, the chimpanzees and gorillas live in a zone that extends approximately across central Africa. Although the apes living in the present period are found only in restricted parts of the Old World, it appears likely that in late Oligocene days and on into the Miocene and Pliocene there were many more varieties and that they ranged over a much wider territory. Just why the Simiidae shou'd have been reduced in numbers, kinds, and zones of habitation, are matters for speculation, but widespread discoveries of fossil ape remains give indisputable evidence of their former diversity and distribution. The deep interest that anthropologists have in trying to understand the origins of the living animals that most nearly resemb!e man's physical form, makes it necessary to look into the material dealing with fossil apes, even though it may be confusing and full of difficult terminology.

The Parapithecus fragment from an Oligocene deposit at Fayum renders it likely, as has been said, that Old and New World monkeys had diverged that far back. It is also thought probable that apes became separated from the line of Cercopithecidae at about the same time. Such an hypothesis is supported by the discovery of another fossil from Oligocene soil at Fayum. This find, named **Propliopithecus,** consists of most of a lower jaw in which several teeth remain imbedded, and which some students of Primate evolution declare to be related in one direction to Parapithecus, and in another to an ancestral line culminating in the gibbon (Fig. 24). From Propliopithecus, which was probably only a little beast about 12 inches high, and which lived about 40 million years back, a trail leads according to some scholars, either to **Pliopithecus,** a fossil ape found in Germany that bears close resemblance to a modern gibbon; or else to **Limnopithecus,** a group of Lower Miocene specimens, recently discovered in Kenya colony, East Africa. Limnopithecus consists of a cluster of remains, and is thought to be connected with three species of yet another African genus called **Proconsul.** Without going into detail it may be said that Proconsul represents a number of separate individuals, whose skulls, jaws, teeth, and limbs betray a mixture of cercopith, gibbon, and large ape traits. Whatever mysteries remain unclarified with respect to ape origins, enough agreement has been reached to warrant the tentative conclusion that the ancestors of the gibbons existed in the Pliocene and that their line of descent is suggested by the series Propliopithecus, Pliopithecus, Limnopithecus, and Proconsul.

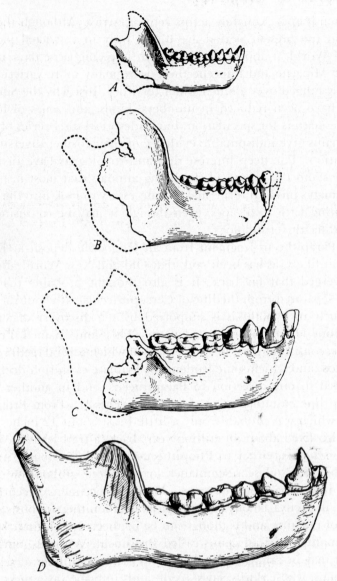

Fig. 24. A series of mandibles from Parapithecus to the
modern gibbon.

A. Parapithecus.        B. Propliopithecus.
C. Pliopithecus.         D. Gibbon.

The dotted portions indicate missing parts. All the jaws and
teeth show many resemblances.

Not content to stop here other qualified experts have tried to demonstrate that this series was in Miocene days closely linked to a different group of fossils called **Dryopithecus-Sivapithecus,** who may have given rise to the large apes. Remains of Dryopithecus or Sivapithecus, or both, have been found widely scattered through parts of Europe, Asia, and Africa. Most of the specimens pertaining to this type consist only of fragments of jaws and teeth, but these have been studied in the greatest of detail. Sufficient variations have been noted to warrant the division of the Dryopithecus-Sivapithecus fossils into about fifteen distinct species.

Close analysis of the formation, number, size, and arrangement of the cusps, ridges, and grooves on the lower molar teeth of these extinct apes has led to the formulation of the so-called Dryopithecus pattern. Several highly trained and competent investigators have concluded that this pattern is basic among chimpanzees and gorillas, and that it exists in two differently modified forms in the orangutan and man. So much significance is attached by these authorities to the molar tooth resemblances among the largest of the Primates, that their descent from an early form of Dryopithecus-Sivapithecus has been postulated.

## H. LIVING ASIATIC APES

Of the four groups of extant apes the gibbons, because of their small body size and brachiating mechanism, are thought to be furthest removed from man. There are two genera, but most gibbons belong to the Hylobates genus, of which several species are to be found in southeastern Asia. Rarely do they exceed 3 feet in height, and adults of either sex commonly weigh only 12 to 15 pounds. Their skins are black, and most parts of their bodies are thickly covered with furry coats that grade from white through gray to black. Ischial callosities, not unlike those of Old World monkeys, are frequently found on the buttocks, but gibbons do not have such distinctive cercopith traits as external tails or cheek pouches. Their heads show low foreheads and large oval eye sockets with thick rims of bone, and their jaws protrude and contain jutting canine teeth that interlock—instead of meeting edge to edge—at the corners of the mouth. The cranial capacity, a term that denotes the size of the skull chamber in which the brain is lodged,[6] is limited to 90 cc., a figure greatly below that of the higher Primates but far in excess of the average for most monkeys.

Nothing is more characteristic of gibbons than their enormous and exceedingly elongated arms (Fig. 25), which are $2\frac{1}{3}$ times as long as the body. Figuratively speaking, a gibbon can pick a dime from the floor without stooping. The greater part of this excessive length is in the forearms rather than the hands and may well be related to the gibbons' brachiating habits. A light, slender body, coupled with powerful arms that culminate in long-fingered hands with short thumbs, seems to be especially well-suited for brachiation. With the greatest of ease and nonchalance a gibbon moves among the trees with a free-swinging, pendulum motion, rapidly shifting its hold from one hand to another. Distances of 10 feet are readily covered with each graceful swing by young and old; mothers with infants clinging to them do not hesitate to make 15-foot leaps; and the members of a whole troop will occasionally jump 30 or more feet through the air. Such skill in brachiating and hurtling through space implies that gibbons must have excellent eyesight, acute judgment of distance, accurate and instantaneous perceptions of depth and size, extraordinary co-ordination of hand and eye, splendid motor controls, and exceedingly fast reaction speeds. All this requires adequate representation in the brain.

Gibbons are so well adjusted to an arboreal environment that they seldom descend to earth, but in the course of their daily wanderings in search of food, they occasionally find it necessary to walk or run over open ground. At such times they rise up on their hind legs, keeping their bodies vertical, and getting their big arms out of the way by lifting them above their heads or holding them out at the sides. As a contrast to the arm-body relationship, the proportion of a gibbon's legs to its torso more nearly resembles man's than does that of any other ape. Despite the fact that gibbons have prehensile feet, in which the big toes are separated by a deep cleft from the other digits, they manage to get about on the ground surprisingly well for short periods of time.

A comparative review of the Primate series reveals a fairly con-

----

[6] To get an approximate measure of the amount of brain that any vertebrate has, anthropologists fill the hollow cranial vault of a skull with a free-flowing material, usually mustard seed, and pour the contents of the vault into a measuring glass or graduate. The resultant reading, expressed in cubic centimeters, is known as the cranial capacity and provides a convenient measure of gross brain size.

A. A gibbon at home in the trees, showing its easy swinging motion, and its prehensile hands and feet.

B. Exceedingly long and strong hands and forearms are typical of all gibbons.

Fig. 25. Gibbons.

sistent increase of body size from lemurs and tarsiers to monkeys and apes. Against this background the short stature and light weight of the gibbons stand out sharply in contrast to their nearest simian neighbors, **orangutans,** who inhabit portions of Sumatra and Borneo off the coast of southeastern Asia (Fig. 26). Orangs stand nearly 5 feet high and adult males weigh from 165 to 200 pounds. In brain size, too, they show a great advance over the gibbons, for their cranial capacities may reach up to 400 cc.

Big and bulky though they are the orangutans are still arboreal, but they are by no means such expert and graceful brachiators as gibbons. They move cautiously and ponderously through the trees, and while they sometimes swing by the hands and arms from one

Fig. 26. Orang-utan mother and child. Although possessed of long and powerful arms, the adult orang-utan is too bulky to leap across wide stretches of open space. As the illustration shows, it has a strong, prehensile grip and rotating forearms, and uses its feet in the same manner as the hands.

stout bough to another, they never attempt to leap across wide stretches of open space. Their arms are long and strong, but less elongated than the gibbons'. To use another figure of speech, an orangutan can tie its shoe laces without bending over.

When they are compared to the size and strength of the forelimbs, the legs and feet of an orangutan are singularly small and weak, the feet long and narrow; the great toes are stunted, devoid of nails, and held at right angles to the main axis of the foot; the toes are perpetually curved and bent so that they cannot be straightened out; and the heel is poorly developed. Such feet resemble hands in structure and are ill-suited for supporting the weight of a heavy creature. Consequently, it is not surprising that orangutans do not walk upright when they come to earth. Instead, they either go on all fours, or rest their knuckles on the ground and swing their bodies between hands and arms as if on crutches. Neither method seems to be comfortable and orangutans prefer to remain aloft.

There is only one genus of orangutan, Simia, all of whose members tend to have dark brown skins and extensive coverings of long, reddish hair. The eye orbits are large and set closely together, and above each one occurs a prominent brow ridge of bone. The tooth-bearing portion of the upper jaw juts forward (alveolar prognathism), all the front teeth are large, and the lower jaw is massive and forward-projecting, but chinless. Two anatomical specialties, whose origins and functions are little known, are typical. They are large, fatty cheek pads that cause the sides of the face to bulge out, and enormous pouches of skin in the region of the throat, which can be inflated, particularly by males, to produce a swollen, goiterous appearance. Like gibbons, orangutans are not thought to be very close to the line of human evolution, partly because of the biological specialties that each reveals. In one particular or another the Asiatic apes may make a very close approximation to man, but on the whole the differences outweigh the resemblances.

## I. LIVING AFRICAN APES

Because they can be more readily raised and trained in captivity, and because they are more frequently exhibited in public than other apes, it is popularly believed that **chimpanzees** are nearly human. Such a judgment is only partially confirmed by primatolo-

A. Chimpanzee being helped to stand up. The upper limbs are much longer and stronger than the lower ones. The great toe is not in line with the others, and the foot on the ground is flat, without an instep arch or a well-developed heel.

B. Young chimpanzee in walking position. The hind limbs show how poorly the feet are adapted for walking or supporting the body upright. Much of the weight is placed on the elongated front limbs, which rest on their knuckles. The thumb is high on the hand, apart from the other fingers. Compare the stance of the gorilla in Fig. 28B.

Fig. 27. Two chimpanzees.

A. Gorilla in sitting position. The huge supraorbital torus and low forehead are plainly revealed. Although the feet can be differentiated from the hands, their prehensile structure is noteworthy.

B. A grounded gorilla. The quadrupedal stance of a walking gorilla resembles that of a chimpanzee.

Fig. 28. A pair of gorillas.

gists, and it would be an error to accept it uncritically. Under natural conditions chimpanzees reside only in those parts of equatorial Africa that are drained by the Congo and Niger rivers. They are divided into several species, all of which are of the genus Pan. Bodily proportions are much like those of man, with full-grown males standing just over 5 feet high and weighing around 110 pounds. Most species have brownish-black skins and are covered with coarse, straight black hair, but brown, gray, and even white-haired varieties are known. As a group chimpanzees have round, low-vaulted heads, and their cranial capacities average about 400 cc. With the approach of adolescence a male develops a solid, transverse bar of bone over the sockets of the eyes (supraorbital torus), and his big chinless jaws bulge forward. Lips are thin but unusually flexible or mobile, and while the front teeth are big and strong, with interlocking canines, the back teeth are apt to look quite human.

Unlike orangutans chimpanzees have long, slender bodies (Fig. 27A). The upper limbs, especially the forearms, are massive and elongated by human standards, but the finger tips reach only a little below the knee when the animal stands up. Hands are narrow and long, thumbs are diminutive, nails are rather strongly curved, and the outer fingers may be connected by a web of skin that runs as high as the first joints. Fruits and tender vegetal growths of many sorts make up the bulk of their diet, and eggs, small birds, and rodents are probably also eaten. Food is most often plucked or grasped by hand and then brought to the mouth, and while feeding in trees a chimpanzee may sit, stand, recline, or squat.

Chimpanzees are fine climbers and expert brachiators. They swing easily from one limb to another, but observers have noticed that they never travel for long distances without resorting to the ground for part of the way. This is somewhat unexpected because they have long, narrow, prehensile feet, with massive but opposable great toes, rudimentary heels, and partially webbed outer toes. Ordinarily, a grounded chimpanzee uses the crutchlike stance of the orangutan and has an ungainly, waddling, sidewise gait (Fig. 27B); but under special conditions, as when the ground is wet or cold, a chimpanzee may walk erect for a few paces.

Largest by far of all the Primates is the African ape genus of **gorilla**. These beasts may grow to prodigious sizes, with adult males standing up to 70 inches high and weighing from 350 to as much as

600 pounds. Although gorillas comprise only a single genus, two major types are customarily distinguished. One is a lowland group that inhabits the Cameroon district, and the other is the mountain gorilla that lives in the Belgian Congo. The most typical skin color for the whole genus is black, and the hair, too, is usually black, but streaked with gray. Particularly noteworthy among full-grown males is a massive skull, with great bony crests on top running from front to back, and an enormous supraorbital torus of solid bone that goes from left to right above the eye openings (Fig. 28). Cranial capacities average 500 cc., but may run a little higher in exceptional cases. This is the greatest amount reported for any of the living apes, but is surprisingly little in relation to the over-all size of the skull. Most of the big cranium consists of solid bone, and there is comparatively little hollow space to contain a brain. Truly may the gorilla be described as a big bonehead!

Heavy though they are, gorillas spend much time in trees and are good swingers and climbers. When they come to the ground, as they apparently do more frequently than other apes, they have a tendency to stand erect from time to time. They have even been observed to take a few strides forward, placing the feet flat on the ground and moving ahead in a fairly straight line. On such occasions the knees are flexed and the hands dangle at the sides. As is true of the other big apes, gorillas have proportionately long forearms, but in their case the fingertips come only to the knees when the animal is standing. They have short but thick, stumpy legs; broad, short feet that are proportioned somewhat like man's; great toes that are massive but shorter than those of the chimpanzee; and a heel that projects backward and is fairly well developed to help support the body in an upright position. Webs of skin may reach to the middle joints of the lesser toes, and the big toe is opposable to the others. This suggests that the foot is a prehensile rather than a supporting organ, yet it is said to be only infrequently used for lifting or carrying things. Hands are readily differentiated from the feet and have proportions not too unlike the human.

Among the least humanoid of gorilla features are the face and jaws. The latter are particularly massive in adult males, forward protruding, and devoid of chin. The huge jaws contain formidable incisors, great tusklike, projecting and interlocking canines, and molars that are large but of manlike shape. The nose is long, and is narrow at the root but broad at the nostrils. It is not elevated above the rest of the facial plane and the nasal bones that underlie the fleshy parts are flat and low. The lips are elongated and thin, and the external ears are rather small.

## J. THE PUZZLE OF MAN AND APE RELATIONSHIPS

The kinship of the living apes to humans is still far from being understood. About thirty years ago it used to be fairly well agreed that the gibbons were too specialized to be close to man's ancestry, but that the Pongidae were quite near. Nowadays it is almost the universal consensus that the big apes represent recent specialties of the Primate form, and are far to the side of the path leading to human beings. In the older hypothesis much was made of the fact that apes and men share a great many traits of the bony skeleton, body organs, nervous and muscular systems, and physiological processes. Only in particular details are there noteworthy biological differences. These resemblances and differences were thought to be explained, in the theories of a few decades past, by the fact that man was descended from an ancestor common to the ape and human lines, and that this ancestral creature was a big, arboreal simian who forsook brachiating tree life for the ground, began to walk upright on his hind legs, and started to use his emancipated forelimbs in the manner of human hands and arms. As the supposed ancestor became better adjusted to the requirements of upright posture on the ground, ran the old argument, modifications took place in the feet, legs, pelvis, spinal column, and head, which provide most of the bodily differences that set modern men apart from their apish cousins who failed to come to earth.

Today a different viewpoint is making headway. Now it is argued that the human and simian lines began to follow separate evolutionary paths far back in late Oligocene or early Miocene times, and that the ancestors of man may have been monkeylike quadrupeds who never passed through a brachiating ape stage.[7] According to this view the differences of ape and human anatomy are given emphasis, and the resemblances are somewhat played down.

[7] Some of the principal arguments on both sides of the controversy are conveniently summarized in E. A. Hooton, *Up from the Ape*, rev. ed., New York, 1946, pp. 130-33.

Proponents of neither theory have made out an entirely satisfactory case. The riddle of man's ancestry remains a riddle. Each side is caught on the horns of a dilemma. If it is assumed that a large, brachiating simian was the common ancestor of apes and men, an impressive list of distinctively human traits remains to be explained. But if one argues that the Pongidae are only far distant cousins of man, whose ancestors never went through a brachiating stage, a host of anatomical similarities demand explanation. Supporters of the modern view sometimes try to account for the resemblances by invoking "parallel evolution," or "convergence," but these phrases are unconvincing without detailed supporting evidence. We shall return briefly to this controversy on page 74.

## K. NONHUMAN PRIMATES IN BRIEF REVIEW

As far back as 1758 the great Swedish naturalist, Linnaeus, gave the name Primate to that order of Eutherian mammals which includes lemurs, tarsiers, monkeys, apes, and men. Only a few positive traits of anatomy characterize the Primates, but as a rule they have prehensile hands and feet, opposable thumbs and great toes, flat nails on the digits, one pair of breasts located on the chest, bony eye sockets, large and wrinkled brains, keen and stereoscopic vision, differentiated front and hind limbs, and excellent coordination between hands and eyes. By nearly every test of biology man is a Primate, yet he is sufficiently different to make it evident that he belongs to a separate category.

For the Primates that have survived to the present the tree shrew seems to fulfill the requirements of an ancestral type, although in itself it does not have the status of a Primate. The lowliest creatures generally admitted to this order are the lemur and the tarsier. Neither of these comes anywhere as close to approximating man's bodily form as do the monkeys. They are divided into New World (platyrrhine) and Old World (catarrhine) varieties, with the latter being the more highly evolved in the sense that they are biologically nearer to the structure of humans.

Closer still are the apes (Simiidae), of whom the least humanoid are the small, lightweight, brachiating gibbons. Their ancestral line seems to start with an Oligocene fossil variety called Propliopithecus, and to run through a series of presumably related extinct forms consisting of Pliopithecus, Limnopithecus, and Proconsul. As for the large apes (Pongidae), made up of orangutans, chimpanzees, and gorillas, they seem to go back to Miocene beginnings. Many think that the existing genera of big apes are descended from ancestors collectively known in fossil form as Dryopithecus-Sivapithecus.

All of the apes are arboreal to some extent, but all of them occasionally resort to the ground. They are not well equipped for walking and they seldom assume an upright (orthograde) posture for more than a few moments at a time. In numerous respects the large apes show so many biological resemblances to man as to hint that they may share a common ancestry with him, but in other regards man has so many distinctive anatomical features that his relations to the great simians are far from clear. The most that can be said conclusively is that man is a distant relative of the other Primates, but is certainly not descended from any of the living varieties.

People who seek to discredit the science of man sometimes proclaim that anthropologists teach that human beings have descended from monkeys or apes. As a careful reading of this chapter shows, it would be more accurate to say that anthropologists teach that man's course of evolution has been diverging from that of all other Primates for well over thirty millions of years.

### SELECTED REFERENCES

Clark, W. E. Le Gros, *History of the Primates,* rev. ed., London, 1950.
Hooton, E. A., *Man's Poor Relations,* New York, 1942.
Howells, W. W., *Mankind So Far,* New York, 1944.
Jones, F. W., *Arboreal Man,* London, 1916.
———, *Man's Place among the Mammals,* New York, 1929.
Montagu, M. F. Ashley, *An Introduction to Physical Anthropology,* rev. ed., Springfield, 1951.
Yerkes, R. M., and A. W., *The Great Apes,* New Haven, 1934.

# CHAPTER 5

# Man-Apes and Man

## A. THE TROUBLESOME MAN-APES FROM SOUTH AFRICA

Within the last few years South Africa has been the focus of two vexing problems of world-wide significance. One is in the field of race relations, and need not detain us here. The other stems from the rapid-fire discovery of a great number of man-ape fossils, scientifically known as the **Australopithecinae.**

The story begins in 1925 at Taungs in Bechuanaland, where Professor Raymond Dart came across the remains of a skull that he called **Australopithecus Africanus.**[1] It pertained to a youngster about six years old at the time of its death, with some of its milk teeth and first permanent molars intact. On the whole the "Taungs skull" was apelike in most ways, but the teeth were remarkably human except for their large size. Then, in 1936, Dr. Robert Broom collected the relics of several adults that had been blasted out of a cave at Sterkfontein. These were named **Plesianthropus,** and again they proved to have a combination of apelike and manlike characteristics. The year 1938 brought to light, at Komdraai, portions of skeletons from an adult male and a three- or four-year-old baby. They were labeled **Paranthropus** (Fig. 29), and once more disclosed a previously unsuspected assortment of human and simian aspects.

In 1947 Dr. Broom was back at Sterkfontein in time to discover more parts of Plesianthropus individuals who were of varying age and both sexes. At about the same time his colleague, Professor Dart, came across a new type of fossil that he called **Australopithecus**

[1] R. A. Dart, "Taungs and Its Significance," *Natural History,* Vol. 26, 1926, pp. 315-327.

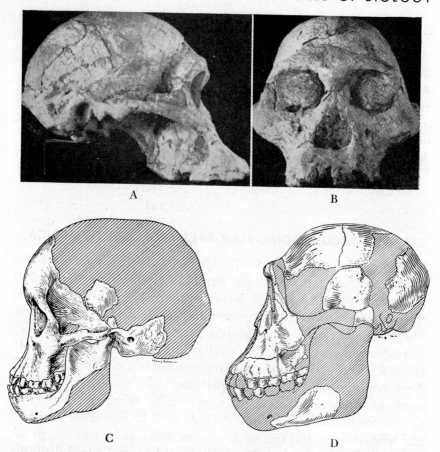

Fig. 29. Some South African man-apes (Australopithecinae). A and B. Two views of Plesianthropus (after Broom and Robinson). The big torus, pronounced prognathism, low-lying nasal bones, and the space in the upper jaw (diastema) to accommodate an interlocking canine tooth, are simian characteristics, yet the cranial capacity far exceeds that of any living ape. C (Australopithecus africanus) and D (another Plesianthropus; both after Montagu) illustrate other combinations of apish and hominid traits.

**Promethus,** because he believed it to be associated with the use of fire. Not everyone is in accord with Dr. Dart, but he is of the opinion that Australopithecus Prometheus was a small, upright-walking creature, capable not only of utilizing fire,[2] but also of hunting game, smashing skulls, and splitting bones.

[2] The association of Australopithecus Prometheus with deliberately made fires has recently been seriously questioned.

Many additional discoveries were made in South Africa between 1948 and 1950, and while no two are identical, the most extraordinary ones probably pertain to Paranthropus Crassidens. Paranthropus Crassidens, first found at Swartkrans, may be described as very large, and with a good number of humanoid features in the jaw and teeth. He probably walked in fairly erect fashion, yet there are enough simian attributes in the skull and face to make the proper classification of this fossil a matter of grave uncertainty.

The discoveries of the numerous and astoundingly diversified Australopithecinae have posed many baffling problems for students of human origins. It will take years of hard work before experts will be in a position to make reasonably acceptable hypotheses of the proper placement of these assorted fossils in the animal kingdom. Some authorities feel that all the Australopithecinae are variants of one species, but Dr. Broom maintains that they represent several distinct types. It is really hard to see how so many varying combinations of skeletal traits as the Australopithecinae exhibit can be lumped into a single species. Some forms have chinless jaws but human dentition, with no indication of projecting canines. Other specimens show a heavy supraorbital torus, but a few have less bone above the eye openings than modern man. No wonder the experts are puzzled when it comes to classifying the material from South Africa.

The dates during which the Australopithecinae flourished will also have to be established before their place with reference to man's emergence can be ascertained. If they prove to be of fairly recent date, as many scholars at present believe, it will have to be acknowledged that they cannot be regarded as ancestors of modern humans. Unfortunately, there is no general agreement on this point. Some physical anthropologists think that the diversity of the man-apes, found in a comparatively restricted portion of one continent, in itself furnishes a presumption of time depth. On this basis they stand ready to accept a date as early as the borderline between the Pliocene and Pleistocene periods.

By way of a general summary Dr. Broom [3] is of the opinion that it has been conclusively shown that there once existed in South Africa, and remained on the scene for many thousands of years, a family of higher Primates that were practically human. Although they had relatively small brains which reached an upper limit of

3 R. Broom, "The Ape-Men," *Scientific American*, Vol. 181, 1949, pp. 20-24.

900 cc., he is certain that they moved about on their hind feet and that their hands were too delicate to have been used for walking on the ground. Dr. Broom agrees with Dart that these creatures probably used tools, at least for hunting baboons. This raises a difficult question. Everyone is willing to concede that the Australopithecinae had perfectly erect posture, but many question their ability to have used tools because of their limited cranial capacities. What cannot be settled at present is whether Primate tool-usage automatically goes with the assumption of upright posture, or whether it also requires a very big brain.

Returning to the problem of human origins, it is no longer necessary in the light of the South African material to rely entirely on the older notion that man has derived his distinctive body from some arboreal, brachiating simian who may have grown too heavy for tree life and began walking erect on earth. Instead, the Australopithecinae give additional support to the hypothesis that the human line may have begun veering away from the ape direction starting from some ancestral catarrhine such as Parapithecus or Propliopithecus.[4] At the moment it seems best to look upon the man-apes from South Africa as representatives of a humanoid branch that was moving slowly and incompletely in the direction of man, while elsewhere in the Old World some of their more highly evolved contemporaries were approaching and perhaps crossing the threshold of humanity.

According to a theory ably argued by Dr. William L. Straus, Jr., as many as four or five divergent lines may have arisen from a catarrhine ancestor that lived in the late Oligocene or early Miocene.[5] One line could have led to the Old World monkeys, another to the gibbons, a third to the big apes, and others to man-apes and man (Fig. 30). From this point of view human ancestry goes back in remote times to a nonbrachiating quadruped, and the living apes must be classified as distant cousins who became specialized for tree life after their line of evolution had long parted from man's.

[4] J. T. Robinson, "The Evolutionary Significance of the Australopithecines," *Yearbook of Physical Anthropology* (G. W. Lasker and J. L. Angel, eds.). The Viking Fund, New York, 1950, pp. 38-41.

[5] W. L. Straus, Jr., "The Riddle of Man's Ancestry," *Quarterly Review of Biology*, Vol. 24, 1949, pp. 200-23. In this article Straus does not give special consideration to the man-apes.

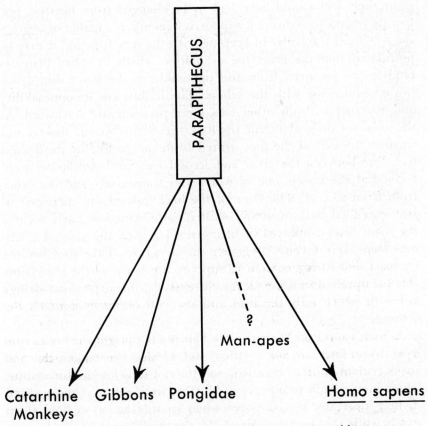

Fig. 30. Postulated lines of Primate descent from Parapithecus.
(Modified from W. L. Straus, Jr.).

## B. WHEREIN MAN DIFFERS FROM OTHER PRIMATES

For all that has been written on the subject no one knows exactly how or when the immediate forebears of modern man acquired their most distinctive body traits. Most often it is assumed that the process was somehow connected with the assumption of upright posture on solid earth. Despite the doubts raised by the discoveries of the South African man-apes, the process can be most meaningfully discussed if it is tentatively assumed to have taken place while large, arboreal, basically quadrupedal Primates were changing to terrestrial bipeds.

Starting from the ground up it is apparent that if such assumed prehominids were to get into the habit of successfully walking upright their feet would have had to be changed from flexible, pre-hensile organs to stabilized, supporting members capable of bearing the weight of the body. In keeping with the new function it may be postulated that the great toe or hallux, which in other Primates tends to be set apart from and opposable to the lesser digits, was brought into line with the others. The hallux lost its opposability and, together with the other toes, faced permanently downward. As the great toe drew alongside the foot, the others became shorter and smaller, the axis of the foot shifted from the middle or third digit to a line between the great and second toes, and two arches were formed at the instep, one of which ran transversely and the other from front to rear. The bone of the heel (calcaneum) increased in size, extended backward, and with its attendant soft parts became the main lever employed in lifting the leg from the ground when-ever steps were taken. Altogether the structure of the foot became compact and sturdy enough to support the body, at the same time that the upraised arches made it sufficiently flexible to permit a springy stride in which only the heel and the ball of the foot touch the ground.

As man's ancestors came to walk habitually upright the bones run-ning from knee to ankle (tibia and fibula) became longer and stronger than in other Primates, and the calf muscles (gastrocnemius) which men delight to observe in females, were enlarged and utilized to help raise the legs and feet when in motion or to hold them steady while standing still. Similarly, the thigh bone (femur) became elongated and straight of contour, and the muscles attached to it (gluteus maximus below the hips, and biceps femoralis lower down) became larger and more powerful in order to extend the leg fully and to give it strength for walking (Fig. 31). With the attainment of these modifications in the lower limbs the body was given firm sup-port or flexibility as needed, and the distinction of forelimbs from hindlimbs, first foreshadowed among the lowliest of Primates, re-ceived its greatest emphasis.

On the assumption that the human body represents a change-over from an original quadrupedal to a bipedal form, modifications are to be expected in the trunk and pelvic regions. By comparison with other Primates, man's pelvis seems to have been rotated forward and downward so that body weight is transmitted in a straight line to the lower limbs; also, the pelvis has been considerably shortened and broadened. Wide hips may not be stylish, but the wider they are the more human they are. Simply stated, it appears as though the pelvic girdle was transformed from a long, narrow, horizontally-

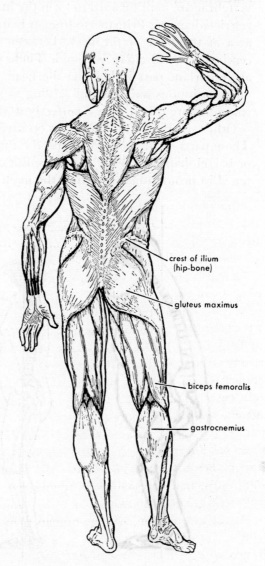

Fig. 31. Major leg muscles in man (after Clendening and Rogers, Hubbell, and Byers). These are the muscles primarily concerned with upright posture and bipedal walking.

crest of ilium (hip-bone)

gluteus maximus

biceps femoralis

gastrocnemius

placed cylinder in a pronograde body to a short, wide, flat, vertically-situated basin that was nevertheless firmly articulated to the thigh bones and spinal column.

In terms of the hypothesis being developed, changes of trunk and backbone above the pelvis also took place. Within the rear space between the lowest rib and the upper margin of the pelvis the lumbar vertebrae are bent forward to form the lumbar curve, a configuration restricted among Primates to human beings. Correspondingly, in the area at the back of the neck, between the head and shoulders, a cervical forward curve is found. These curves are thought to play an important part in keeping the head, trunk, and lower limbs in one continuous axis, and in serving as springs to make the spinal column more pliant than a perfectly straight shaft (Fig. 32).

Other significant modifications occurred in the chest and rib cage. These parts of the body comprise the thorax, and are usually round or barrel-shaped in other Primates, but appear to have become flattened in proto-humans. Within the main body cavity are located the

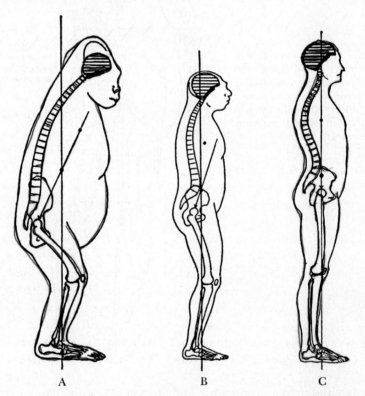

Fig. 32. Upright posture and spinal curves (after J. Dudley Morton). A comparative view of (A) a gorilla; (B) Neandertal Man from La Chapelle-aux-Saints; and (C) *Homo sapiens.*

internal organs or viscera, some of which lie within the thorax while others are contained in the pelvic basin. These organs are supported in four-footed beasts primarily by the pelvic floor on which they rest. In a two-footed position, however, the force of gravity tends to pull all the viscera downward, out of place. To counteract this dangerous tendency, the human body is provided with strong membranous sheets (mesenteries) that wrap around some of the internal organs and help attach them to the backbone so that they cannot readily be dislodged. Assistance is also provided by the remnant of a tail which, in human beings, normally curves under the pelvic outlet where it helps close the bottom opening and provides a means of attachment for many tissues that also aid in keeping the viscera in place.

The most important modifications that occurred in the hands, arms, and shoulders as prehominids are thought to have become committed to orthograde posture, are concerned with a general shortening of the total arm length, from finger tips to shoulders, and a shift in the relative proportions of the forearm to the upper arm. Most varieties of modern man have a forearm that is short in relation to the upper arm, but the reverse is true of the existing apes. Likewise, when human beings stand erect, the finger tips reach only to a point approximately midway between the hips and knees.

A great number of highly significant alterations are thought to have taken place above the shoulders and are believed to be related to the manner in which the head is balanced on top of the spine. In quadrupeds, or animals that only infrequently walk semierect like some of the apes, the spinal column is held horizontally or nearly so, and enters the skull through an opening (foramen magnum) near the rear (occiput). Such an arrangement necessitates a set of strong ligaments or nuchal muscles in order to hold the poorly poised head firmly in place. The nuchal muscles, in turn, require sturdy points of attachment, and these are provided by a rugged area of bone in the occipital region at the back of the skull, in conjunction with elongated bony projections that protrude backward from the cervical or neck vertebrae. Such a set of structures may be readily observed in the skeleton of a gorilla (Fig. 33), and when one of these beasts is seen in the flesh its neck appears to be exceedingly thick, short, and muscular, while its head gives the impression of being sunk between the shoulders.

To the simian arrangement of neck, head, and upper spinal column, the body of an orthograde being like man provides a marked contrast. A human carries his spine vertically with the backbone entering a foramen magnum that is centrally situated at the base of

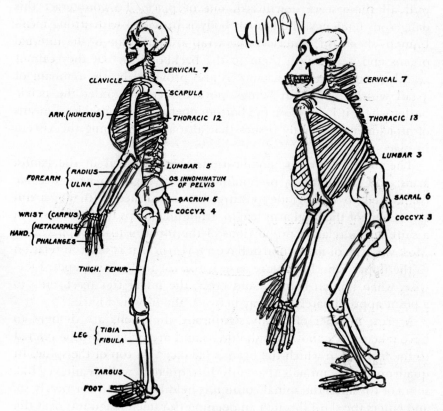

Fig. 33. Comparison of human and gorilla skeletons (after Stibbe). Particularly striking are the differences in the skulls, vertebral columns, poise of the head, hand and arm length, rib cages, pelvic girdles, stance, legs, and feet.

the skull. Thus, the head is neatly balanced and poised on top of the vertebral column, and neither the occipital portion of the skull nor the cervical vertebrae are particularly rugged, for only a slight nuchal musculature is needed to bind the head securely in place. Man has, as a result, a good deal of free space between the shoulders and head, so that his neck appears long and slender when compared with an ape's (Fig. 33).

Although it must be admitted that the cause-and-effect relationships of the changes discussed in this section are not properly known, it certainly seems reasonable to assume that modifications of feet, legs, pelvis, visceral attachment, spine, neck, and head, were somehow connected with the attainment of bipedal, terrestrial locomotion. Simultaneously, while these presumably functional adjustments were going on, another series seems to have been taking place that has little or no direct connection with the position in which the body is held and carried. Of these the most significant, in the light of man's later development, pertain to the size and form of the bony braincase and its contents.

## C. MAN'S SWOLLEN BRAINCASE

In most species of apes, but best exemplified by the gorilla, the eye sockets are crowned in adult males by a great, thick, transverse supraorbital torus. Such an ape, it has just been explained, is also apt to have a great deal of rugged bone at the back of the skull to provide attachment for ligaments and powerful nuchal muscles. Compressed between the front and rear areas of solid bone the cranial vault has only a small hollow chamber in which the brain may lodge. This arrangement seems to limit the cranial capacity of the gorilla to an average of about 500 cc.

Very important, indeed, are the differences to be noted in all these respects among living humans. The heavy bars of bone over the eye orbits have diminished almost to the vanishing point in modern

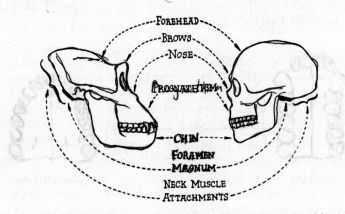

Fig. 34. Comparison of gorilla's and human skull (after Howells). Many essential distinctions are plainly indicated.

men and women; and with the attainment of an evenly poised head on the upper end of the spine, the nuchal muscles and ligaments have become so delicate that they do not require massive areas of bone for attachment. The cranial vault gives the appearance of having expanded upward, backward, and from side to side, increasing threefold the size of the hollow chamber which holds the brain (Fig. 34). These conditions make possible an average cranial capacity of around 1350 cc. for modern man, and the upper limit may even run over 1600 cc. Some of the cultural consequences of man's expanded brain will be discussed later, but from any point of view the swollen cranial vault is one of the most outstanding features of man's physical evolution.

## D. WHERE DID YOU GET THAT FACE?

Whereas the braincase is thought to have grown larger among early hominids, the facial region was becoming smaller and more delicate, while the forehead was getting higher and broader and the brow ridges and jaws were shrinking. In particular, the lower jaw (mandible) looks as though it had diminished in bulk and receded in position. At the same time the rear branches (ascending rami), which join the skull near the temples, had to become splayed out if they were to accommodate themselves to man's broadened braincase. From a different viewpoint the inner area of any lower Primate's jaw is shaped like a long and narrow "U," whereas the inner area of a true hominid's jaw has a parabolic shape (Fig. 35).

Development of a prominent, bony chin is another exclusively human feature of the lower jaw. When viewed in profile, the outer

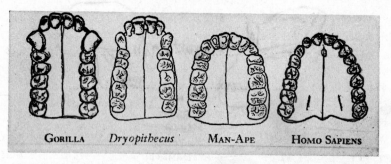

GORILLA    *Dryopithecus*    MAN-APE    HOMO SAPIENS

Fig. 35. A series of palates (after Howells). Typical of apes are long "U-shaped" palates, with pointed and projecting canines. *Homo sapiens* has a short, parabolic palate, with less pointed and non-projecting canine teeth.

line of almost any nonhuman Primate's mandible appears at the
center to curve under and away like the arc of an old-fashioned rock-
ing chair. Conversely, the same region in man shows a very pronounced forward bulge (Fig. 36). No adequate explanation for this

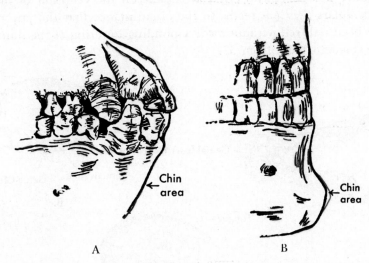

Fig. 36. Lower jaws of ape and man (after Hooton). An ape's lower jaw (A)
protrudes and shows prognathism, but is entirely without a chin. Man's lower
jaw (B) is far less protrusive, but the chin area juts prominently forward.

phenomenon has yet been offered, but a prominent, forward-projecting, bony chin is one of the most distinctive traits of the human body.

Another significant aspect of man's mandible may be found on the
inner side of the central point, "opposite" the chin. Here are rooted
the genio-glossus muscles that manipulate the tongue. These muscles
originate in apes from a depression or pit, above which there extends
a bony ledge known as a simian shelf. In contrast to this arrangement,
human tongue muscles are attached to small, rough excrescences of
bone known as genial tubercles, above which there is no shelf at all
(Fig. 37). Despite these anatomical differences, the failure of other
Primates to develop speech is more likely to be based on a small brain
than on any restriction of tongue movements.

Although jaw dimensions have decreased, the mouths of living
men contain the same dental formula as do the higher Primates.
There has been a reduction in the over-all size of human teeth; the
canines neither project beyond the closed mouth nor interlock; dif-

ferences of spacing and in length-breadth proportions have come about; and there are variations of cusp pattern on the molars that are peculiar to man. On the whole, though, human teeth do not differ radically from those of the higher Primates. Some students attribute the difficulties often attendant on the eruption of man's third molars (wisdom teeth) to the circumstance that the jawbones have been reduced without a corresponding lowering of the number of permanent teeth from 32.

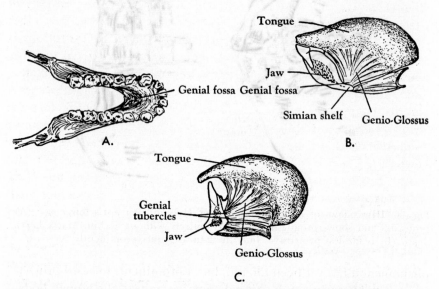

Fig. 37. Tongue attachments of ape and man (after Hooton and Keith). In apes (A and B) the tongue and its associated muscles originate from a pit or fossa on the inner side of the lower jaw (mandible). In humans the tongue and its attendant muscles are affixed to bits of bone, known as genial tubercles.

Few things contribute as much to the distinctive appearance of the human countenance as do thick, fleshy, and sometimes everted or outrolled lips that expose the reddened, mucous portions to view; and a nose that rises well above the rest of the face. Since other Primates generally have thin, taut lips that seem to be tightly stretched over bulging mouths, it has been suggested that the recession of the human jaws has left behind a considerable amount of slack skin that has somehow become furled into lips. This hypothesis is not quite satisfactory, nor has any likely theory been advanced to account for the uniqueness of the human nose. Reference is made only to the underlying nasal skeleton, and not to the soft parts that rest on it. Simians have low-lying and flat nasal bones that scarcely rise above the rest of the facial skeleton. To possess high, elevated nasal bones, therefore, is to show one's self to be a true representative of modern man.

## E. MAN STANDS ALONE, AND PAYS A PRICE

Physical anthropologists think it likely that man has retained a highly generalized and typical form of Primate body, except for his expanded braincase, long legs, and stabilized feet. His other organs and members are neither exceedingly large nor exceptionally small, and their usefulness is not confined to a restricted environmental range or a sharply delimited kind of function. Nonetheless, humans make up the only species of Primates that customarily walk or run on the ground in an upright posture. Some think that the acquisition of this ability was a slow process, which was so complex and difficult that it has not been successfully completed even in our own day. A surprising number of adjustments remain imperfect, and until they are perfected they will continue to plague mankind. Without stopping to dwell on the frequency of flat feet, degenerate small toes, fallen arches, excessive curvatures of the spine, backaches, faulty wisdom teeth, and the difficulties of females who must give birth to babies with swollen braincases, let us consider the stress imposed on the circulatory system which, in upstanding men and women, must pump blood against the force of gravity to and from the heart and such distant extremities as the fingers, toes, ears, and brains. In their minor manifestations the difficulties of circulation may cause no greater discomfort than cold feet or readily frostbitten ears or finger tips, but in extreme cases they may be responsible for the grave ailments lumped under the phrase, "heart failure."

A heavy burden is also imposed by the force of gravity on the mesenteries that help hold some of the viscera in place. When abdominal wall muscles weaken, as they not infrequently do, a rupture or tear may occur that permits an organ to slip out of place. Abdominal hernias are the most common of these displacements, but various other forms of rupture are known to surgeons.

## F. THE RELATIONSHIP OF MODERN MAN TO
## EXTINCT HOMINIDS [6]

Although scientists disagree on the details of man's immediate ancestry they stand firm in the belief that the long list of distinctively human characteristics is matched by an equally impressive list of biological resemblances shared by man and higher Primates. If the arrangement of evolutionary lines shown in Figure 5 approximates the truth, it indicates that two related but different paths appear close together when they are just starting to separate, but become more widely divergent with the passage of time. The figure of a caret, $\wedge$, demonstrates the basic idea in simple fashion. The top represents the start of divergence, and the bottom shows separation at a much later date. As we trace the two lines backward in time (upward), the less far apart they are. Such is the case with the living simians and modern man. Today they seem very far apart but we can discover their common ancestry by tracing their evolutionary lines back in time.

Not many decades ago the quest for predecessors of modern man used to be spoken of as a "search for missing links." Such a description has fallen into disuse because it gives the impression that there once existed crosswise connections between other Primate and human branches. Anthropologists do not believe in the existence of such fanciful cross-ties, but they do believe that if man's line is followed back it will lead to creatures less humanoid than living men and women.

Remains of so many partially manlike forms have been discovered that a figure like a caret is greatly oversimplified and fails to show the multiplicity of lines that actually exists. Far from having too few remains to guide them, anthropologists find themselves embarrassed with riches. Out of the mass of early hominids already found they do not know which ones belong in the direct path leading to modern man, and which represent side branches that culminated only in dead-ends. They do not know with certainty where each of these hominids originated, and they cannot recite the entire cast in the or-

---

[6] In other anthropological textbooks the phrase "fossil men" is used in place of "extinct hominids." However, since the remains discussed are neither invariably fossilized nor completely human, "extinct hominids" seems to give a more precise description of what is meant.

der of its appearance. Moreover, they are forced to deal with the vagaries of asymmetrical evolution.[7] According to this concept the course of evolution proceeds irregularly, with some body parts evolving more rapidly than others. Only with such a concept in mind can we understand why some specimens of early hominids, as is literally the case, have human thighbones but apish skulls, or simian jaws containing humanoid teeth. Confronted with such assortments, who is to say whether a particular example should be classed with man or with some other Primate?

Out of the welter of puzzling details several facts may be selected as valid. Before man had achieved his present body form there lived many kinds of less completely evolved hominids. No one of them is as old as one million years, which marks the start of the Pleistocene period, and the great majority go back only to mid-Pleistocene times, about 500,000 years ago, or less. Some of the early humanoids are probably in the main line of man's descent, but most of them died without known issue, and not one has survived to our day in his original form. Because the **extinct hominids** help mark the path that man followed after leaving the simian line, anthropologists pay much attention to their study.

### SELECTED REFERENCES

Broom, R, "The Genera and Species of the South African Fossil Ape-Man," *American Journal of Physical Anthropology*, Vol. 8, 1950, pp. 1-13.

Broom, R., and Robinson, J. T., "Notes on the Pelves of the Fossil Ape-Men," *American Journal of Physical Anthropology*, Vol. 8, 1950, pp. 489-494.

Broom, R., and Schepers, G. W. H., "The South African Fossil Ape-Men, the Australopithecinae," *Transvaal Museum, Memoir No. 2*, Pretoria, 1946.

Dart, R. A., "Taungs and Its Significance," *Natural History*, Vol. 26, 1926, pp. 315-327.

Hooton, E. A. "The Asymmetrical Character of Human Evolution," *American Journal of Physical Anthropology*, old series, Vol. 8, 1925, pp. 125-141.

Morton, D. J., *The Human Foot*, rev. ed., New York, 1937.

[7] E. A. Hooton, "The Asymmetrical Character of Human Evolution," *American Journal of Physical Anthropology*, Vol. 8, 1925, pp. 125-41.

Straus, W. L. Jr., "The Riddle of Man's Ancestry," *Quarterly Review of Biology,* Vol. 24, 1949, pp. 200-223.

Von Koenigswald, G. H. R., "The South-African Man-Apes and Pithecanthropus," *Carnegie Institution,* publication No. 530, Washington, 1942.

CHAPTER 6

# Extinct Hominids

## A. THE CLASSIFICATION OF EXTINCT HOMINIDS

When Charles Darwin published *The Origin of Species* in 1859, and *The Descent of Man* in 1871, he showed no awareness of the existence of extinct hominid remains. Yet, even in his day, two important discoveries had already been made. Within the last century a surprising number of additional finds have been reported throughout the Old World. At the outset, each new form was assigned by its enthusiastic finder to a separate species or genus, more or less at random. There thus came into existence a chaotic hodgepodge of terms that made it difficult to figure out the relationships of the various remnants to one another and to modern man. Only recently has the problem been somewhat clarified by means of painstaking comparative studies. These have made possible a tentative classification in which all the extinct hominids are grouped into a single genus, *Homo.*

So far the most comprehensive classification has been proposed by the late Dr. Franz Weidenreich. He was of the opinion that even before the middle of the Pleistocene *Homo* had become separated into at least three major divisions, each of which contained several

different types. Weidenreich named the large divisions, in the supposed order of their resemblance to modern man, **Archanthropinae**
("ancient hominids"), **Paleoanthropinae** ("old hominids"), and **Neoanthropinae** ("new hominids").[1] Weidenreich's scheme will be followed in this chapter, but with some modifications. Only a selected
number of extinct hominids will be treated, and it is essential to bear
in mind that the order in which the material is presented depends
on the nearness of a specimen's resemblance to modern man and
not on the time when it is supposed to have lived.[2] The dates when
discoveries were made will have no bearing on the order of classification.

## B. ARCHANTHROPINAE FROM EAST ASIA—GIANT SIZE AND REGULAR

Together, the Archanthropinae comprise the earliest and in many
respects the least highly evolved of the creatures that may be called
men. They consist of three main divisions which had inhabited either
the island of Java or the region of China. Most of the specimens are
assumed to have been discovered in mid-Pleistocene or somewhat
earlier soil deposits, so that in the aggregate they may be said to be
over a half million years old.

## I. Gigantopithecus

Full of doubts and unanswerable questions, yet packed with interest for anthropologists, is the account of the first specimen to be
considered (Fig. 38A). It consists only of portions of three molar teeth
obtained between 1934 and 1939 by Dr. von Koenigswald at Canton
and on the island of Hong Kong. They came, of all unlikely places,
from the drawers of apothecary shops. No one knows exactly where
they were originally found or what geological age they represent.
It is impossible to establish a full case on the basis of such scant
evidence, yet Professor Ashley Montagu has written, "These are
the teeth of an early giant form of extinct man"; [3] and Professor

---

1 F. Weidenreich, *Apes, Giants, and Man*, Chicago, 1946, pp. 29-31.
2 This method is known as morphological dating, and is not free of scientific ob-
jections. See T. D. Stewart, "The Development of the Concept of Morphological Dating . . . in America," *Southwestern Journal of Anthropology*, Vol. 5, 1949, especially
pp. 15-16.
3 M. F. Ashley Montagu, *op. cit.*, p. 134.

Franz Weidenreich has gone so far as to say that the teeth are those not of a giant ape but of "a giant man and should, therefore, have been named Gigantanthropus and not Gigantopithecus." [4]

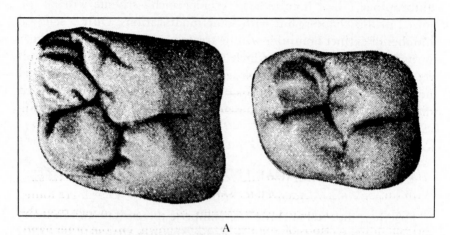

Fig. 38. Fragments of giant Archanthropinae (after Weidenreich). A. Right upper molar tooth of Gigantopithecus (left, x 1½), and a corresponding tooth of *Homo sapiens*. B. Lower jaw fragment of Meganthropus (left, x 2), compared with the same portion of a modern man's mandible (right). Both specimens are x ½.

Dubious as were the circumstances of discovery, experts agree that the teeth of **Gigantopithecus** are human in every respect but size, for they are more than five times as big in volume as are the corresponding teeth of modern men. Were they the only indication of the

[4] F. Weidenreich, *op. cit.*, p. 59.

existence of early human giants they would scarcely deserve mention, but they gain extra credence from their resemblance to the teeth of another gigantic humanoid that Dr. von Koenigswald discovered in Java.

## II. Meganthropus

At Sangiran, Java, in 1940-41, von Koenigswald found the remains of two jaw fragments (Fig. 38B) that he named **Meganthropus paleojavanicus** ("giant man from old Java"). The exigencies of World War II prevented the finder from publishing the facts of his discovery, so the welcome task fell to his old friend and co-worker, Dr. Weidenreich. Von Koenigswald's main fragment consisted of a portion of a huge lower jaw, with three of the teeth in place, but he came to the conclusion that the relic was humanoid despite its size. With this opinion Weidenreich expressed complete accord. He found the mandibular fragments to be chinless, thicker, and higher than the corresponding sections of any Primate jaw known. On the other hand, he reported the shape of the dental arch to be intermediate between ape and man, and he considered the teeth to be enormous yet recognizably hominid. From so small a sample nothing definite can be said of the total size and shape of Meganthropus, but Weidenreich has ventured to guess that the ancient Javanese giant was bigger than any living gorilla. He also regarded Meganthropus as probably linked to Gigantopithecus and ancestral to the smaller Archanthropinae.

## III. Pithecanthropus erectus

Less than ten years after the death of Charles Darwin, a young and energetic Dutch surgeon named Dr. Eugene Dubois applied for colonial service in the Netherlands East Indies. He was a zealous student of human evolution, and so great was his faith in the theory that Primate-like hominids had once roamed on earth that he spent his spare time deliberately searching for their remains. Despite the overwhelming odds against him Dubois persisted until, in the years 1891 and 1892, his diligence and faith were rewarded. While working along the banks of an ancient channel that had been cut in Pleistocene days by the Solo River near Trinil in central Java, he picked up in the fall of 1891 an unusual kind of tooth. Three feet away he came across the upper part of a skull, and nearly fifty feet further off he located a left thighbone. Before he was through two more teeth

and a piece of a lower jaw, found at a more distant spot, were added
to his collection (Fig. 39).

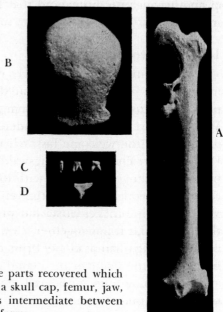

Fig. 39. Pithecanthropus Erectus. The parts recovered which
are shown here, include fragments of a skull cap, femur, jaw,
and teeth. The whole assemblage is intermediate between
apish and hominid forms.

From his knowledge of comparative anatomy Dubois became convinced that all the skeletal fragments pertained to an intermediate
sort of hominid whom he designated as **Pithecanthropus erectus**
("ape-man erect"). As can readily be imagined a heated discussion
arose when Dubois published his findings in 1894. Cautious scholars
insisted, not without reason, that the materials had been so widely
scattered that they might have come from several different creatures
instead of from the same individual. Perhaps, it was argued, the
simian portions were the remains of an ape, and the human parts
remnants of a long-deceased man. While this moot point has never
been satisfactorily settled, the consensus of anthropologists favors the
view that Dubois' original interpretation was essentially correct.

What, then, was Pithecanthropus erectus like? Judged by the skull
cap he was rather apish. His cranial vault was thick and heavy; a solid
torus of bone protruded above the eye cavities; the forehead was
exceedingly low and narrowly constricted just beyond the eye sockets;
and the nuchal area was so extensive and ran so high up the occiput

that the head must have been poorly poised on the spine. Based on the portion of the cranium that was actually found several competent specialists have reconstructed the entire skull and measured the cranial capacity. Their results vary somewhat but an average of about 950 cc. is pretty representative of all the estimates. This figure is nearly twice that of an adult gorilla, but only about two-thirds that of an average modern man. Judged in this way, Pithecanthropus occupies a sort of midway position between ape and man. Such an appraisal is supported by the jaw fragment, which is big and chinless but lacks a simian shelf on the inner side. Similarly, the teeth also combine hominid and apelike features.

Markedly different from the other fragments is the femur, which is quite modern in every way. The shaft has a straight contour, a sign of upright posture, and its size indicates that its owner stood around 5 feet, 7 inches high, and weighed about 150 pounds. When all the evidence is put together it gives the impression that Pithecanthropus erectus had a sort of ape's head mounted on an essentially human body.

Had all knowledge of Pithecanthropus been limited to the fragmentary discoveries made by Dubois, all conclusions would have been forever tentative and open to question. Luckily, investigators have persisted in searching through Java for additional remains that might confirm or alter the status ascribed to Pithecanthropus erectus. Between 1936 and 1939 Dr. von Koenigswald was fortunate enough to have located in early to middle Pleistocene formations the shattered cranium of an infant Pithecanthropoid, known from the site of its discovery as *Homo* modjokerto; as well as parts of three adult specimens, one of whose skulls resembles that found by Dubois "as closely as one egg another." Dr. von Koenigswald's material has strengthened the conclusion that Pithecanthropus erectus represents a kind of ape-man that walked erect in Java at least a half million years ago.

Somewhat different from other Pithecanthropoid remains is the fragment usually called Skull IV or Pithecanthropus robustus. Found by von Koenigswald in 1939 in the vicinity of Sangiran, Java, it consists of a braincase, with only the front quarter missing, and an upper jaw that still holds in their original positions most of the teeth. Except for extremely large and projecting canines the teeth of Pithecanthropus robustus are humanoid. The upper jaw is wider and

longer than in any other known hominid; and the braincase is long
and excessively broad, but low in elevation. Dr. Weidenreich has
interpreted Pithecanthropus robustus as belonging in the direct ancestral line of man, and as an intermediate form between the giant
and man-sized Archanthropinae.

## IV. Sinanthropus pekinensis

About thirty years or so after Dubois had made his original discoveries in Java, a number of persons began to suspect the presence
of extinct hominids in a limestone quarry situated at Chou Kou
Tien, 40 miles southwest of Peking. Up to 1927 the evidence was
extremely meager, but a brilliant analysis by the late Professor Da-
vidson Black led him to the conclusion that one tooth in particular
represented a hitherto unknown type of creature which he named
**Sinanthropus pekinensis** ("Chinese man from Peking"). In subsequent years Dr. Black's daring assumption was completely vindicated,
for more and more skeletal material came to light from Chou Kou
Tien, all of which pertained to the same kind of hominid.

Unlike the Pithecanthropoid relics the Sinanthropus specimens
were found in rapid succession, and were imbedded in stone so near
each other as to leave no doubt of their belonging together. By 1939
various bones and teeth representing approximately forty different
individuals had been excavated from deposits at Chou Kou Tien that
reach back to the middle Pleistocene. No single skeleton is complete,
but the collection includes a dozen or more skulls, numerous jaws
and femora, a great many teeth, one arm bone, and other fragments.
These remains are slightly variable in character, but it is not impossible to group them into one composite picture.

Sinanthropus skulls (Fig. 40) are provided with heavy, bony, brow
ridges; the foreheads are low and retreating; the jaws massive, protruding, and relatively chinless; and the nuchal areas are as rugged
and extensive as in Pithecanthropus. The teeth are far from uniform,
but they approach the human rather than the ape condition. Estimates of cranial capacity vary, but an average of over 1000 cc. is
indicated; and the thighbones show that the Chinese men from
Peking walked fully upright. Most writers on the subject accept as
reliable cultural objects found associated with Sinanthropus, which
suggest that he may have been a good hunter, capable of fabricating

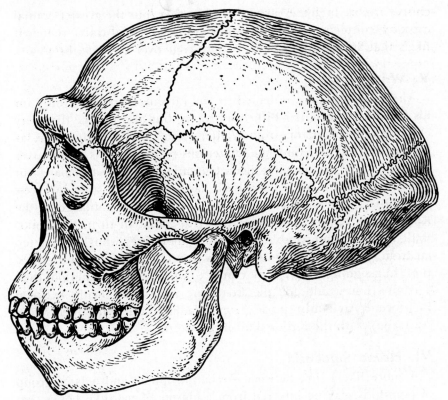

Fig. 40. Reconstruction of a female Sinanthropus skull (after Montagu, following Weidenreich). There is a surprisingly heavy supraorbital torus for a female, the forehead is retreating, the arch of the skull vault is low, prognathism is pronounced, and there is no forward projection of the chin.

stone tools and kindling fires, and that he might possibly have been addicted to cannibalism.

Although Dr. Black had ventured the belief, soon after the first discoveries were made, that Sinanthropus might have been related to Pithecanthropus, nothing much was done about classifying them together for a decade. Then, in 1939, Dr. Weidenreich, who had succeeded Dr. Black, and Dr. von Koenigswald, published a joint article in which they stated their conviction that all the remains of Pithecanthropus and Sinanthropus established a close relationship between the two types.[5] Neither of these branches of Archanthropinae is con-

[5] G. H. R. von Koenigswald and F. Weidenreich, "The Relationship between Pithecanthropus and Sinanthropus," Nature, Vol. 144, 1939.

clusively more highly evolved than the other, but the greater cranial capacity, coupled with one or two minor anatomical traits, render it likely that Sinanthropus holds a slight edge over Pithecanthropus.

## V. Wadjak Man

Anthropologists are indebted to Dr. Eugene Dubois not only for his finds of the original Pithecanthropus, but also for the discovery of two interesting crania from Wadjak, Java. They were found as far back as 1889-90, but for some mysterious reason Dubois waited over 30 years before announcing them. One might have been female, but the other was probably male. Each has a cranial capacity in excess of 1500 cc., and together they show a striking resemblance to the Keilor skull, found near Melbourne, Australia. In turn, the Keilor skull is closely comparable to existing aborigines who live not too far from Melbourne. If Dr. Dubois is correct (which is open to question) in assigning the Wadjak crania to the Pleistocene period, then a connection would for the first time have been made between Pleistocene Archanthropinae (from Wadjak) and living men (from Australia), with the Keilor skull in between.

## VI. Homo Soloensis

A more likely link between Archanthropinae and a later group of hominids may be inferred from a cluster of manlike bones that came to light from upper Pleistocene gravels at Ngandong in Java, a scant half-dozen miles east of Trinil where Dubois had located Pithecanthropus. The finder of these extinct hominids was Dr. W. F. F. Oppenoorth, of the Geological Survey of Java, who discovered portions of eleven crania and two tibiae between 1931 and 1936. In keeping with the custom of the day, Oppenoorth took the Ngandong remains to represent a new species which he termed **Homo soloensis** (Fig. 41). No conclusive judgment of the evolutionary status of the remains can be made because the skulls are all badly broken, and most of the jaws and teeth are missing.

From the general appearance of the skull vaults, which are low-pitched, with receding foreheads and big brow ridges of bone, but which have cranial capacities of 1200 cc., some authorities incline to regard *Homo soloensis* as related partially to Pithecanthropus-Sinanthropus and partially to Neandertal man, who typifies the Paleoanthropinae. Many also recall that when Oppenoorth first reported his

discoveries he called attention to the resemblance that the Solo
hominids bore to Rhodesian man, another of the Paleoanthropinae
with Neandertaloid characteristics. There is now a strong tendency
to agree with the general notion that *Homo soloensis* represents a
transitional form between the Archanthropinae and the Paleoanthropinae.

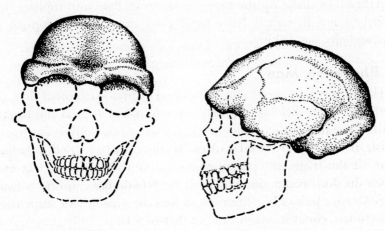

Fig. 41. Solo Man (after Howells). Only the shaded area was found. It reveals a
heavy supraorbital torus, and a low, backward-projecting skull vault.

## C. PALEOANTHROPINAE ROAM THE OLD WORLD

As indicated in the brief account of *Homo soloensis* there is no
sharp break between the hominids grouped under the term Archanthropinae and those classed as Paleoanthropinae. Nevertheless, anthropologists believe that a line between them ought somewhere to
be drawn. This is hard to do because there is no check list of anatomical traits to serve as a guide for assigning hominid material with
certainty to one division or the other. Fortunately, there is practically
no disagreement about the Paleoanthropic character of the specimens
to be treated in this section. Remains of Paleoanthropinae have been
discovered at varying depths in the Pleistocene, and in places ranging
from Spain to Central Asia. Under such conditions it is not surprising that they show a considerable amount of variability. Where
so many differences exist it is dangerous to make generalizations
about the type as a whole, but the feeling persists that the Paleoanthropinae appeared somewhat later than the Archanthropinae and

that in their cranial capacities, at least, they had approached closer to modern man.

Not many years ago there was a tendency to use the term Neandertal Man more or less interchangeably with Paleoanthropinae, but recent research has demonstrated that this usage is unsatisfactory. More than one kind of Neandertal man is now distinguished, and together they make up the major division of Paleoanthropinae, but it is best not to regard Neandertal man and Paleoanthropinae as one and the same thing.

## I. Rhodesian Man

Hardly any humanoid relic has caused greater excitement than the skull and other skeletal parts that were found in 1921 at the Broken Hill mine in Southern Rhodesia, Africa. Conservative anthropologists, headed by the late Dr. Ales Hrdlicka, flatly refused to believe that all the fragments pertained to the same individual, but even when the skull is examined by itself the **Rhodesian** cranium is amazing. Above a pair of big, high eye sockets there projects a stupendous bony torus, equal in magnitude to that of a large, fully-grown, male gorilla. Coupled with this is an exceedingly retreating forehead and a very low-roofed cranial vault. These features give Rhodesian man (Fig. 42) a singularly bestial appearance.

Curiously enough, the skull conforms in other regards to human standards. Its cranial capacity is estimated at 1300 cc.; the nasal bones are not quite as developed as in men of today, but they are by no means simian; the palate is huge in dimension but humanoid in shape; and the teeth are large but of hominid proportions. No one mentions Rhodesian man without calling attention to his poor health, for his teeth are badly decayed, he had trouble with his mastoids, and he probably suffered from arthritis.

No matter how it is to be interpreted the Rhodesian skull is an astonishing relic. Within itself it provides a striking illustration of asymmetrical evolution, for the stupendous torus and apelike face are accompanied by a cranial capacity and a set of teeth that fall well within the range of contemporary human averages. As to its relations with other extinct hominids, there is room for argument, but it shows a good deal of resemblance both to *Homo soloensis* and to some of the Neandertaloids from Western Europe.

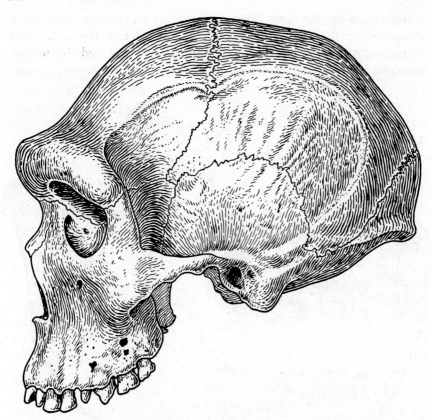

Fig. 42. The skull of Rhodesian Man (after Montagu). Despite a stupendous torus and low-arched skull vault, the cranial capacity of this extinct hominid was up to modern standards. Asymmetrical evolution is also apparent from the contrast between the hominid teeth and the slightly elevated nasal bones.

## II. Heidelberg Man

Just when or where the so-called classic Neandertaloids of Western Europe had their origin it is impossible to say, but the possibility must be recognized that they might have descended from a type of extinct hominid such as is known from the **Heidelberg jaw,** one of the most amazing relics ever attributed to the Paleoanthropinae.

The Heidelberg jaw was found in 1910 in the lower to mid-Pleistocene horizon of a sandpit at Mauer, half a dozen miles from Heidelberg, Germany. Only a lower jaw and its associated teeth, still resting in their original sockets, were recovered, a circumstance that makes it inadvisable to try to guess how the creature walked or what its

cranial capacity may have been. Suffice it to say that the jawbone is
exceptionally massive, minus a chin, and apelike in the occurrence
of such features as a simian pit to which were attached the tongue
muscles. However, the teeth are entirely human in size, proportions,

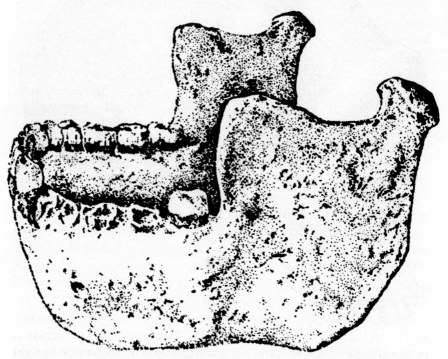

Fig. 43. The Heidelberg jaw (after Hooton). This huge, chinless jaw contains
unexpectedly human teeth.

number, arrangement, and projection. All experts dealing with extinct hominids have the impression that the person who is represented by the Heidelberg jaw (Fig. 43) may well have been a forerunner of Neandertal man.

## III. Homo Neandertalensis

Between 1848 and the present the remains of nearly a hundred
**Neandertal** men, women, and children have been discovered in the
Old World. They lived over a time span that covers more than
100,000 years, from the later stages of the Early Pleistocene well into
the Late Pleistocene. When their spread in time and space is con-

sidered, it is small wonder that they should be greatly diversified. A recent article by F. Clark Howell [6] makes explicit a distinction that had for some time been suspected between Early and Classic Neandertaloids. The Early group is best represented in an easterly direction from Central Europe, while the Classic division tends to be concentrated toward the West. Howell finds that the Early variety approaches more nearly the structure of modern man than the Classic, because it has shorter and narrower skulls, more highly arched cranial vaults, smaller facial skeletons, and other anatomical resemblances to living men. He regards the Early branch as more likely to have given rise to contemporary forms of man, and he looks upon the Classic group as a later offshoot, isolated, peripheral, and lacking in modern descendants.

Because of the profusion and variety of Neandertaloid remains it is exceedingly difficult to select specimens that accurately typify each of the two main units, but the skeleton of an elderly man that was found in 1908 at La Chapelle-aux-Saints in France, has for many years served as a model of the Classic Neandertal men from Western Europe. By using the measurements taken on the individual from La Chapelle-aux-Saints in conjunction with data from his nearby contemporaries, a reasonably good picture of Western European Classic Neandertaloids may be obtained.

Adult males appear to have stood 2 or 3 inches more than 5 feet high, and females were slightly shorter. This relatively low stature is attributed, partially, to failure to have achieved a completely upright posture. Classic Neandertal man had short leg bones with bowed shafts, which indicates that they could not be fully extended when he stood up. He is believed, consequently, to have walked with a dip at the knees, a mode of progression known as the bent-knee gait. The feet, too, seem imperfectly adjusted to orthograde locomotion. Heels are small and do not project very far backward, ankle arches are low, great toes are somewhat set apart from the rest, and there is reason to believe that in walking the weight of the body was transmitted to the outer borders of the feet (Fig. 44).

Generally speaking, Classic Neandertal man has a rather high and narrow pelvis, the chest is rounded, the lumbar curve is only

6 F. C. Howell, "The Place of Neanderthal Man in Human Evolution," *American Journal of Physical Anthropology*, Vol. 9, 1951, pp. 379-416. Howell's analysis is based on studies of crania only.

slightly developed, and the processes at the back of the cervical vertebrae are long and prominent. The latter feature, it should be recalled, is associated with heavy neck muscles necessitated by a poorly poised head. There is little reason to doubt that Classic

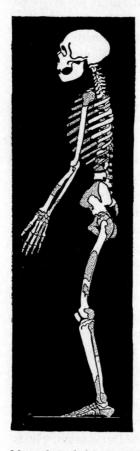

Fig. 44. Restoration of a Neandertal skeleton from La Chapelle-aux-Saints (after MacCurdy, following Boule). Particularly noteworthy are the poorly poised skull, slightly developed spinal curves, rounded rib cage, and bowed femur.

Neandertaloids had short thick necks and outthrust faces and jaws. Their skulls had big supraorbital ridges of bone, although the Early type may have had even larger tori. Bun-shaped prominences are occasionally found at the back of the head in all varieties of Neandertal man. Mandibles are inclined to be bulky and to have little or no chin, but all have genial tubercles and teeth that are almost entirely modern. Cranial capacities run high, usually ranging from 1300 cc. to 1600 cc.

Except for his inability to stand completely upright, which may have interfered with his speed and agility, *Homo Neandertalensis* was not significantly inferior in physical fitness or gross brain development to human beings now living. Furthermore, much of the era during which the Classic Neandertaloids lived in Western Europe was subject to the frigid weather conditions of a protracted Ice Age. With this difficult environment they were able to cope by developing cultural aids in the forms of cave homes, fireplaces, possibly clothing, and well-made tools and weapons. We shall meet the Classic Neandertaloids again when we take up the Mousterian phase of culture in Western Europe.

Two variants of *Homo Neandertalensis* require brief mention. One is known as Steinheim man and exhibits a blend of Paleoanthropic and Neoanthropic traits; and the other is called Ehringsdorf man, a Neandertaloid that makes a surprisingly close approach to the Neoanthropinae.

## IV. Neandertal Man from Mount Carmel

In the not too distant past it used to be said that the Classic Neandertaloids were eliminated from Western Europe by new forms of man, equipped with more efficient weapons. Recent discoveries at Mount Carmel in Palestine have rendered such statements obsolete. Expeditions headed by the famed British archeologist, Dr. Dorothy Garrod, located in 1931 and 1932 the remains of about a dozen individuals who had lain since middle Pleistocene times in two limestone caves on the western slopes of Mount Carmel. Both caves have picturesque names, being known as Mugharet es-Skuhl ("Cave of the Kids"), and et-Tabun ("The Oven"). Within them reposed a group of greatly varied skeletons, ranging from a Tabun woman who is practically indistinguishable from a Classic Neandertaloid of Western Europe, to a man from Skuhl whose anatomical structure is essentially modern. The other ten relics show differing degrees of admixture between the extremes. Two different explanations have been put forth to account for the wide range of hominid types at Mount Carmel. One opinion holds that the Palestinian Neandertaloids represent stages of evolution that culminated in modern man; and the other maintains that recent forms of man had evolved independently elsewhere, and had then migrated to Mount Carmel where they interbred with local Neandertaloids.

Howell has diagrammed both suggested interpretations (Fig. 45).

He inclines to the latter which, in his belief, indicates a line of evolution that begins with Heidelberg man and runs through Swanscombe (a Neoanthropic form to be discussed below), to Steinheim. There the line leads into a large division, within which

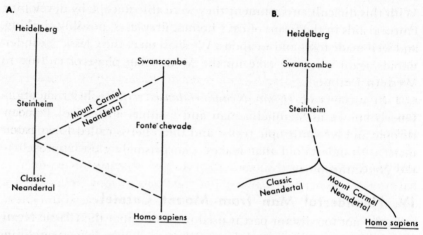

Fig. 45. Postulated relations of extinct hominids to *Homo sapiens* (modified from Howell).

Ehringsdorf man and the Classic Neandertaloids are set apart from the Mount Carmel Neandertaloids and modern man. In this graphic way Howell expresses the opinion that the Classic Neandertaloids reached a deadend, while the Mount Carmel Neandertaloids gave rise to fully evolved human beings.

## D. NEOANTHROPINAE TAKE OVER

Those hominids that lived prior to the end of the Pleistocene period yet show a near approximation to the structure of contemporary man are ordinarily classified as Neoanthropinae. Two theories have prevailed concerning their relationships to the Paleoanthropinae, particularly Neandertal man. One group of writers favors the notion that the Neandertalers became completely extinct and are to be regarded only as collateral relatives who contributed nothing to the formation of modern man. The other group avers that some Neandertaloids are directly ancestral to some of the forms of living man. An up-to-date but conservative statement would be to the effect

that Neandertal man as such did become extinct during the Pleistocene, but not before some Neandertaloid genes had been contributed through evolution or interbreeding to the basic stock that
produced the present human population.

Anthropological opinion has also undergone a change with respect
to the dating of Neoanthropic remains. At first it was commonly held
that the more modern-looking forms of Pleistocene man could not
possibly have appeared as early as Neandertal man. Next, the consensus favored the opposite view. On the basis of reputed Neoanthropinae reported to have come from the lowermost Pleistocene, or
even Pliocene levels, opinions were expressed to the effect that ancestral forms of modern man were actually much older than Neandertal man. Thanks to a new method of dating ancient remains, based
on the principle that under fixed conditions a long-buried bone absorbs and retains more fluorine than a more recently-buried one,[7] it
has been demonstrated that some of the Neoanthropic relics are not
as aged as was once claimed. However, there is still reason to believe
that some Neoanthropinae are at least of the same age as Neandertal
Man, and that a few specimens may even be older. Fortunately, the
problems that plague specialists deal only with the early and middle
phases of the Pleistocene. By the time that period was drawing to
a close the Archanthropinae and Paleoanthropinae had disappeared
from the scene throughout the Old World, and Neoanthropic forms
predominated and led directly to the varieties of men who now inhabit the earth.

## I. Swanscombe Man

Anthropologists are reasonably well agreed, with the support of
recent dating by fluorine analysis, that the earliest of the Western
European Neoanthropinae is represented by fragments of a hominid
skull that were uncovered in 1935-37 at Swanscombe, Kent, England,
from a section of a gravel pit that goes back to an early stage of the
mid-Pleistocene. All that was found of the so-called **Swanscombe
Man** was the occipital bone from the back of a youthful, probably
female cranium, and an adjoining piece of the left parietal bone that
lies above the temple (Fig. 46). These remnants hardly provide a

---

[7] For an account of the technique of dating by fluorine analysis, as well as its application to extinct hominids, see K. P. Oakley, "The Fluorine-Dating Method," *Yearbook of Physical Anthropology*, The Viking Fund, Inc., New York, 1949, pp. 44-52.
Not all authorities accept the antiquity of the Swanscombe remains.

complete picture, but when the available portions of the Swanscombe skull are compared with similar parts of other individuals of the same sex and age (insofar as these can be determined), it becomes

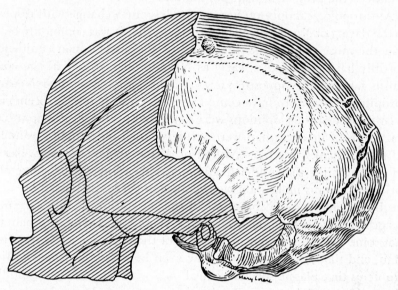

Fig. 46. Remains of Swanscombe Man (after Montagu). Only the light portions were discovered. Although they are fragmentary, they give every indication of having come from a modern-appearing skull.

perfectly clear that the young lady from Swanscombe had a cranial capacity of about 1325 cc., and was much more highly evolved than any of her Neandertal contemporaries.

## II. Piltdown Man

Another supposedly Neoanthropic relic from southern England has been the center of one of the longest debates in the history of modern anthropology. It goes back to 1908 when Charles Dawson, an amateur archeologist, reported the first of a series of finds made in a gravel pit bordering on the Piltdown Common in Sussex. From time to time until 1913 Dawson and others continued to remove bits of bone from the same pit, and the combined fragments are known as **Piltdown** man or woman, or else as Eoanthropus Dawsoni ("Dawson's Dawn Man"). Briefly stated, the Piltdown remains consist of a sizable portion of a mandible and several segments of a cranial vault (Fig. 47).

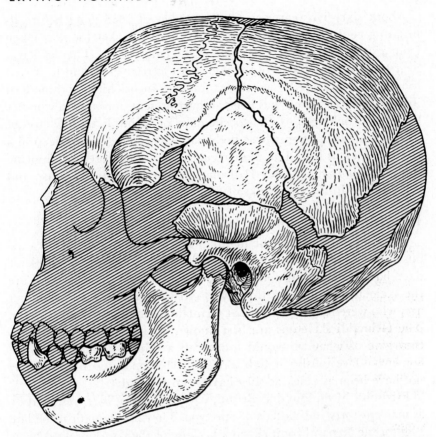

Fig. 47. The controversial Piltdown skull (after Montagu). Sometimes regarded in times past as an outstanding example of asymmetrical evolution, but recently proclaimed a hoax, this specimen has an admittedly apish jaw, which was supposedly found together with a modern kind of upper skull. The fragments actually discovered are shown in light color.

The argument that has raged for so long revolves around the question of whether the two main fragments belong together and pertain to the same individual. The lower jaw is apelike, but the upper part of the skull is perfectly modern and has a cranial capacity that has been estimated to fall between a low of 1200 cc. and a high of 1400 cc.[8]

[8] K. P. Oakley and C. R. Hoskins, "New Evidence on the Antiquity of Piltdown Man," *Nature*, vol. 165, 1950, pp. 379-382. In this article the authors show that similar dates apply to the jaw and skull fragments. While this book was in press a number of newspapers reported that Dr. Oakley and two fellow-scientists had branded the Piltdown

About sixty-five years ago, in September of 1888, long before its meaning could have been properly evaluated, a skeleton was taken from a spot called Galley Hill, along the banks of the Thames River near London. Almost all of the skeleton was recovered, and it proved to represent a man who was about 5 feet, 3 inches high, and modern in every respect. There has been an ever-present doubt as to whether he actually belonged to Pleistocene days, or is simply the skeleton of a contemporary person whose body happened to be buried deep in a layer of ancient soil. The most recent conclusion, based on fluorine analysis, eliminates Galley Hill man from the Neoanthropinae and flatly assigns him to the ranks of modern man.[9]

## III. Grimaldi, Predmost, and Fontéchevade Man

From several spots on the mainland of Europe discoveries of various kinds of Neoanthropinae, usually of mid-Pleistocene or later date, have been announced. Among the more important of these are the skeletal remains of a thirty-year-old woman and a boy half her age, who were found in a cave at Grimaldi along the Italian Riviera. The **Grimaldi** skeletons are best known because of the indications they give of what we would today call a Caucasoid-Negroid cross. Somewhat facetiously, though, Professor Hooton states that they may not have been as black as they have been painted.[10]

**Predmost Man,** found at Brünn, Czechoslovakia, is represented by as many as forty individuals of one type. They are thought to be late Pleistocene Neoanthropinae who, because of their pronounced brow ridges, might possibly have interbred with Neandertaloids. All of them have large faces, and rugged and massive braincases. A variant form, **Combe Capelle,** is known from France, and also shows a possible combination of Neoanthropic and Neandertal traits.[11]

material as an out-and-out hoax. This is not the first time that such a charge has been made. Even if it turns out to be absolutely true, it would not greatly alter our knowledge of human evolution. Anthropologists have always regarded as dubious the circumstances under which Piltdown man was found, and no evolutionist has ever based his conclusions on the authenticity of Dawson's discoveries. A full account of the Piltdown hoax is given in "The Solution of the Piltdown Problem," by J. S. Weiner, K. P. Oakley, and W. E. Le Gros Clark, in *Bulletin of The British Museum (Natural History) Geology,* Vol. 2, No. 3, 1953, pp. 141-146.

[9] M. F. Ashley Montagu and K. P. Oakley, "The Antiquity of Galley Hill Man," *American Journal of Physical Anthropology,* Vol. 7, 1949, pp. 363-84.

[10] E. A. Hooton, *Up from the Ape,* New York, rev. ed., 1946, p. 374.

[11] Professor Carleton S. Coon holds strongly to the opinion that the Combe Capelle type is directly ancestral to an important strain of living Caucasoids.

Portions of two skulls, one of which came to light near the village of Montbrun, France, as recently as 1947, provide all the evidence there is for the existence of **Fontéchevade Man.** They are unquestionably Neoanthropinae from a late Pleistocene horizon, and have been tentatively classed with the Swanscombe relic.

## IV. Cro-Magnon Man

During the later phases of the Pleistocene there appear in steadily increasing numbers in Western Europe types of individuals known

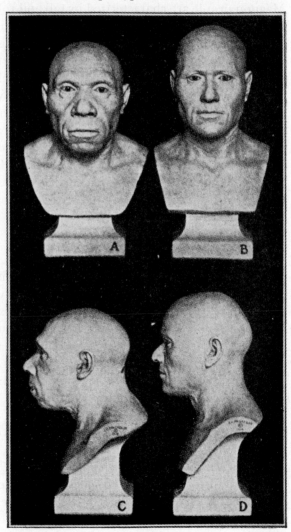

Fig. 48. Restoration of Cro-Magnon and Neandertal men (after McGregor). Cro-Magnon man's head is higher, his neck is longer, his head and jaws are less out-thrust, his brow ridges are more delicate, and his chin is well developed. In short, he is a modern human in all respects.

as **Cro-Magnon.** They are a highly evolved group of Neoanthropinae who, by absorption, displacement, or elimination of earlier populations came to dominate the areas where they settled. Originally, the term Cro-Magnon was applied only to a cluster of five skeletons that were found in 1868 in the Dordogne region of southern France, but nowadays the designation is often used for all of the modern-looking forms that lived toward the end of the Pleistocene.

Once again we encounter the difficulty of trying to give a single description to cover many divergent types. As a whole, the Cro-Magnon people are characterized by tall and robust bodies, with long arms and shins, and total statures that go as high in males as 5 feet, 10 or 11 inches. Their heads are large and high-vaulted, with moderate brow ridges, elevated foreheads, well-formed chins, and capacious braincases that may accommodate as much as 1600 cc. (Fig. 48). Apart from some unimportant face and body features, which are not unknown among living human beings, there is really nothing to differentiate the Cro-Magnon men from tall and powerfully built people of our day. Many students are convinced that a fraction of Europe's population is directly derived from Cro-Magnon ancestry. It thus becomes a matter of personal preference whether one calls the Cro-Magnons the last of the extinct hominids or the first examples of modern man.

## E. RECAPITULATION

This chapter makes an effort to picture some of the steps in the process by which living humans came to be so widely separated from such other Primates as are typified by the existing apes. For this purpose a review was made of some of the extinct hominids that had preceded modern man on earth. No attempt was made to provide exhaustive summaries of all the specimens or of the many controversies that have sprung up as new discoveries have been announced, and no scheme was formulated for fitting all of the data into one great timetable. Only enough materials were selected to furnish a tentative outline of the last evolutionary events that took place before modern man's emergence.

Even if the uncertainties that go with each step in the story are frankly admitted, the main episodes in the divergence of the human and simian stocks stand out fairly well. Apparently, by early Pleistocene times the separation had progressed far enough to produce those manlike forms known as Archanthropinae who once inhabited parts of Java and China. If the Weidenreich-von Koenigswald hypothesis is correct, the first hominids were of giant proportions like Giganto-pithecus and Meganthropus, but later forms were smaller and had the dimensions of Pithecanthropus and Sinanthropus, which approximate those of living mankind. About the time that the mid-Pleistocene horizons were being reached the Archanthropinae seem to have given rise, in the more southerly latitudes of the Old World, to such late Archanthropic or early Paleoanthropic forms as Solo and Rhodesian man. These may possibly have been ancestral to the kind of hominid represented by the Heidelberg jaw, from whom may have stemmed one or more varieties of the fully-developed Paleo-anthropinae typified by the Early and Classic Neandertaloids. Contemporaneously, different sorts of hominids, the Neoanthropinae, who closely resemble modern men, began to show up in Europe in growing numbers, especially during the middle and later stages of the Pleistocene. Some of these, notably the Swanscombe specimen, give no evidence of mixture with Neandertalers but others, including the Predmost population, suggest a degree of contact.

Before the Pleistocene drew to a close, about 20,000 years ago, very highly evolved Neoanthropinae, making up the Cro-Magnon group, penetrated into Western Europe from some place further east where they are presumed to have originated. They became widespread and dominant in their new environment, and there gave rise to some of the varieties of modern man that still exist.

### Selected References

Howell, F. C., "The Place of Neanderthal Man in Human Evolution," *American Journal of Physical Anthropology,* Vol. 9, 1951, pp. 379-416.
Keith, Sir A., *New Discoveries Relating to the Antiquity of Man,* London and New York, 1931.
———, *The Antiquity of Man,* London, 1929.
McCown, T. D., and Kieth, Sir A., *The Stone Age of Mount Carmel,* Vol. II, London, 1939.
Oakley, K. P., "The Fluorine-Dating Method," *Yearbook of Physical Anthropology,* The Viking Fund, Inc., New York, 1949, pp. 44-52.
Weidenreich, F., *Anthropological papers* (compiled by S. L. Washburn and D. Wolffson), The Viking Fund, Inc., New York, 1950.
———, *Apes, Giants, and Man,* Chicago, 1946.

# CHAPTER 7

# The Living Varieties of Man

## A. PUTTING MAN IN HIS PLACE

By every estimate that has yet been made the number of human beings alive is set at a fraction over two billion. It is not easy to appreciate how vast a sum this is, but an idea of its magnitude may be achieved if we imagine a football stadium capable of seating 100,000 persons, which can be completely emptied and refilled in half an hour. Assuming, at this rapid rate, that 200,000 people entered and left the stadium every hour of the day and night, it would take almost fourteen months (416.6 days) for two billion people to hurry in and out.

Faced with the overwhelming problem of trying to deal with so huge a number of subjects no two of whom, with the possible exception of identical twins, are absolutely alike, the anthropologist is forced to classify them into large groups. Customarily, initial attempts at gross classification are based on procedures that have long been practiced by students of all forms of living things. Biologists who specialize in the systematic arrangement of plants and animals are known as **taxonomists** and today, after two centuries of effort, they have succeeded in grouping all varieties of things that live into a series of units called kingdoms, phyla, classes, orders, families, genera, and species. Each of these units may have one or more subdivisions, and the entire scheme provides a measure of presumed degrees of relationship. The largest categories, kingdoms and phyla, contain a great many organisms that may be only distantly related, but smaller groupings like genera and species are more exclusive and limited to close kindred. Experience has shown that similarities of anatomical structure, known technically as *homologies,* provide the most reliable tests of relationship, but in some instances a taxonomist finds it necessary to examine such *analogies,* or resemblances of organic function or behavior, as may exist between two specimens. As a general rule it is felt that taxonomy rests on a firmer foundation when it is based primarily on homological evidence.

Suppose now that a taxonomist thoroughly familiar with all other living things were asked to classify a number of men and women from all parts of the world. If he were to use the standard techniques of his profession, to what categories would he assign them? A quick glance at their heads, eyes, noses, limbs, and genital organs would be enough to convince him that they were not plants but belonged to the animal kingdom. At the same time, their size would indicate that they pertained to the subkingdom of Metazoa, which comprises all organisms made up of multiple cells. A hasty examination of their backs would disclose the presence of a bony, segmented spinal column, which would be enough to assign them to the phylum Chordata and the subphylum Vertebrata. Moreover, their warm blood, body hair, breasts, and nipples would suffice to place them in the class of Mammals. Up to this point our imaginary taxonomist would work speedily and without hesitation. However, he would then have to witness a pregnancy in order to observe the formation of a placenta, after which he would rapidly decide to put the creatures under study into the subclass of Eutheria.

There are so many kinds of Eutherian mammals that it has been found necessary to group them into nine orders, eight of which contain creatures as diversified as sloths, shrews, bats, dogs, squirrels, sea cows, whales, deer, and horses. It would not take long for a qualified taxonomist to decide that human beings bore only a slight general resemblance to all of these animals, but observation of man's prehensile hands, collar bone, acute vision, and complex brain would soon reveal enough fundamental homologies to warrant assigning him to the ninth, or Primate, order. This order includes lemurs, tarsiers, monkeys, and apes, and close inspection would justify a taxonomist in ruling out the former two and putting monkeys, apes, and men into a separate suborder of Anthropoidea. Further study by an experienced classifier would show enough anatomical differences of hand, foot, posture, face, and brain to warrant man's assignment to the separate family of Hominidae.

If now our taxonomist were given the opportunity of comparing his specimens with earlier hominids he would doubtless decide that they ought all to go into the genus *Homo*. As for variations among the living peoples, they would be found so trivial biologically that a classifier would unfailingly group the present human population into one species, traditionally called *sapiens*. To summarize what any skillful taxonomist would decide, the biological classification of modern man would run as follows:

| | |
|---|---|
| Kingdom | Animal |
| Subkingdom | Metazoa |
| Phylum | Chordata |
| Subphylum | Vertebrata |
| Class | Mammalia |
| Subclass | Eutheria |
| Order | Primate |
| Suborder | Anthropoidea |
| Family | Hominidae |
| Genus | Homo |
| Species | Sapiens |

## B. SPLITTING THE SPECIES

When the physical anthropologist takes over from the taxonomist he must deal with over two billion diversified members of a single species. A student of humanity may decide to pay no attention to such differences as exist within the species, or else he may decide to investigate the distinctions in the hope of determining just how extensive they are, how they originated, and what they signify. Invariably, anthropologists have chosen to take the latter course.

Only a small minority of scholars think that the physical variations in the human population have resulted from different lines of evolutionary descent, with divergent groups deriving from different sets of ancestors. An overwhelming majority takes the position that all the living varieties of mankind stem from a common background, but that they long ago acquired distinctive traits as they settled in variegated environments. As a starting point for such an hypothesis, let us postulate that considerably more than 20,000 years ago there appeared in the Eastern Hemisphere a generalized kind of modern man (Cro-Magnon), whose descendants gradually spread throughout the Old World. Professor Wilton M. Krogman has suggested that a type of the sort we are postulating may have carried in its reproductive cells varied genes for skin colors that ranged from white to very dark brown, head shapes that ran from narrow to broad, hair forms that varied from very straight to curly (Fig. 50B), and so on.[1]

Since it is known that the first humans lived by hunting, fishing, and gathering wild foods, it is reasonable to assume that they moved about in small units that could readily have become isolated from one another. Under these circumstances the conditions for forming distinct physical varieties were practically ideal. Each of the separate bands would, of necessity, become an inbreeding community. This means that in the course of time its original genetic variability would have been greatly reduced. Within the inbreeding population environmental, social, and sexual selection would operate to perpetuate some types at the expense of others. Furthermore, mutations taking place in the germ cells of one of the isolated groups would not be likely to be duplicated in any of the others. In this fashion, after many generations of geographical and biological separation all of the inbreeding units, despite their originally common genetic background, would differ from each other genotypically (in the actual composition of their genes), as well as phenotypically (in outward form or appearance).[2] Then, as means of communication and travel improved, the once-isolated, varied bands of modern man would be enabled to establish contacts with each other, thus paving the way for the high degree of intermixture that is an outstanding phenomenon of our day.

Even a superficial examination of the variations among human beings makes apparent two orders of magnitude. Major distinctions set apart from one another the universally recognized divisions of **Caucasoid** (White), **Mongoloid** (Yellow), and **Negroid** (Black); and lesser differences separate groups of individuals contained within each of the big units. We must not forget that both the major and

---

[1] W. M. Krogman, "The Concept of Race," *The Science of Man in the World Crisis* (R. Linton, ed.), New York, 1945, p. 46.

[2] Individuals who are genotypical are supposed to be much alike because they have inherited the same kinds of genes. Phenotypes, however, may look the same either because different genes sometimes produce similar results, or else because the environment sometimes molds the products of diverse genes into features that are outwardly much alike.

minor sets of distinctions pertain to members of a single species, hence, whatever subdivisions are made must be recognized to apply to something less than a species. A suggestion has been put forth, and will be followed here, to call the greater units by the term **stock,** with the implication that each of them corresponds to a subspecies.[3] Then the smaller groups within a stock may be called **races,** with the understanding that they correspond to sub-subspecies. It is a matter of record that taxonomists find it increasingly difficult to establish clear-cut categories as these become smaller than a species. Anthropologists have exactly the same trouble. Only the exception here and there refuses to admit that all living men comprise a single species; there is relatively little disagreement about stocks,[4] but races are hard to distinguish satisfactorily, and on this score a degree of confusion prevails.

## C. TECHNIQUES OF STOCK AND RACE CLASSIFICATION

Absence of great and outstanding biological differences among the various subgroups of *Homo sapiens* has forced the classifiers of living man to deal with anatomical minutiae. On the whole, they have gone about their tasks by using a combination of three techniques. Wherever possible, on skeletal material or live bodies, they try to make careful measurements between recognizable points. Where this is impossible, as in dealing with color differences, they resort to detailed observations based on agreed-upon standards. For computing averages or establishing proportions between one body part and another, they utilize a number of statistical devices.

Until the current generation of physical anthropologists began to work, the traditional techniques were universally employed and seldom questioned. It was firmly believed that they would yield an accurate knowledge of the nature, range, and meaning of the variations among mankind; throw light on the evolutionary processes that produced man and divided him into stocks and races; afford a sound point of departure for studies of the relationship of race to health and disease, longevity, fertility, crime, alcoholic tolerance, or intelli-

[3] For further details, see W. M. Krogman, *op. cit.,* p. 48.

[4] The Caucasoid, Negroid, and Mongoloid stocks are universally accepted. Almost in the same category are **Australoid** and **American Indian.** Beyond these there is no large-scale agreement. Not all anthropologists use stock in the sense of a subspecies, as it is used here.

gence; and help to elucidate the biological consequences of such practices as inbreeding or race mixture. Not all of these goals have been achieved and a great many contemporary specialists are impatiently objecting to the continued use of old procedures. Some of their criticisms and a few of the new approaches employed will be treated in the chapter that follows, but it has not been proved that the conclusions reached by the older workers are invariably false or worthless. There is still a need for understanding how traditional physical anthropologists work and what they are finding out. Only a small sample of methods and results will be offered here, but interested readers may readily find more complete treatments in other works.[5]

## I. Measurements and Indices

With the help of specially designed instruments and with precisely designated landmarks, it is possible to measure accurately several segments of the body—alive, dead, or skeletalized. A tall, calibrated, metal rod with a sliding bar attached (anthropometer) is used for determining a subject's total stature, the height of his head and neck, the length of his limbs, the width of his shoulders and hips, and similar items. A smaller implement of comparable construction (sliding caliper) is used for taking such measurements as the length and width of the nose. Still another tool, with arms that open outward (spreading caliper) is made to measure rounded or spherical parts, and is handy for getting the length and breadth of the head, or the width of the face (Fig. 49). All the data obtained with these and other more highly specialized implements are recorded in the metric system in order to make possible comparisons with results secured by fellow scientists throughout the world. Figures gotten by trained investigators using standardized tools, methods, and landmarks, are likely to be accurate and to provide a sound basis for mathematical comparisons and analyses.

For example, it is a general practice to determine the proportions of one body segment to another. This is done by finding the ratio between them, and the result is called an **index.** One which is very

[5] Much additional information, and many more bibliographic sources may be obtained by consulting E. A. Hooton, *op. cit.*, pp. 699-764; M. F. Ashley Montagu, *op. cit.*, pp. 440-524; and E. P. Stibbe, *An Introduction to Physical Anthropology*, rev. ed., New York and London, 1938.

widely utilized in racial studies is the cephalic index. It expresses ✓ the ratio of the head's breadth to its length, and is conveniently calculated as a percentage by the use of a simple, mathematical formula: Breadth of head × 100/Length of head. If an individual's cephalic

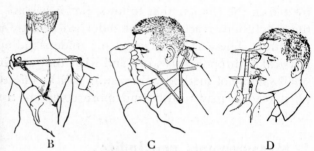

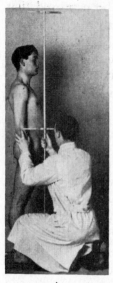

Fig. 49. Some anthropometric techniques (after Martin and Hooton). A and B show how an anthropometer is used for taking, respectively, upper arm length and the width of the shoulders. C illustrates how a spreading caliper measures the length of the head, and D pictures the measurement of upper face height with a sliding caliper.

A

index is under 77, which is the same as saying that the breadth of the head is less than about ¾ of the length, a person is considered to be **dolichocephalic** or long-headed. If the result is between 77 and 82, a person is classed as **mesocephalic** or medium-headed; and a figure of 82 or more is interpreted as **brachycephalic** or broad-headed.[6]

Another commonly used index expresses the proportion of nasal width relative to length. Again, a simple formula suffices: Nasal breadth × 100/Nasal length. A nasal index of less than 70 on a living subject is taken to indicate a narrow-nosed or **leptorrhine** condition; 70 to 85 is medium-nosed or **mesorrhine;** and over 85 means broad-nosed or **platyrrhine.**

Many other indices are in use among professional physical anthropologists, and their calculations and interpretations are patterned along lines similar to the two examples here given.

[6] These figures apply to measurements on live subjects. When dealing with skulls long-headedness applies to 75 or less, and broad-headedness means anything over 80.

## II. Observations

Accurate measurements between definite landmarks unquestionably provide the most satisfactory method of determining anatomical variations between groups of humans, but, unfortunately, there are bodily aspects that cannot be readily measured. These include skin, hair (Fig. 50A), and eye color; nasal prominences and profiles; face

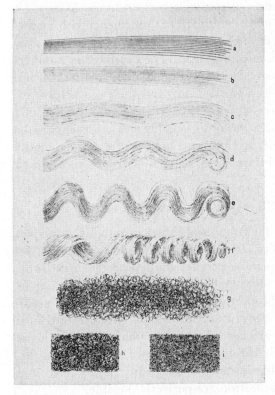
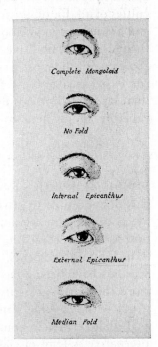

Fig. 50. Observational guides to hair and eye forms. A. Varieties of human head hair. Mongoloids have types a and b, and, occasionally, c. Caucasoids have some c, but are usually d, e, or f. Negroids generally have the spiral forms lettered g, h, and i. B. Eye folds. Although eye folds are most characteristic of the Mongoloids, they may sometimes be noted in individuals of other stocks. (After Martin and Hooton)

and jaw projections (prognathism); straight, wavy, curly, or frizzly hair forms; lip thickness; and so on. Moreover, it must not be overlooked that many of these features can be altered from their original or inherited appearance by tanning, bleaching, plastic surgery, or the ministrations of imaginative beauty-parlor operators. Anthropologists are aware of the difficulties involved in making accurate, unbiased, systematic, and standardized observations, but rather than abandon this technique altogether they prefer to use it with caution and in conjunction with data obtained by other means.

Sometimes, in an effort to achieve uniformity of results, physical anthropologists employ things like color charts, not much different from those used for selecting paints or ladies' stockings. Even so, it is virtually impossible to make observational judgments with mathematical precision. And that, of course, is one of the most serious difficulties of all, for observations cannot readily be expressed in numbers and are not easy to elaborate statistically. Some mathematical formulas and coefficients have been worked out, and their use helps overcome one of the most serious drawbacks of this approach. In the long run experienced observers get far more reliable and consistent results than laymen think possible, and observational data provide a highly valuable supplement to information secured by other techniques.

## D. PLACING MAN IN THE STOCKS

Without deviating too far from established taxonomic principles it is now possible to classify *Homo sapiens* into stocks or subspecies by grouping into divisions those people who live in one area; function as an interbreeding unit; and have bodies that are similar in terms of measurements, proportions, and observations. Such classifications have been adversely criticized on many grounds, but until more valid arrangements are agreed upon an old-fashioned scheme is not without value. Only the three best-known stocks will be described here. Their boundaries are by no means rigidly fixed and alternative systems of classification are perfectly possible.

Out of the generalized ancestral hominids from whom all living humans are thought to be descended, the **White** or **Caucasoid** stock was differentiated quite early. It is the least specialized and most variable of the three subspecies to be treated.[7] Within this category may be found individuals with skin colors ranging from clear white through pink or ruddy to light brown or ripe olive. Hair color runs from platinum blond to red and dark brown; and eye color goes from pale gray-blue or green to various shades of brown. Hair form on the

---

[7] Stock and race descriptions customarily take the adult male as a standard.

head is usually wavy or lightly curled, and the face and body show considerable hairiness. Noses are predominantly high-bridged with profiles that vary from straight to concave or convex. There is little facial protrusion (prognathism), lips are only moderately thick and slightly turned out (everted), and the chin is usually prominent and well developed. Cephalic indices fluctuate all the way from very dolichocephalic to frankly brachycephalic, and body builds are too variable to be classified, although pelves are proportionately broad in both sexes.

Our second subspecies comprises the **Negroid** or **Black** stock. Its members are characterized by dark brown to black skins and eye colors, and by black head hair that tends to loop into narrow or intertwined spirals. Beard and body hair is generally black but less abundant than in the Caucasoid stock. Most Negroids are dolicho-cephalic, with considerable prognathism, broad, low noses, thick, greatly everted lips, and somewhat receding chins. Body sizes and proportions vary, but the pelves are relatively narrow, calf muscles may be poorly developed, and the arch of the foot is often low.

Although adequate proof is lacking, and there are ample grounds for skepticism, some writers claim that the **Mongoloid** or **Yellow** stock was the last subspecies of *Homo sapiens* to make its appearance. On the whole, members of the Mongoloid division may be described as broad-headed, broad-faced, and broad-shouldered. Skin colors generally show a yellowish tint but may vary from lemon-colored to reddish-brown. Eyes are dark brown as a rule. Head hair is long, coarse of texture, straight, and black. On face and body Mongoloids are distinctively devoid of hair (glabrous). Several special characteristics are found in the facial area. The eyes are slanted, and have narrow openings, and the lids are heavy, with extra folds of skin (Mongoloid or epicanthic folds) stretched across the upper lids from the eyebrows to the lashes and from the outer corners to the nose. Nasal bridges tend to be of medium breadth but very low, and cheekbones are prominent, jutting out from back to front as well as from side to side, and padded with fat. Prognathism, chin, and lip development are all average, but the incisor teeth frequently have an unusual concavity that gives them a "shovel-shaped" appearance. Stature is variable, but not uncommonly a little short of the male average for all mankind (about 5½ feet), and the body build is most often compact and sturdy. Infants are sometimes born with purplish blue areas of skin (Mongoloid spots) at the small of the back, but these usually disappear by adolescence. Comparable spots may also occur in Negroids.

## E. RACIAL GROUPINGS

While there is reasonably close agreement on the classification of *Homo sapiens* into stocks, there is much less uniformity when it comes to subdividing each stock into its component races. After all, one cannot expect anything but minor, and perhaps trivial, differences to occur between units of so low a biological level as sub-sub-species. Still, each stock does comprise so many different-looking groups that it seems justifiable to make an effort to fit them into the most logical arrangement possible.

Instead of attempting to give exhaustive accounts of all the races that have been described by former writers, we shall limit ourselves to brief synopses of the distinctive traits that differentiate the most representative ones. Each of these units, one must not forget, is likely to have all or most of the features associated with the stock to which it belongs. It is also important to be forewarned that there is a great deal of individual variation, so that a single person cannot be expected to show every one of the characteristics that are typical of his race.

## I. Caucasoid Stock (Fig. 51).

1. **Archaic White.** Short, thick-set, dolichocephalic brunets, with large and bulging brow ridges, depressed or sunken nasal roots, large palates and teeth, and a profusion of wavy brownish hair on head, face, and body. Apparently an early Caucasoid variety, now almost extinct, that once spread widely along a zone from eastern Europe across Asia, and into several Pacific islands where they mixed with native peoples. Best represented at present by the "hairy" Ainu of northern Japan, and presumably an element in the make-up of the Australian natives, who are sometimes given the status of a distinct stock, the so-called pre-Dravidians or Dravidians of India, and the Veddah of Ceylon.

2. **Mediterranean.** Long-headed brunets with brown eyes and olive skins. Generally short and slender, with delicate features in-

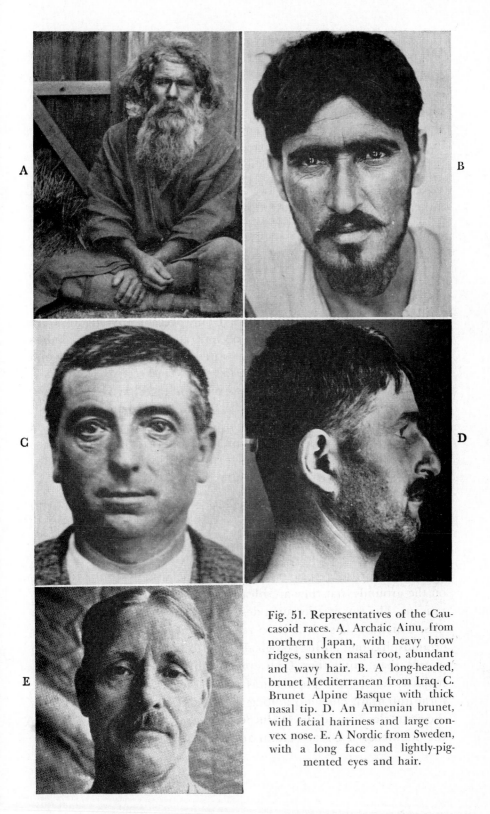

Fig. 51. Representatives of the Caucasoid races. A. Archaic Ainu, from northern Japan, with heavy brow ridges, sunken nasal root, abundant and wavy hair. B. A long-headed, brunet Mediterranean from Iraq. C. Brunet Alpine Basque with thick nasal tip. D. An Armenian brunet, with facial hairiness and large convex nose. E. A Nordic from Sweden, with a long face and lightly-pigmented eyes and hair.

cluding straight, high-bridged, narrow noses, oval faces, and no extremes of prognathism, lip fullness, or chin development. Several subvarieties of Mediterranean have been recognized, particularly among Arabs in the Near East and north Africa. Typical forms occur in such Mediterranean countries as Spain, Italy, and Portugal, but they also are common in England and Wales.

**3. Alpine.**   Broad- and high-headed brunets, with broad and rather heavily-bearded faces, and short, fleshy ("blobby") noses. They have dark skins and brown hair and eyes. Stocky and moderately short bodies predominate. They are distributed in a wide belt across central Europe, from France through Germany and deep into Russia.

**4. Armenoid.**   Brachycephalic brunets, colored much like Alpines, and typified by "sugar-loaf" heads that are flat and steep at the back but rounded and sloping in front. Recent investigators are inclined to regard the flattened occiput as due to cradling habits rather than as an expression of inherited genes. Noses are outstanding because they are high-bridged, long, full, and convex, with thick, fleshy tips, and prominent nostrils. Armenoid men have hairy bodies, full beards, and bushy eyebrows that usually merge above the nose. They are found from Asia Minor eastward to the Balkans and throughout most of the countries of Western Asia. In cartoons, Jews often are drawn with Armenoid features. A related group, called Dinarics, is sometimes given separate racial status.

**5. Nordic.**   A medium-tall, long-headed, light-skinned group with blond or reddish hair, and green or gray-blue eyes. Noses are high, narrow, and straight of profile. They are apt to have long, narrowly compressed faces, culminating in deep jaws with prominent chins. Several authorities refuse to give separate racial status to the Nordics, on the grounds that they are bleached out or depigmented Mediterraneans. Hooton irreverently describes them as "horse-faced" Nordics. This race, if such it is, so recently idolized on purely fictitious grounds, has one anthropological claim to fame—it has less coloring matter than any other Caucasoid group. Nordics are nowhere a majority among the populations where they exist, but such people form important elements among the inhabitants of Scandinavia and the countries around the Baltic Sea, and are well represented among the populaces of Great Britain and the United States.

## II. Negroid Stock (Fig. 52).

1. **Forest Negro.** These are moderately tall, somewhat barrel-chested, broad-shouldered, and muscular. In other respects this race conforms closely to the Negroid stock description on p. 121. Most Forest Negroes live in west-central Africa, between the Atlantic Coast and the Congo Basin. Many Negro athletes in the United States appear to have Forest Negro ancestry.

2. **Nilotic Negro.** Very tall and slender, with long but thin legs, and short trunks. Customarily, the members of this race are less prognathous, narrower-nosed, and thinner-lipped than others of the same stock. The apparent modification of typically Negroid features is interpreted by some as an indication of ancient admixture between Forest Negroes and Mediterranean Caucasoids from Western Asia. Those who support this view point to the distribution of Nilotic Negroes, concentrated among the upper courses of the Nile River, not far from Western Asia, as partial support for their hypothesis.

3. **Oceanic Negro.** On a good many of the South Pacific islands, especially those from New Guinea to Fiji, there live dark-skinned natives of average height who resemble the Negroes of Africa. Although there are many kinds of Oceanic Negroes all of them, as a rule, are brown rather than black in skin color, and their head hair is less tightly coiled, with some exceptions, than is true of their presumed African relatives. They also have fuller beards and more body hair, their faces are less prognathous, and their lips are neither as thick nor as everted. Noses tend to be narrower and higher-bridged, and some individuals have such high, thick, convex, and fleshy-tipped noses as to approximate those of Armenoids. Genetic relationships between African and Oceanic Negroes have not been worked out, but it seems that the latter migrated to their Pacific homelands from continental sources of origin.

4. **Pygmy Negro.** This racial term applies to a diversified group of Negroids, all of whom can be readily distinguished by the fact that even fully adult males seldom reach 5 feet in height. Sometimes Pygmies from Africa are called Negrilloes to differentiate them from Asiatic varieties known as Negritoes but the distinction of names is going out of common use and both groups are being termed Negrito. Whether in Asia, Africa, or Oceania, Pygmy Negroes are

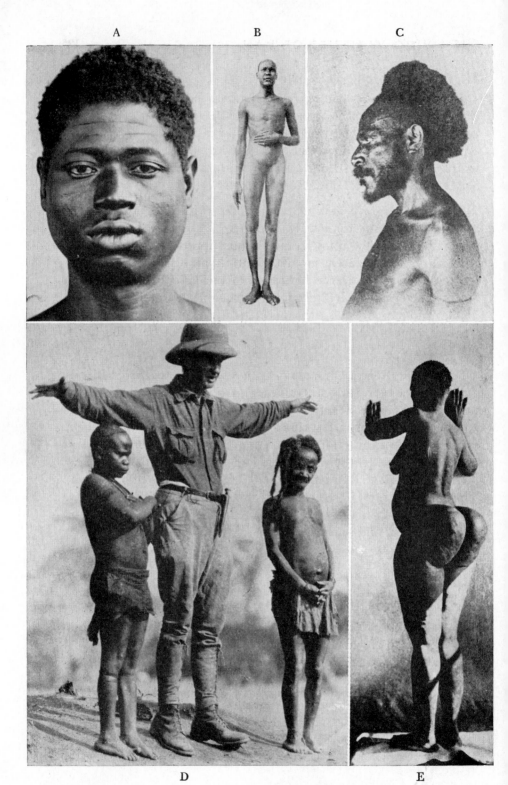

A　　　　B　　　　C

D　　　　　　　　　　　E

likely to have head shapes that fall into the mesocephalic range, and head hair that tends to grow in small, separated, spiral clusters, a condition called "peppercorn." Lips are very full, and noses are exceptionally platyrrhine and low-bridged. Two different body builds have been noted: a so-called infantile type, with narrow shoulders, short trunk, prominent abdomen, and slender legs; and an adultiform type having broad shoulders, a long torso, strong musculature, and sturdy lower limbs. Both kinds of Pygmy Negro occur in the Congo Basin of Africa, the Malay Peninsula, and in nearby Pacific islands from Sumatra to the Philippines.

Whatever connections may exist between African, Asiatic, and Oceanic Pygmy Negroes are completely unknown; nor does any one understand why it is only the Negroid stock that is divided into normally tall and Pygmy divisions.

**5. Bushman-Hottentot.** A puzzling racial group believed to have affiliations with African Pygmies, whom they somewhat resemble in shortness of stature, head-hair form, and a few other respects. Each sex has a minor anatomical peculiarity of the genital organs, consisting of a tendency for the male member to be partially erect at all times, and an extra flap of skin (apron) over the vagina of a woman. Females, too, are addicted to great accumulations of fat on the thighs and buttocks (steatopygy) (Fig. 52E). These traits have never been explained. Even more troublesome for physical anthropologists to understand is the presence of apparently Mongoloid features including a yellowish cast to the skin, high cheek bones, extra folds of skin covering the upper eyelids, and the occasional occurrence during early infancy of a Mongoloid spot. There are several cultural differences between Bushman and Hottentot, but physically they are much alike. Both peoples live in the vicinity of Africa's Kalahari desert.

---

Fig. 52. Races of the Negroid stock. A. Forest Negro. A man from Dahomey, with all the main features of his stock, including dark pigmentation, spiral-shaped head hair, low, broad nose, and thick, everted lips. B. Nilotic Negro. A tall, thin, Dinka male, from East Africa. He is less dark than a Forest Negro, and his Negroid traits are sufficiently modified to suggest the possibility of ancient race mixture with Caucasoids. C. Oceanic Negro from New Guinea. A Papuan tribesman whose hair form and abundance, as well as whose nasal configuration, differ from those of African Negroes. D. Pygmy Negro adults from the Ituri forest of Africa, shown with a Caucasoid man to contrast their statures. E. A Hottentot woman, with a pronounced degree of steatopygy.

### III. Mongoloid Stock (Fig. 53).

1. **East Asiatic (Classic) Mongoloid Stock.** Ranging eastward from Tibet and Mongolia, across much of southern Siberia, northern China, Manchuria, Korea, and Japan, are many tribal and national groups whose members conform very closely to the Mongoloid stock description on p. 120. Strictly speaking, no racial term has been applied to them, but since they are so typical of their stock they are sometimes called Classic Mongoloids.

2. **Arctic Mongoloids.** To this racial division belong the Koryak and the Chukchee of northern Siberia and the Eskimo of northern Canada. Some of them differ from Classic Mongoloids because their heads are less brachycephalic and higher roofed, their skins are browner, and their noses are higher-bridged and narrower.

3. **American Indian (Amerind).** Although several biologically different kinds of American Indians can be readily recognized, lack of detailed information makes it necessary to describe them as a single but variable group of Mongoloids. Unlike their supposed Classic relatives they have somewhat reddish-brown skins, faces that are often both very wide and very long, mesorrhine noses that are frequently high-bridged and convex, facial skin that becomes greatly wrinkled in old age, and brown eyes that do not always show a Mongoloid fold. It is their straight, coarse, black head hair, high cheek bones, and relatively glabrous bodies that lead some race classifiers to call them Mongoloids; but in the opinions of others they deserve separate ranking as a stock.

4. **Indonesian-Malay.** This is another diversified set of people which is only partially Mongoloid. Indonesian-Malays are distributed from the Malay Archipelago and adjacent regions out into the islands of the South Pacific, about as far east as New Guinea. There is fairly good reason to look upon these people as having strains of Classic Mongoloid probably mingled with Pygmy Negro. Most often they look like short, dark Mongoloids, but sometimes they have too much wavy hair, too greatly full, everted lips, and too much prognathism to be taken for Classic Mongoloids.

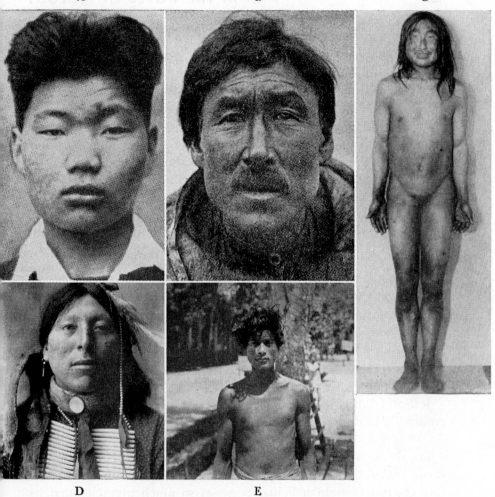

Fig. 53. Mongoloid racial types. A. East Asiatic (Classic) Mongoloid. He is a speaker of the Tungus language, which is widespread in Northeastern Asia, and exhibits all the diagnostic features of his stock and race, including full Mongoloid eye-folds. B. Arctic Mongoloid. Except for his head hair and a partial epicanthic fold, this Koryak man does not look particularly Mongoloid. C and D. American Indians (Amerinds): C. An Eskimo with non-hairy, glabrous body; D. A Sioux Indian, with Mongoloid head hair and cheekbones, but non-Mongoloid nose and eyes. E. Indonesian-Malay. A Batak tribesman from the island of Sumatra. Very likely he represents an ancient admixture of Mongoloid and Negroid.

## F. SOME BALD FACTS ABOUT RACE

Regardless of how crude some of the traditional techniques of physical anthropology are now regarded to be, the older workers made some valuable contributions to a scientific understanding of racial differences. From the outset they showed a marked determination to avoid preconceived notions and to deal with human variations with the same objective detachment that zoologists exhibit when classifying other animals. Although their methods are becoming outmoded, most of their pronouncements on race are still valid and worthy of repetition.

All anthropologists are united in the belief that stock and race distinctions are biological, resulting from geographic isolation and the interplay of evolutionary and reproductive forces. Accordingly, differences of race or stock cannot possibly be expressed in terms of non-heritable or cultural traits. Anthropology does not recognize such so-called "races" as Aryan (linguistic), Mohammedan or Jewish (religious), Italian (geographic), or British (political). Students of man must never allow themselves to forget the fundamental distinction between biologically determined, lifelong, racial characteristics that one receives involuntarily at conception, and cultural attributes that are acquired in postnatal life.

Racial boundaries are not rigidly fixed, and physical traits are constantly in the process of being modified or changed. In fact, races are sometimes thought to be embryonic species, or groups that are going through a process of change which may ultimately convert them to new species. More than one study has shown that any given race or unit of human beings possesses so much plasticity that its members are likely to become phenotypically quite different from each other if some of them grow up in dissimilar environments. Practically, this amounts to saying that the offspring of migrating members of a race will vary considerably from the children of stay-at-home members of the same race.[8]

No race or stock, taken in the aggregate, can be judged to be more highly evolved than any other. This point is sometimes demonstrated by a sort of game that runs as follows: if we regard as most highly

[8] This demonstration was first made over forty years ago by the very traditional anthropologist, the late Professor Franz Boas, in *Changes in Bodily Form of Descendants of Immigrants*, Washington, 1911. It was then verified by later workers, and was given a new statement by H. L. Shapiro, *Migration and Environment*, New York, 1939.

evolved those human traits that diverge furthest from a generalized apelike condition, then we can show that each of the three main stocks is most advanced in some regards but retarded in others. On this basis, Caucasoids show the highest evolution with respect to elevated nasal bones; Negroids because of their very thick lips; and Mongoloids on account of their hairless or glabrous bodies. At the opposite extreme, Caucasoids most nearly approximate apish conditions in regard to their profusion of face and body hair; Negroids by virtue of their prognathism; and Mongoloids because of their coarse, straight, head hair. This kind of pastime is harmless, but it is of little scientific value because only special traits are singled out for comparison, they are not the same in each case, and because one cannot be sure that the features selected are biologically equivalent.

Insofar as can at present be determined there do not seem to be any important racial or stock differences in terms of essential qualities like vitality, resistance to disease, fertility, and longevity. At the same time there are indications of other important biological differences. Mongoloids appear to have a lower metabolic rate than Caucasoids of the same sex and age; Negroids are the most susceptible by far to sickle-cell anemia; and, in the United States, cancer strikes an exceptionally high percentage of Caucasoids. The question of variable disease rates among the stocks and races of *Homo sapiens* is complicated by uncertainty as to whether they result from biological or sociocultural factors. Measles and whooping cough are known to have played havoc with several American Indian tribes, but this may be due not so much to fundamental differences of biology as to the fact that the pre-Columbian Indians had lived in isolation from the centers of these infections and had had no opportunity to develop immunities. Up to now the data on this topic are too meager to permit the formulation of general laws, but comparative pathology is one of the most interesting fields of research dealing with physical variations among differing groups of men.

To date no convincing proof has been brought forward to show that the races of mankind differ in the *potentialities* of their mental equipment. Vast differences of intellectual *performance* can, assuredly, be demonstrated, but when it comes to measuring *potential* the going gets harder and harder. The reason that anthropologists are more concerned with comparative ratings of mental potential rather than performance is because no one knows to what extent the latter is based on cultural conditioning instead of biological inheritance. Varying scores on intelligence tests between American Negroids and Caucasoids, for example, have been shown to be so directly related to cultural factors such as amount of education and social or economic status, that it is hard to tell whether the tests measure biological differences of mental capacity or differences of training and background. Until techniques are developed for evaluating intellectual potentiality without reference to cultural influences, it can only be maintained that no distinctions of basic mental ability are known to exist among the races of man.

Neither race nor stock mixture produces harmful biological consequences and, contrary to opinions that prevail in some quarters, they may even bring about beneficial results through the agency of **heterosis,** or **hybrid vigor.** On this topic anthropologists speak with assurance because members of the profession have studied the offspring of a great many inter-stock matings in all parts of the world.[9] Nowhere have they found signs of physical deterioration resulting from intermixture. Even the descendants of such varied parents as Dutch (Caucasoid) men and Hottentot (Negroid) women turned out to be vigorous, fertile, and long-lived.[10] Popular prejudices often create difficult social and cultural situations for hybrid individuals or groups, but biologically speaking race mixture produces no harmful results.

Less is known about the consequences of inbreeding, but the few investigations that have been made by unprejudiced observers have led to the tentative conclusion that it is not invariably dangerous.[11] As far as can be determined inbreeding does no more than intensify the usual procedures of heredity. Therefore, if it occurs in a group with a healthy genetic background it should do no harm, but if it takes place among people with many deficient genes it may lead to biological disaster. These findings have been directly opposed in our day to the exaggerated claims of unscientific speakers and writers on racial topics. The term "racist" has come into current usage to denote

9 See, for example, L. C. Dunn, "Some Results of Race Mixture in Hawaii," *Eugenics, Genetics and the Family,* Vol. 2, 1923, pp. 109-24.

10 Reference is made here to the famous study of E. Fischer, *Die Rehobother Bastards,* Jena, 1912. "Bastards" is inaccurate as the subjects were born of legally married parents.

11 Consult H. L. Shapiro, "Descendants of the Mutineers of the Bounty," *Memoir of the Bishop Museum,* Honolulu, 1929.

those who argue about race without reference to observed and known facts. It is to the credit of physical anthropology that it has provided effective material to counteract the extravagant statements uttered by unabashed racists.

And so, as the curtain falls on traditional physical anthropology, the workers who accomplished so much with tools that have become outmoded may step forward and take a bow. If they need any consolation, they may find it in the reflection that the present generation of physical anthropologists could not have ventured into so many new avenues of research, were it not for the training and inspiration that they got from their elders.

SELECTED REFERENCES

Boas, F., "Changes in Bodily Form of Descendants of Immigrants," *61st Congress, second session, Senate document*, No. 208, Washington, 1911.

Coon, C. S., *The Races of Europe*, New York, 1939.

———, Garn, S. M., and Birdsell, J. B. *Races*, Springfield, 1950.

Count, E. W., *This Is Race*, New York, 1950.

Hooton, E. A., *Up from the Ape*, rev. ed., New York, 1946.

Krogman, W. M., "The Concept of Race," *The Science of Man in the World Crisis*, R. Linton, ed., New York, 1944, pp. 38-62.

Shapiro, H. L., and Hulse, F., *Migration and Environment*, New York, 1940.

Stewart, T. D., ed., *Hrdlicka's Practical Anthropometry*, rev. ed., Philadelphia, 1947.

Stibbe, E. P., *An Introduction to Physical Anthropology*, rev. ed., New York and London, 1938.

Washburn, S. L., "Thinking about Race," *Smithsonian Report*, Washington, 1946, pp. 363-378.

# CHAPTER 8

# The New Look in Physical Anthropology

## A. OFF WITH THE OLD; ON WITH THE NEW

On the basis of data collected by Dr. Erminie Voegelin in 1949-50, Professor Georg K. Neumann ascertained that out of 604 teachers of anthropology in American schools no more than 65 were offering work in physical anthropology, and of these only 27 were themselves primarily physical anthropologists. This little band, supplemented by a few specialists who do not teach and a limited number of colleagues abroad,[1] makes up for its size by the vigor with which it attacks its problems and the boldness with which it is searching out and pursuing new lines of investigation. Among the members of the group there is to be detected a feeling of impatience with the methods and accomplishments of the more traditional scholars. The leaders of the new movements are seldom unwilling to acknowledge their debts and links to the past, but they prefer to think of themselves as representing a brand-new stage in the evolution of their profession. As was the case formerly, the chief objectives of physical anthropology remain the study of the evolutionary processes that brought man on the scene and produced his many variations. But there is a profound change in regard to which differences are most basic for study, the techniques by which their extent and distribution are to be determined, and the way they should be classified, analyzed, compared and interpreted. While it is still conceded that an accurate

[1] In 1951 the American Association of Physical Anthropologists had a total of 245 members, by no means all of whom were full-time professionals.

sorting of mankind into races is a desirable achievement, it is argued stoutly that classification should not be an end in itself. The new group charges that there was a time, not so very long ago, when the traditionalists thought that by means of adequate classification they would learn how *Homo sapiens* had evolved, and how the species had become separated into stocks and races. When this hope was disappointed, so it is charged, the older workers did not seek new methods of investigation but tried only to refine their customary techniques by making them more painstaking and elaborate. All this was love's labor lost, in the modern point of view, and classification as such is felt to be valueless as a problem-solving device.

A primary cause of failure, it is being said, was undue reliance on measurements and observations made exclusively on the final appearance of body parts in adult males. No search was made for the genes that give rise to mature anatomical features, women and children were just about omitted from consideration, and no account was taken of environmental or cultural influences. Hence the older school could never hope to learn how body parts developed, what they were like at various stages of growth, what influences sex factors exerted, or what may be the effects of mating customs. Dissatisfaction has also been expressed because so many observations and measurements were taken on surfaces of bones or their nearest equivalents in the flesh. It is true that this custom persisted in part because of historical accident or mere repetition of established procedures; but it is equally true that efforts to understand evolution require comparison of living populations with dead or extinct hominids whose remains consist only of teeth and bones. Furthermore, museums and laboratories can house collections of skeletal fragments for study much more readily than they can large numbers of whole bodies. Just the same, it must be admitted that measurements of gross, external features, such as head length and head breadth are incapable of throwing light on the formative processes by which long or broad heads come into being. Hence, it is not always possible to refute the charge that the old custom of measuring was deteriorating into a kind of ritual procedure that led to the compilation of vast amounts of data of dubious worth.

Even statistics, the new voices proclaim, were inadequately handled in the past. Most of the time they yielded little but averages that might or might not have been really typical of a given group.

As to indices, it does not take much appreciation of mathematics to become suspicious of the three-fold pattern into which they consistently fall. Modern physical anthropologists are also correct when they point out that the most widely used indices were arbitrarily established long ago, and that they have no reference at all to known biological mechanisms. A great many new mathematical procedures have been developed of late, and their use holds forth the promise of furnishing clues to analysis and interpretation that no one had previously suspected and which could have come to light in no other way. Also occupying a prominent place in the current bill of complaints, is the failure of orthodox physical anthropologists to have developed theories of human origins or variations that might have led the way to greater insights or new techniques. There was too much speculation and not enough formulation of hypotheses that could be experimentally confirmed or disproved. Worst of all was the relative inflexibility of former approaches. Professor Washburn stated the case effectively when he wrote: "The methods of observation, measurement, and comparison were essentially the same, whether the object of the study was the description of evolution, races, growth, criminals, constitutional types, or army personnel." [2]

Thanks to the increase of scientific knowledge, development of new techniques, interest in different sets of problems, and the creation of fresh points of view, it is not surprising that physical anthropologists are no longer willing to follow blindly in the footsteps of the pioneers of their profession. With very few exceptions they are less interested in refining and perfecting the old procedures than they are in striking out boldly along new paths.

## B. IN THE BEGINNING WAS THE GENE

As the science of genetics developed many physical anthropologists sought to apply its findings to their work. **Genes,** ran the argument, are the very stuff of heredity, variation, and evolution, and to study man's genes is much more fundamental than to investigate their ultimate expression in human anatomy. Genes are much less subject than external features to environmental influences, they are strictly biological in character, they are transmitted only through sexual

[2] S. L. Washburn, "The New Physical Anthropology," *Transactions of the New York Academy of Sciences,* new series II, Vol. 13, No. 7, May, 1951, p. 298.

*genotype*
*in lieu, phenotype*

reproduction, and they remain practically unaltered during an individual's entire lifetime. So, in some quarters, the genotype rather than the phenotype was proclaimed to be the object of research in physical anthropology. There can be no quarrel with a modest statement along these lines, but human genetics is so complicated a subject that very little has been accomplished in the primary business of identifying particular genes, with the noteworthy exception of those genes that are responsible for the blood groups.[3]

One of the most uncompromising critics of old-style racial classification, Professor William C. Boyd, has written the most comprehensive work yet published on human genetics.[4] He has shown that the particular genes that have been identified as affecting the blood groups may be used as a basis for subdividing *Homo sapiens* in a new way. These genes, or the blood groups derived from them, are labelled in three series: A, B, AB, O; M, N; RH; each of which may be subdivided. By studying the percentages in which these genes occur in human populations throughout the world, Professor Boyd has drawn up a tentative scheme of six racial groups. There is a hypothetical Early European category, now represented by the Basques of France and Spain; a European (Caucasoid) group; an African (Negroid) class; an Asiatic (Mongoloid) group; an American Indian division; and an Australoid classification. Professor Boyd readily admits that his six divisions correspond pretty well to the traditional scheme of stocks and races. Oddly enough, he interprets this to mean that his own system is probably soundly based, but he gives no credit to the older catalog. An unbiased observer cannot escape the conclusion that the two approaches supplement rather than contradict each other.

Although the genes that affect the blood groups are the best known and most clearly understood, other human genes have been tentatively identified and may, in time, provide other bases for classifying mankind. In this connection the next best known are two genes that control the ability to taste low concentrations, in solution, of phenyl-thio-carbamide (PTC). "T" represents the gene that makes taste

[3] Long ago it was discovered that the blood streams of various human beings contained different ingredients, some of which could be harmoniously mingled while others could not. Transfusions of whole blood are dangerous if the two sets of elements are inharmonious. All blood types result from particular genes that every person inherits from his parents.

[4] W. C. Boyd, *Genetics and the Races of Man*, Boston, 1950.

possible, and "t" stands for the nontasting gene. It is believed that inheritance of these genes follows the regular pattern of biological transmission through sexual reproduction.

Other human genes that have been recognized but not as precisely identified as those dealing with blood groups or the capacity to taste PTC, are thought to be connected with a disease (favism), restricted to the Mediterranean race, that results from eating horse or broad beans; baldness, although its inheritance is complicated by sex and age factors; color blindness; albinism, or the absence of coloring matter (pigment) in body cells; occurrence of extra digits (polydactyly); absence at birth of hands or feet; and a small number of others.[5] Most of these factors, it is readily apparent, are in the nature of deficiencies or diseases, and are important for medical research and studies of inheritance.

One of the earliest criticisms of the use of blood groups was based on the limitation that samples could be obtained only from live subjects or recent corpses. Blood groups were thus considered of little use in evolutionary studies concerned with remote ancestors of modern man. Now, two ingenious investigators, Drs. Candela and Laughlin, have shown that while it is impossible to get blood out of a stone it is possible to get blood groups out of mummies and old bones.[6] Thus has the exciting prospect been revealed to the scientific world of finding out the blood groups of ancient kinds of men. It is hoped that extensions of the new techniques will enable physical anthropologists to discover the blood groups of all extinct hominids, which will make it possible for them with greater certainty than ever before to establish the links that bind ancestral forms of man to living stocks and races.

[5] Altogether the locations of nine universal human genes have been identified.

J. N. Spuhler, "On the number of genes in man," *Science,* Vol. 108, 1948, pp. 279-280, estimates that the gene loci in a human being are of the order of 20,000 to 42,000. Physical anthropologists believe that the bulk of the gene loci are the same for the species, and that all stock and race differences arise from variations in only a small number of assumed gene loci.

[6] P. B. Candela, "Blood-group reactions in ancient human skeletons," *American Journal of Physical Anthropology,* old series, Vol. 21, 1936, pp. 429-432; and W. S. Laughlin, "Preliminary tests for presence of blood-group substance in Tepexpan Man," in H. de Terra, *et al.,* "Tepexpan Man," *Viking Fund Publication,* No. 11, New York, 1949, Appendix F.

## C. THE PHENOTYPE MAKES A COMEBACK

It was not too long before the first alluring calls for physical anthropologists to abandon phenotypes for genes and genotypes began to lose some of their effectiveness. Few were the anthropologists who became convinced that they could better understand man by investigating submicroscopic chemical particles than entire human beings. On the other hand, the impact of genetics made a lasting impression on all fields of biology, not excluding physical anthropology. Genetic approaches have become thoroughly incorporated into the new techniques, and knowledge of genetics plays an important part in modern interpretations of data.

One of the principal fields of endeavor that combines genotypical and phenotypical inquiries is the study of human populations. A population is defined as an interbreeding unit, or that segment of any society which customarily pools its genes by marriage or mating. In the words of Professor Frederick P. Thieme, one of the most articulate of the current students of population, "The problem for these studies is, in the last analysis, to examine and obtain knowledge about the interrelationship between genetic and environmental factors in shaping the phenotype. The phenotype is largely our unit of study. This is the individual." [7]

To achieve their objectives students of population find it necessary to make careful, reliable samples of the total group under investigation, to determine the genetic composition of the selected sample, to examine in detail the environmental factors most likely to affect human beings, to gain knowledge of the physiological characteristics of individuals living in similar and contrasting environments, to interpret the known history of the population being studied, and to take into account whatever cultural factors influence the selection of mates and the begetting of children.

Population studies are most effective when conducted among isolated groups. Members of an isolated populace will, in due time, come to be different from the rest of the group from which they became separated, through the agency of random **genetic drift.** This is based on the probability that the members of a unit which becomes isolated, especially if it is of small size, do not take with them all of

[7] F. P. Thieme, "Problems and Methods of Population Surveys," *Cold Spring Harbor Symposia on Quantitative Biology,* Vol. XV, 1951, p. 25.

the genes that exist among the people from whom they break away. Thus, the isolated population will come to show different characteristics from the parent group. Then, as the result of inbreeding among themselves, all the members of the isolated segment will tend to acquire comparable frequencies of similar genes. As time goes on, other changes will occur to differentiate the isolated populace from its former neighbors. These will result from the same forces that make for evolution. Differences will arise from mutation (spontaneous changes occurring within the genes), or from an aspect of natural selection (influences of the external environment). As new types are formed, some will be perpetuated over others if they make for better adjustments to the environment, or if they are more likely to be selected for breeding. An understanding of all these factors is the goal that students of population have set for themselves.

Before turning to the next point, it should be recalled that part of the attraction of gene study in man was based on the assumption that nonadaptive features which resist environmentally induced changes offer the most satisfactory data for racial and evolutionary studies. From this viewpoint there has been a complete about-face in many quarters. Modern physical anthropologists realize that in one form or another it is changes of anatomical structure that are the main targets of their attack. Consequently, they are deliberately concerning themselves with investigation of phenotypical traits that are likely to show change.

An outspoken work along this line deals with the problems of race formation.[8] The authors are entirely aware of physical anthropology's past errors in technique, the sterility of many older hypotheses, and the temptations of genetics, yet they cleverly try to steer around all three. They state their thesis boldly: "Human beings differ in their physiological reactions to their different environments and consequently differ in appearance as much as do the members of any other animal species." [9] They then proceed with an original and provocative effort to explain how race differences may be brought about by responses to differing environmental conditions. The short stature of some Mongoloid groups is attributed to a diet of polished rice; meat eaters in mid-latitudes grow large, heavy, and muscular; life at

[8] C. S. Coon, S. M. Garn, and J. B. Birdsell, *Races: A Study of the Problems of Race Formation in Man*, Springfield, Illinois, 1950.
[9] *Ibid.*, p. 4.

high altitudes pays a premium to those with spacious lungs and big chests; desert dwellers thrive best if they are tall and lean; and inhabitants of the Arctic are most likely to survive if they are short and thick-set. Peppercorn hair is advantageous in hot zones because it permits sweat from the scalp to evaporate; cold weather has engineered the Mongoloid face with large pads of fat resting on distended cheekbones, and a flat nose designed to provide maximum heat for air passing to the lungs; and absence of pigment is associated with life in cool, damp, and cloudy areas.

At the moment very few physical anthropologists are willing to accept so frankly functional an approach, or to attribute so much direct causation to environmental determinants. Among other things, this method of analysis fails to explain why the Indian occupants of the hot and humid Amazon basin have thick-set bodies and long, black, straight, head hair, much like the Eskimo inhabitants of the Arctic circle. Nevertheless, the hypotheses proposed by the authors provide a refreshing departure from conventional methods of race classification that so often deal with human populations as if they lived in vacuums, out of contact with any environment.

## D. SHAPE-PRODUCING FORCES

Another approach that takes full cognizance of new developments in genetics and general biology, without being enslaved by them, is best exemplified by the work of Professor Sherwood L. Washburn. Long in revolt against the static aspects of traditional physical anthropology, he has turned from efforts at race classification to attempts at understanding the dynamic processes that result in differences of body shapes, and to the relations between biological forms and functions. Not satisfied to speculate about these matters, nor to deal with groups of so large a size that precise analysis is impossible, Professor Washburn prefers to ask the kinds of questions that give promise of being answered by laboratory experiments. Many writers on vertebrate anatomy had wondered, for instance, about the connection between the size of the eyeball and the dimensions of the socket that contained it. In 1943 Drs. Detwiler and Washburn sought a reply through experimentation.[10] They removed the natural eyes from

[10] S. L. Washburn and S. R. Detwiler, "An Experiment Bearing on the Problems of Physical Anthropology," *American Journal of Physical Anthropology,* Vol. 1, 1943, pp. 171-90.

embryonic specimens of the amphibian *Amblystoma punctatum,* a salamander, and transplanted extremely large eyes from a related species. As the embryos grew they developed abnormally large orbits that encroached on surrounding portions of the olfactory and optic regions. This demonstrated that the pressure of growth exerted by a very large eyeball directly influences the form of nearby areas of the face and head.

Another effort to understand the forces that shape the body led Washburn to remove temporal muscles from one side only of the heads of day-old rats. Several months later it was found that the associated skull parts on the operated side were much less well developed than on the corresponding normal side. Such experiments have established that bones do not independently assume their characteristic sizes and shapes. What, then, is one actually measuring when he measures a skull, external bones or the end-products of dynamic stresses caused by various muscles?

Quite recently Washburn has been advocating use of the "split-line" technique, which makes possible separate analysis of different portions of a single anatomical structure like the lower jaw. On a larger scale he has cited evidence which suggests the possibility that the total body of man is actually a combination of three distinct regions, each of which may develop at a totally different rate (Fig. 54). In this new concept of asymmetrical evolution, Washburn considers it likely that the upper body segment, consisting of the entire chest area and the forelimbs, was the first to attain its current pattern; that the bipedal complex, centering about the pelvis and lower limbs, was the next to be evolved to its present form; and that the skull, with its attendant face and brain was the last to reach modern proportions. In none of the three regions are important evolutionary changes known to have arisen since the emergence of the Cro-Magnons.

Different attacks on the problem of body formation have been made in a large number of studies devoted to growth. One of the leaders in this aspect of physical anthropology is Professor Wilton M. Krogman, who has published a valuable, comprehensive syllabus that gives references to numerous works covering the entire field.[11] In addition, Dr. J. M. Tanner has prepared a guide to growth studies,

11 W. M. Krogman, "The Physical Growth of the Child," *Yearbook of Physical Anthropology,* The Viking Fund, Inc., New York, 1949, pp. 280-99.

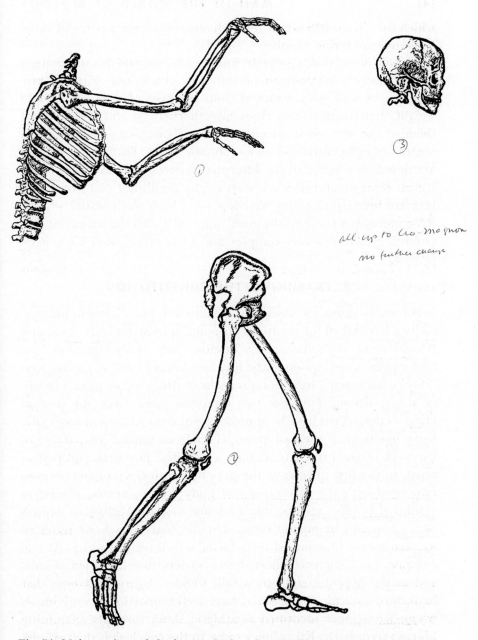

all up to Cro-magnon
no further change

Fig. 54. Major regions of the human body (after Washburn). Each of the three areas appears to have had an independent evolution. Thorax and arms were the first to attain modern form, followed by pelvis, legs, and feet. The head and brain were the last to evolve fully.

which lists all the important research centers and the particular problems they are trying to solve.[12]

Among other things growth studies are concerned with changes of the entire configuration of the body, including shifts of proportions, as well as the more obvious increases of total stature and weight. Investigators also chart growth rhythms and try to relate them to age, sex, environment (including diet), race, disease (both mental and physical), and socioeconomic status. Students of growth are thoroughly aware of the interplay between physical and physiological changes, and they are alert to the possibility that everything they are investigating may have a genetic basis. As a matter of fact, Krogman neatly sums up the entire approach with the statement that physical growth is a very complex and highly integrated bio-genetic process.

## E. EXAMINING THE CONSTITUTION

For many centuries observers of mankind, both laymen and specialists, have taken for granted a correlation between body build and temperament or behavior. Expressions like "jolly, fat man," or Shakespeare's description of the lean and hungry-looking Cassius who "thinks too much," have not always been dismissed as mere folklore or poetic license. For over two thousand years, since the days of Hippocrates, efforts have been made to put these ideas on a systematic basis, but none of the past attempts made an impact comparable to the work of Dr. Ernst Kretschmer, a Viennese physician and psychiatrist, in the first quarter of the present century. Kretschmer was so impressed with the relationship of body type to mental disease as exhibited by his patients, that he made a studied effort to express the connection in precise terms. On the basis of a fixed series of measurements, he grouped body forms into three categories. At one extreme was a compact, short, heavy variety that he called pyknic, and at the opposite end was a tall, slender, lightweight type that he termed asthenic. In between were well-proportioned individuals whom Kretschmer identified as athletic. After carefully examining his case records Dr. Kretschmer came to the conclusion that pyknics were most likely to suffer from manic depressive ailments, while

---

[12] J. M. Tanner, "A Guide to American Growth Studies," *Yearbook of Physical Anthropology*, The Viking Fund, Inc., New York, 1947, pp. 28-33.

asthenics were much more apt to become schizophrenic.[13] Despite a number of keen and justifiable criticisms of Kretschmer's methods and classifications, he is known as the first modern student to have put into quantitative terms a long-suspected connection between a definite body type and a specific kind of mental activity.

At about the same time as Kretschmer, Dr. George Draper, a physician from New York, was engaged in making somewhat similar studies. With the help of anthropometric (body-measuring) techniques, taken over and modified from the practices of physical anthropology, Dr. Draper made accurate determinations of the body structures of his patients, and then sought to relate their physical types to their ailments. Dr. Draper did not always find a close correlation, but sometimes he got surprising results. Most widely known of these are the tie-ups that seem to prevail between gastric ulcer and tall, thin, narrow-chested men; and between gall-bladder ailments and members of both sexes who are rather soft, fat, and rounded in build.[14]

By all odds the most ambitious studies conducted along similar lines have been those of Dr. William H. Sheldon and his associates. Their first efforts were directed toward the establishment of well-defined body or constitutional types, after which they tried to relate them to particular kinds of temperaments and other aspects of behavior. Not satisfied with the standard measurements taken by physical anthropologists Dr. Sheldon devised a technique known as "somatotyping." Its essence rested on his conviction that each human being develops in greater or lesser degree from a combination of three basic components: **endomorphy, mesomorphy,** and **ectomorphy.** Endomorphy means a comparative predominance of soft and rounded body parts, particularly in the region of the stomach or digestive tract; mesomorphy stands for a relatively great development of muscle and bone; and ectomorphy implies a tall, thin body, with much skin surface and little depth or volume behind it, coupled with a sensitive nervous system and a big brain.

[13] E. Kretschmer, *Körperbau und Charakter*, Berlin, 1921. For an English translation, see *Physique and Character*, by W. J. H. Sprott, London, 1925. A manic depressive goes through cycles of extreme elation and extreme depression. A schizophrenic lives in a world of his own, cut off from reality.

[14] G. Draper, *Disease and the Man*, London, 1930; and G. Draper, C. W. Dupertuis, and J. L. Caughey, Jr., *Human Constitution in Clinical Medicine*, New York and London, 1944.

By means of measurements and observations taken, for the most part, with specially designed tools on carefully standardized photographs in the nude, Sheldon rates five sectors of each individual's body in terms of the three components. His scale runs from 1 to 7, so that an extremely endomorphic person averages 7-1-1; extreme mesomorphs average 1-7-1; and extreme ectomorphs average 1-1-7 (Fig. 55). A person who exhibited absolutely no extremes of body build would earn an average rating of 4-4-4. Other subjects would vary from 1 to 7 in each of the three components.[15]

Hardly had Sheldon's account of somatotyping appeared than physical anthropologists divided into two camps. Some felt that he had broken new ground which promised to produce a rich scientific harvest, but others maintained that he was a visionary employing an unsound and biased, subjective approach. Unperturbed by the caustic comments of many of his colleagues, Sheldon went on to relate his constitutional types to forms of temperament or behavior. Again he rated his subjects on a seven-point scale for each of three components. Extraverts, who enjoyed comfortable living, good food, and pleasant companionship were called **viscerotonic** and were found to predominate among endomorphs; those who liked vigorous exercise and other forms of strenuous muscular activity were labelled **somatotonic** and linked with mesomorphs; while introverts who were shy and studious were described as **cerebrotonic** and associated with ectomorphic body build.[16]

Since then Sheldon has published a third book, in which he and his co-workers have tried to relate constitutional types and temperaments to various kinds of delinquent behavior.[17] Like the volumes that preceded it, it has been praised and damned. Without doubt the last work is so full of personal opinion and preaching that it can scarcely be taken at face value.

Among the outstanding weaknesses of Sheldon's entire approach has been his insistence that under all conditions a somatotype remains the same throughout a person's life. When a research worker demonstrated that starvation actually changes a person's somatotype, Sheldon brushed off the criticism with the implication that the in-

---

15 W. H. Sheldon, S. S. Stevens, and W. B. Tucker, *The Varieties of Human Physique,* New York, 1940.

16 W. H. Sheldon, and S. S. Stevens, *The Varieties of Temperament,* New York, 1942.

17 W. H. Sheldon, E. M. Hartl, and E. McDermott, *Varieties of Delinquent Youth,* New York, 1949.

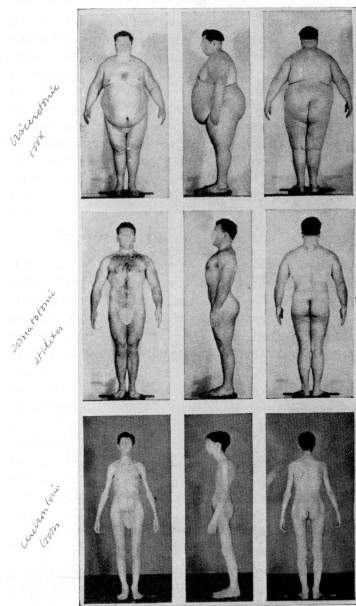

Fig. 55. Extreme varieties of human somatotypes (after Sheldon). At the top is an endomorph with a rating of 7-1-1; the center is a mesomorph, rated as 1-7-1; and at the bottom is an ectomorph who rates 1-1-7.

vestigator was incompetent. In his latest book, however, he has
yielded a little on this score by differentiating between a morpho-
phenotype that is changeable, and an unchanging morphogenotype
with which he identifies his somatotype. Needless to say, the invention of new terms has failed to stifle criticism.[18]

Whatever the final evaluation of Sheldon's work turns out to be,
he has already exerted a profound influence on many students of
man and his behavior. Very likely, the most lasting results will be
achieved by those who, stimulated by Sheldon, are revising and
modifying his techniques, rather than by the few disciples who are
adhering rigidly to his concepts and methods.[19]

## F. NEW USES FOR PHYSICAL ANTHROPOLOGY

The habits of careful measurement and observation of human
bodies that were the principal stock-in-trade of physical anthropologists have lately been diverted from some of their old pursuits
to a surprising number of new and practical applications. Between
1937 and 1939 precise measurements were obtained on 147,000
American boys and girls from four to seventeen years of age in order
to establish more accurate standards in the making and distribution
of children's clothing. Pressure for the study came especially from
mail-order companies whose customers, lacking opportunities for
preliminary fittings, found that former label sizes were consistently
misleading. To be effective, the standard techniques of anthropometry had to be altered to fit the conditions of the particular project
under consideration. Apparently, so much success was achieved, that
the decade of the 1940's saw many more measurements being taken
on women and children, and applied to practical use in the manufacture and sale of countless garments.[20]

While this was going on, engineers were also seeking anthropometric information that would permit the making of machinery that
was best suited for handling by a large percentage of potential opera-

18 For a brief summary of critical comments on Sheldon's work, consult W. A. Lessa,
"Somatomancy—Precursor of the Science of Human Constitution," *The Scientific
Monthly,* Vol. 75, 1952, pp. 364-65.

19 E. E. Hunt, Jr., "Human Constitution: an Appraisal," *American Journal of Physical Anthropology,* Vol. 10, 1952, especially pp. 65-72.

20 For a review of these studies, consult R. W. Newman, "Applied Anthropometry,"
*Anthropology Today* (A. L. Kroeber, ed.) Chicago, 1953, pp. 741-49.

tors. One specific program, undertaken in 1945 at the Naval Medical Research Institute, sought to determine how far a man could reach in various directions from a fixed position. Some of the results were put to use in designing military aircraft, but the basic information has also proved of value in civil aeronautics.[21]

Both in the United States and Great Britain many problems during World War II were turned over for solution to teams that included personnel trained in physical anthropology. Among other things these teams dealt with questions connected with sizing and fitting wearing apparel, handling of weapons, vehicle guidance, personal equipment of the nature of gas or oxygen masks, and seating devices. Again the results obtained were deemed so valuable that civilian agencies continued to seek similar information after the war. Professor Hooton of Harvard has gained no small amount of fame from a comfortable chair he designed to suit the sitting contours of riders in Pullman cars.

Long after peace had followed World War II, the American Air Force continued to maintain an Anthropometric Unit at Wright Field, on which Dr. H. T. E. Hertzberg served as anthropometrist. This team made many contributions that were intended to be of value not only to the armed forces, but also to the general populace.

First, Professor W. M. Krogman, and later, Drs. T. D. Stewart, and Marshall T. Newman, physical anthropologists on the staff of the National Museum in Washington, have often been asked by the Federal Bureau of Investigation to help identify skeletal remains found under suspicious circumstances. They have become expert at sorting human from other animal bones, and in making estimates of age, stature, and sex. Race is so frequently only skin deep in its main characteristics that it is hard to determine from skeletal fragments, but even here the physical anthropologists sometimes make startlingly accurate analyses. Similar identifications of unknown war dead have been made by Drs. Harry L. Shapiro of the American Museum of Natural History in New York, and Charles E. Snow of Kentucky University. It is estimated that over 80 per cent of 1500 unknown war dead are being definitely identified.[22]

21 For further details about this project and some of those mentioned in the remainder of this section, see "Symposium on Applied Physical Anthropology," *American Journal of Physical Anthropology*, Vol. 6, 1948, pp. 313-80.

22 *Ibid.*, p. 327.

Far from having remained an obscure, academic and impractical field of endeavor, physical anthropology has turned out to have wide usefulness in many ways. Apart from the projects already mentioned it has been applied to numerous programs of dental and medical research.[23] Whenever necessary, revisions of old-fashioned procedures have been unhesitatingly made, and have often proved to be of great value. In a review of this branch of the science of man it is not surprising to discover that many questions concerning the biology of human beings remain unanswered, but it is little short of amazing that so much has been accomplished by so few in the short space of several decades.

## SELECTED REFERENCES

Boyd, W. C., *Genetics and the Races of Man,* Boston, 1950.

Candela, P. B., "Blood-group Reactions in Ancient Human Skeletons," *American Journal of Physical Anthropology,* old series, Vol. 21, 1936, pp. 429-432.

Draper, G., *Disease and the Man,* London, 1930.

———, Dupertuis, W. C., and Caughey, J. L., Jr., *Human Constitution in Clinical Medicine,* New York and London, 1944.

Kretschmer, E., *Physique and Character,* (Sprott), New York and London, 1925.

Laughlin, W. S., "Preliminary Tests for Presence of Blood-group Substance in Tepexpan Man," in H. de Terra *et al.,* "Tepexpan Man," *Viking Fund publication No. 11;* New York, 1949, Appendix F.

Sheldon, W. H., *et al., The Varieties of Human Physique,* New York, 1940.

———, *et al. The Varieties of Human Temperament,* New York, 1942.

———, *et al. Varieties of Delinquent Youth,* New York, 1949.

Spuhler, J. N., "On the Number of Genes in Man," *Science,* Vol. 108, 1948, pp. 279-280.

Symposium on Applied Physical Anthropology, *American Journal of Physical Anthropology,* Vol. 6, 1948.

Washburn, S. L., "The Strategy of Physical Anthropology," *Anthropology Today,* A. L. Kroeber, ed., Chicago, 1953, pp. 714-727.

---

[23] A summary of this important topic may be found in W. M. Krogman, "The Role of Physical Anthropology in Dental and Medical Research," *American Journal of Physical Anthropology,* Vol. 9, 1951, pp. 211-18.

# CHAPTER 9

# The Biological Foundations
# of Culture

## A. THE HUMAN ANIMAL

By the time the first truly hominid forms made their appearance their organs for meeting the requirements of the biological imperatives were of considerable antiquity and time-tested utility. Except for matters of degree there were almost no differences between the ways in which human and other Primate bodies breathed, chewed and swallowed food, digested, excreted waste matter, reproduced, or used their sense organs. It seems safe to postulate that the biological conduct of the earliest hominids was not significantly different from that of their Primate contemporaries. Yet the later stages of man's behavior stand out in sharp contrast because of his dependence on nonphysiological mechanisms. Herein lies a problem that is worthy of the most careful consideration, for it involves the basic question of how human beings, only, came to fashion on a generally Primate form of biology a whole system of extra-biological patterns of action.

Scientists know absolutely nothing about the grandparents of *Pithecanthropus erectus* but, as a point of departure, it is worth trying to imagine how their generation lived. As a guess, their lives were adjusted to meet the needs, exclusively, of the bio-physico-chemical world. Involuntarily, their lungs took in oxygen, their hearts pumped blood, and their body temperatures normally remained at a constantly high level. Whenever they exerted themselves they breathed harder than usual and they felt tired; when they were cold their teeth chattered and their bodies shivered; when

151

they were hot they sweated; and whenever they grew sufficiently weary they rested or slept. If their stomachs contracted they felt hunger pangs and sought to put food into their mouths, where it was moistened, chewed, and swallowed into the digestive tract. When there was pressure on the bladder they urinated, and when their bowels were full they defecated.

Male bodies were organized to form sperm cells in the testes and female bodies to produce egg cells in the ovaries. From time to time their genital organs were stimulated to engage in copulation. If fertilization followed, the female's menstrual periods were suspended and an embryo formed within her body, where it was nourished through a gestation of about nine months by means of a placental arrangement. After giving birth to her child the female discharged the placental mechanism from her body, suckled the baby, and aided it in many ways until it reached a stage where it could shift for itself. As years passed the bodies of males and females became subject to some fatal disease or else grew old and deteriorated. Then death came to terminate the biological aspects of their behavior, and the corpses decomposed in response to fixed laws of chemistry and physics.

This is purely animal (mammalian) behavior, even when it applies to hominids. Within the limits mentioned every mechanism for action is bio-genetically inherited and developed, and every response is biologically directed and controlled. Had man continued to live in such fashion, his way of life would have been virtually indistinguishable from that of other large Primates.

## B. TOOL-MAKING AND THE ORIGIN OF CULTURE

Soon after the appearance of hominids, at the very latest by the time level of *Sinanthropus pekinensis* in the mid-Pleistocene, there are signs that man was no longer living exclusively in the bio-physico-chemical world, but had entered into the realm of culture. The most conclusive proof rests on the occurrence of manufactured stone tools that were found directly associated with the skeletal remains. Manufactured stone tools, it need hardly be emphasized, are not a part of any animal's bio-genetic inheritance. They have to be fashioned with the help of a body, but they carry on an independent extra-bodily existence. We may speak of inheriting a kit of tools, but we realize full well that the manner of transmission is quite apart from sexual reproduction. Only hominids regularly and consistently manufacture tools. By following out all the implications of this statement of fact, it is possible to learn a great deal about how man came to use his inherited biological equipment for nonbiological purposes and in nonbiologically determined ways.

Many creatures employ bits of wood, stone, grass, or earth for a variety of purposes. As long as these things are used in their natural condition they should not be classed as manufactured tools, even if they are fashioned into complicated structures. To make a tool requires the mental capacity to plan ahead freely without biological predetermination, to look unrestrictedly into the future, to deal with imaginary situations in the sense that all future events are imaginary before they have come to pass. Anthropologists have learned not to confuse the two different levels at which planning ahead may be found. One kind is bio-genetically inherited, as when squirrels store nuts before the coming of winter, or when birds migrate from north to south and back again. The other kind is cultural and is neither biologically inherited nor a fixed response to environmental clues. The essential difference between these two levels of planning ahead is the matter of freedom of action. Biological planning ahead leaves no room for individual choice but is imposed, with very little flexibility, on all the members of a given species; but cultural planning ahead permits each individual to act or not at his own discretion, and with no limitation on how he may decide to meet a future contingency. Squirrels of a particular species must store nuts at certain times, in certain ways. Men, by contrast, may store any or no kinds of nuts, may decide to hoard instead potatoes or cans of soup, or may prefer to put money into the bank, or to go on relief when winter comes.

## C. PEEKING INTO THE FUTURE

Man's special ability to plan ahead freely marks one of the most essential traits that separates him from the rest of the animal kingdom. Yet, there is a convention among ourselves that we cannot guess about the future, and all of us are familiar with remarks like, "No one knows what the future will bring," or "It's ridiculous to try to predict the future." Of course there are many vast and important areas in which prediction is futile, as in trying to guess who will be President of the United States in 1990. Just the same, in spite of the wealth of proverbs and popular sayings to the contrary, human beings constantly indulge in predictions. Late in the winter of 1952 the National Safety Council predicted that during the month of December the one millionth traffic fatality in the United States would occur. They could not foretell who the victim would be, where he would be struck down, or how the accident would happen, but insofar as the main point of their forecast is concerned they were absolutely correct.

Every day, and at practically every moment of the day, huge numbers of men and women are constantly predicting and, to a great extent accurately predicting, many important future events. Countless schoolchildren select their colleges and professions years in advance; lovers decide to marry "when John gets out of the Army"; youngsters repeatedly make dates for "after school"; wives ask husbands each morning to bring something or other "on the way home from the office"; people make travel or hotel reservations months ahead; and invitations to great affairs go out long before they are scheduled to take place. Obviously, death or sickness, or some other unforeseen contingency may upset one's predictions, but human beings persistently and to a large extent successfully base their lives on the premise that their plans for the future will be carried out.

It is time now to see how man's nonbiological aptitude for looking ahead applies to the making of tools. If one decides to manufacture even the simplest of implements, say a homemade toothpick of wood, he must plan for the future in several ways. He must know where he can get the necessary raw material, and where he can secure the needed tools. More important still, he must have clearly in mind before he begins manufacturing, the size and shape of the finished object that he wants to make. Unless he has in mind an advance blueprint of the completed product, he is unlikely to turn out even so elementary an implement as a simple, wooden toothpick.

Once he had demonstrated the capacity to think ahead in ways that were not biologically predetermined, man was able to escape the limitations of the bio-physico-chemical world and to begin fashioning culture. Yet, he could not entirely divorce himself from biology for, if he refused to obey its imperatives, as by failing to breathe while manufacturing tools, he would surely die. Moreover, even if a man had the clearest of mental pictures of something he wanted to make, he would still require strong and flexible fingers, hands, wrists and arms, accurate muscular controls, and keen hand-eye coordination in order to be a successful manufacturer. Thus it can be shown that cultural behavior must rest on biological foundations, and that toolmaking is a biocultural activity.

## D. WORDS, WORDS, WORDS

Man's capacity to deal with future or imaginary situations, including preparation of advance blueprints, calls for a kind of mentality that is, as far as is known, unique among animals. Thanks to his special ability the test of reality among human beings is no longer restricted to physical, chemical, or biological standards. Man can and does deal with non-existent things with just about as much assurance as he does with tangible objects. Mermaids are not supposed to be real, but humans can count them, paint or carve them, and write stories or poems about them. It is easy to give a human being instructions that will enable him to go to some place where he has never before been and to take up an object which he has never before seen. One of the most extraordinary accomplishments along these lines is man's capacity for dealing with abstractions. By no test of bio-physico-chemical reality can one establish the existence of such abstract ideas as "pride," "civic duty," "loyalty," or "thoughtfulness"; yet, humans have no trouble in measuring or comparing these intangibles as when we say that one person has more or less pride than another. With the emergence of the mental ability to deal with abstractions the way is opened for the development of higher mathematics, philosophy, religion, and similar fields.

Abstract ideas achieve a kind of reality, as a rule, only when they have been expressed in words. Accordingly, the human capacity for dealing with abstractions cannot be separated from the use of language. In essence, a spoken word is a sound or combination of sounds to which a group of persons (a society) has assigned a particular meaning. Take the sound "C" as commonly uttered in the English-speaking world. By itself it has absolutely no meaning, as any skeptic can discover if he will travel about the world saying, "C," "C," "C." Nor has this sound any specific meaning even to speakers of English. When used in one context the sound "C," spelled "see," means "look"; but if spelled and used another way the same sound, "sea," means a body of salt water. "C" can just as well stand for the third letter of the alphabet, a note of our musical scale, an athletic award won at Colgate or Cornell, or a familiar form of address for a girl named Celia. How can the same sound "C" mean so many different things in English, to say nothing of meaning, "yes," in Spanish or Italian, and, "if," in French? Paradoxical as it may seem, the reason why "C" can mean all these things, plus whatever else human beings may choose to have it mean, is because in and of itself it has absolutely no meaning. Since it is entirely without meaning it does not restrict any society from assigning to it as many different meanings as it wishes. Even when this has been done with as much variety as in the English use of "C," no one of the ascribed meanings becomes permanently attached to the sound. We can still, if we like, change the meanings of "C" at will. In making up a code we can make "C" stand for an oboe or a windmill.

To deny that other animals are able to use true speech is not to deny that they can utter meaningful sounds. Birds, chickens, dogs, cats, most Primates, and many other creatures produce sounds that convey definite meanings, but on analysis it turns out that their sound-making ability is biologically inherited in its manner of production as well as in its content. Among all species the sounds are almost exclusively limited to the expression of generalized, subjective states like fear, hunger, joy, or sexual desire. There is no capacity for dealing with abstractions, and not even the most ardent of animal fanciers really expects a parrot to discuss philosophy. Moreover, not a single nonhuman creature can make sounds that apply to precise details. Even if one knows from the whine of a pet dog that it has been hurt one realizes that the beast cannot utter detailed information about who injured it, when, or under what circumstances. To make meaningful sounds is a common aspect of animal behavior, but to use true speech is an exclusive, human ability.

## E. PLAYING WITH SYMBOLS

The mental power to assign one or more meanings to something which has no meaning of its own is the basis of **symbolic behavior.** A standard dictionary definition of a **symbol** reads in part, "That which suggests something else . . . especially a visible sign of something invisible, as an idea, a quality. . . ." [1] A symbol does not necessarily have to be a sound. In fact, it is universally agreed that the invention of a mark for zero is one of the highest mental achievements ever made by man because it expresses the very essence of symbolism by providing something that stands for absolutely nothing. Anything at all can be endowed with symbolic meanings or values and the meanings cannot be perceived except by members of the society who have been taught to know them. In purely physicochemical terms two pieces of wood in the shape of a cross are nothing but two pieces of wood and will be so regarded by true pagans. But to believing Christians the symbolic meaning of a wooden cross is very real and of far greater significance than the chemical or physical properties of wood. To cite another instance, a piece of greenish paper with certain markings that include the words, "one dollar," is no more than a small piece of colored paper as far as any physicochemical analysis goes and, to anyone outside our range of economics, it has no more value than any similar piece of paper of the same size, shape, weight, thickness, and color.

## F. LET X EQUAL

Ability to symbolize depends on a kind of mentality for which the term **algebraic** has been suggested.[2] This idea can easily be grasped if we think of the commonest formula used in algebra, "Let $x$ equal." Whenever we use this expression the symbol "$x$," has no meaning of its own, but in problem after problem it can be assigned any meaning within the range of human imagination. The symbol "$x$" can just as well equal 8 railroad cars, or $\frac{1}{2}$ an orange, or 37 women, or 14 pairs of green shoes, or 3 unicorns. Here again we find that no matter how many meanings are assigned to "$x$," the symbol itself remains without fixed meaning and so stands ever ready to have any of its assigned meanings changed at the will of those who manipulate it.

Because the entire range of culture leans so heavily on the use of language and other forms of symbolization, scientists are eager to

1 *Webster's Collegiate Dictionary,* abridged, 5th ed., Springfield, 1948, p. 1010.
2 W. Köhler, *The Mentality of Apes,* rev. ed., New York, 1925, p. 11, speaks of experiments with apes that require "a complicated geometry of movement." L. A. White has carried the concept a step further and describes human mentality as "algebraic."

know if nonhuman animals can use this process, perhaps in a less perfect form. Experimenters have worked with a host of creatures to see whether or not they were able to symbolize. Claims of all sorts, some clearly extravagant and others hard to deny, have been made for beasts that seem to deal successfully with symbols. Seeing-eye dogs that stop at a red traffic light, mice that quickly run a difficult maze, numerous animals that "speak," and rats that learn to distinguish the symbol "A," leading to food, from the symbol "B," that leads to punishment, are only a few that have been cited. Yet, all the doubts that have been raised by these cases can be swept away if we take into consideration two factors.

In the first place, in every experiment of this kind so far devised the symbolic value, such as red light means stop, "A" equals food, and "B" stands for punishment, has been thought up by a human being. There is no record of any other animal that has invented a symbolic meaning and arbitrarily assigned it to a particular sound, mark, color, or object. It is one thing to *recognize* a man-established symbolic meaning, which many animals can learn to do, but it is quite another matter to *invent* a symbolic value, which man alone can do. In the second place all human beings, even small children, can learn to switch symbolic meanings about. If "B" stands for punishment today it can just as well stand for reward tomorrow. To fool an enemy, perhaps, we might decide to stop traffic on green and proceed on red. There might be a little confusion at first, but it would not take long for people to learn the new system. With non-human animals the situation is very different. Once they have learned to associate "B" with punishment, it is no easy matter to retrain them to link "B" with reward.

Man and man only has the mental capacity to think up symbolic values, practically without limit; and only human beings can switch about and change symbolic meanings whenever they desire. For these reasons anthropologists are convinced that none but humans have unqualified algebraic mentalities. At this point the scientific world finds itself baffled. Even if it is granted that the use of symbols by *Homo sapiens* is an unique achievement, it is exceedingly hard to single out the particular aspects of human biology which have given the species that special ability.

## G. THE BIOLOGICAL BASIS OF ALGEBRAIC MENTALITY

Only one feature of human biology gives promise of holding the key to man's exceptional mentality, and that is his highly developed brain. Relative to the size and weight of the average body *Homo sapiens* has by far the largest brain of any Primate. Correspondingly, the species has the greatest cerebral cortex of any related group. Within its manifold curves and wrinkles the human cerebrum lodges over nine billion cells, and it is perhaps possible that the combination of gross size and multitudinous cells, coupled with a rich blood supply and, perhaps, other physical traits, may some day yield a clue to man's most distinctive mental characteristic. At the moment, no one dares to speak with assurance about the relationship of gross brain size to symbolic behavior, but certain tentative suggestions may be advanced.

If it is true, as there is every reason to believe, that man alone has an algebraic mentality, then it may not be improper to point out that the average human has a cranial capacity of 1350 cc., which is $2\frac{1}{2}$ to 3 times that of a large gorilla. Running from the living Simiidae, through the man-apes and extinct hominids, there appears to be a continuum that spans the gap between the ape and human brain sizes. Somewhere along the line algebraic mentality is thought to have made its appearance, but no one knows exactly where. Because it is obviously impossible to observe the mental workings of extinct animals, scientists are forced to make comparisons between living humans and living apes, and that may explain why differences of brain size stand forth as seemingly all-important.

While increases of quantity do not invariably result in changes of quality, there are instances where more or less of something leads to a critical point or threshold beyond which a qualitative difference may be noted. A significant case of this kind is that of water temperature. When ordinary water at sea level is chilled below 32 degrees Fahrenheit, it becomes a solid, ice, and remains a solid no matter how much colder it gets. Between 32 and 212 degrees Fahrenheit there is a wide range without critical points, within which water retains the properties of a fluid. But 212 marks another threshold, above which hot water becomes converted from a liquid to a gas, steam.

By analogy with what happens to water, there is a chance that cranial capacities also have critical points. Tentatively stated, it may be that a Primate brain which is normally less than 900 cc. stands for a mentality that is incapable of true symbolization; between 900 and 1000 cc. may represent a threshold zone about which nothing definite is known; and any normal Primate brain above 1000 cc. is probably fully capable of using symbolic speech and other features of algebraic mentality (Fig. 56). Once this point has been reached,

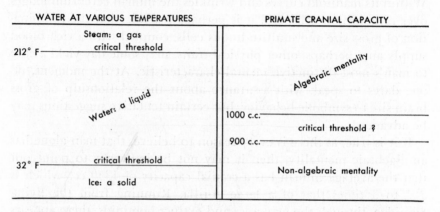

Fig. 56. Quantity may affect quality. Primate cranial capacity, by analogy with water, may have a quantitative threshold above which a qualitative change takes place. If so, it would explain the origin of the mental ability to symbolize.

additional cubic centimeters of cranial capacity do not seem to affect the quality of mental behavior. No tests have ever demonstrated that a brain size of 1000-1200 cc. is any less efficient in dealing with symbols than one of 1400-1600 cc., or more.

## H. CULTURAL VERSUS BIOLOGICAL VALUES

Man-made symbolic meanings, it must be repeated, have significance only to those members of *Homo sapiens* who share a common way of life. These are the intangible meanings that anthropologists describe as nonbiologic cultural values. A human being can no more expect automatically to know the cultural values of a society different from his own than he can expect to know at first hearing the meanings of a strange language. Once more we are confronted with the profound distinction between human biology and culture. There is no way of anticipating the cultural values that an investigator may find prevalent in a foreign society, but it is a foregone conclusion that in terms of biology the members of any human society will behave much alike regardless of their stock, race, or place of residence. As to relative stability, we are again on safe ground for it has been shown repeatedly that it is easier to modify one's culture than his biology. Many a Caucasoid child of American parents has been born in China. If such a child remains in China long enough he is capable of becoming thoroughly Chinese in culture, but under no circumstances would he ever become anything but Caucasoid biologically (Fig. 57).

Fig. 57. Biological fixity and culture change. A young Caucasoid who was brought up in China is shown in an Americanization class. He writes Chinese easily, but is laboriously learning to write English.

Inasmuch as cultural factors are so completely distinct from biological ones, it follows that they do not necessarily need to conform to the same system of logic. Judged only in direct relation to their biological counterparts, cultural values may be called: (a) logical, if they help to satisfy biological imperatives; (b) nonlogical, if they neither help nor retard biological activity; and (c) illogical, if they stand in the way of a response to biological imperatives. When viewed within this particular context, wearing a woolen sweater when the weather is cold is logical; insisting on a light red rather than a deep red but otherwise identical sweater is nonlogical; and refusing to don any sweater at all, though one is available, is illogical.

Just because cultural values are generally intangible, invented by man, subject to change, and sometimes illogical, it does not mean that they are any less real or important than material things to the people who have learned to accept them. There is a widespread belief that human beings are the only rational animals and that they always try to act logically. This is far from true. In case after case it can be shown that, short of inviting death, men and women prefer to follow cultural dictates even if they are frankly illogical by biological standards. A proper Catholic will surely prefer to go hungry rather than eat meat on a Friday in Lent, an orthodox Jew will avoid any food that is not ritually clean or kosher, a true Moslem will abstain from pig flesh regardless of hunger, and a devout Hindu would never consent to make a meal of beef. Large numbers of people throughout the world refuse to indulge in culturally unapproved sexual relations in spite of biological urging; and who among us has not watched the efforts of individuals on their good behavior to suppress the sound effects of the digestive process?

Man is the only animal capable of this type of illogical behavior, nor is it to be regarded as a consequence of low mentality. A coed rushing about with scant clothing and bare legs in zero weather does not have to be a Phi Beta Kappa to realize that she would be warmer if she wore heavy underwear and long stockings, and a teacher sweltering in a summer classroom does not need to be a genius to know that he would be more comfortable if he stripped down to his shorts. Far from being a sign of dim-wittedness such behavior is geared to the highest order of mentality (algebraic) because it rests on the acceptance of cultural values that can be invented by no creatures other than humans.

To understand how exclusively *sapiens* is this sort of behavior, we have but to pose a number of questions. Is there any other animal which habitually eats a certain kind of food but will voluntarily abstain from it in keeping with religious instructions? Does a male of any other species that is sexually desirous refuse to mate with a receptive female because she may be his near relative? Has anyone ever heard of a beast that feels a need to eliminate but refuses to ease itself because a member of the opposite sex is present? To all of these, and to as many similar questions as one can think up, the answer is, "Certainly not!" Only by dint of a great deal of special training at the hands of human beings can any other animal be induced to act contrary to the dictates of its biology.

At the opposite extreme there is no society known to anthropologists where people eat, drink, eliminate, or mate, exclusively in biological terms. Yet, there are fixed limits beyond which even man may not go in modifying biological behavior. No matter how expert a diner is required to be with silver knife and fork or bamboo chopsticks, he must get an adequate amount of nourishing food into his mouth if he wants to grow or live, and after the food has been swallowed the biological process of digestion must take over. A person may read the works of Shakespeare in his bathroom, but the act of elimination remains a biological matter. A woman may be ultrafastidious about keeping her body covered but if she wants to become a mother she must, barring the remote possibility of artificial insemination, submit to the biological act of copulation. The scheme of dual values implied in all cases of this kind makes up the very essence of biocultural behavior. Every human society has formed a set of cultural values in the light of which its biological actions are modified, but no two societies subscribe to the same set of symbolic meanings. Whatever may be the reasons for these variations they certainly do not arise from differences of human biology. Members of any given society, stock, or race can, if they care to make the effort, adjust themselves to any other group's system of symbols. This leads to the inescapable conclusion that, *in theory*, there is no insuperable barrier to prevent all of mankind from learning to live by a single pattern of culture.

### Selected References

Allee, W. C., *The Social Life of Animals*, New York, 1938.
Köhler, W., *The Mentality of Apes*, rev. ed., New York, 1925.
Kroeber, A. L., "Subhuman Cultural Beginnings," *Quarterly Review of Biology*, Vol. 3, 1928, pp. 325-342.

———, "The Superorganic," *American Anthropologist,* Vol. 19, 1917, pp. 163-213.

Tozzer, A. M., "Biography and Biology," *American Anthropologist,* Vol. 35, 1933, pp. 418-432.

White, L. A., "The Mentality of Primates," *Scientific Monthly,* Vol. 34, 1932, pp. 69-72.

Zuckerman, S., *The Social Life of Monkeys and Apes,* New York, 1932.

PART TWO

The March of Culture

# CHAPTER 10

# Archeology and the Beginnings of Culture

## A. THE NATURE OF ARCHEOLOGY

Of the three main approaches to a total understanding of the science of man, archeology contains the greatest number of challenges and is in many ways the hardest. With the study of extinct cultures and, when possible, of the people who lived by those cultures as his objectives the archeologist is deprived by the very nature of his work of any opportunity to ask questions of living persons. Professionally, he is dedicated to an investigation of the past, often the remote past, and the materials with which he deals are accordingly strictly limited by an inexorable rule. They must be capable of resisting the forces of decomposition and disintegration over long periods of time. Only under the most exceptional of circumstances does the archeologist have the advantage of studying extinct people with the help of soft body parts, and rarely does he get a glimpse of an ancient culture except in terms of objects made of stone, bone, baked clay, metal, or some other durable substance. And, of course, he must be prepared to find that even the goods which he does discover are broken or damaged or are only fragments of things that were originally much larger.

To add to his woes the archeologist is committed to try to reconstruct from the physical objects that come into his hands something of the nonmaterial aspects of the culture that they represent, its system of symbolic values, its ideas of right and wrong, its social regulations, or the forms of its religion. Without the help of the language that was spoken when the culture was flourishing, and generally lacking the benefit of accompanying written documents, the archeologist is seldom in a position to make dogmatic statements about the intangible features of an extinct way of life. Yet, it would be a serious error to think he is completely shut off from this feature of human activity. Surely, no one will deny that when an archeologist comes across a large stock of weapons and many skeletons showing wounds he is justified in deducing a battle or something else of a military nature. And if he finds the remains of a large and well laid-out city, he is certainly correct to infer that the inhabitants must have had a system of social planning. Instead of being content, therefore, to limit themselves to descriptions and analyses of imperishable, physical objects, archeologists throughout the world have labored to develop subtle techniques for reading into their materials interpretations and meanings that may penetrate into the intangible and nonmaterial spheres. Even so there is much that cannot be recovered by any known method and there is always the danger of grave error, but archeologists are well aware of the pitfalls and try hard to avoid them.

Most of the material that makes up the subject matter of archeology is found at sites that have been abandoned by their former occupants for so long that they have become covered with layers of dust, dirt, or solid earth. Consequently, a standard part of a field archeologist's equipment consists of implements suitable for digging. Places chosen for large-scale study are not picked at random. Sometimes they are selected after careful ground or air reconnaissance in an area whose surface exhibits signs of former habitations, burials, or objects of recognizably human make. Sometimes a place is discovered by a farmer whose plow turns up ancient bones or tools; and sometimes old histories provide clues to buried settlements. It is only when he has reason to think that a spot is likely to yield worthy material that an archeologist undertakes a major job of excavation.

## B. PICK, SHOVEL, TROWEL, AND BRUSH

When a suitable site has been located and all necessary arrangements have been made with its owner an archeologist does not immediately plunge his shovel into the earth. Instead, he closely

A

B

Fig. 58. Archeological methods. A. View of a site which has been cleared
by the grid method. B. A stage during the digging at the Lindenmeier
site. Careful evacuation of a fixed area, a few inches at a time, has produced a step-like effect.

examines the terrain and, often with the help of a geologist, tries to figure out what the nature of the place was in former times, where its sources of water may have been, what the climate was like, what plants and animals lived in the area, what fuels and raw materials were available, how close it was to an old road or trade route, what factors led man to come to that spot, and what in the external environment may have killed him off or driven him away.

When, at last, it is time to start digging the archeologist does not tunnel straight down, unless he is deliberately making a test pit that may yield a sort of synopsis of the things that are likely to be encountered underground. Today, archeologists prefer to mark a site into regular squares or rectangles and to excavate only a fixed distance downward at a time (Fig. 58). The depth of each stage depends on internal conditions such as marked changes in the layers of earth, the occurrence of walls, fireplaces, or other structures, or noteworthy differences in the kinds of objects found. There are times, though, when the depth of excavation stages is arbitrarily set so that accurate records can be kept of the vertical and horizontal positions of everything that is uncovered. A field worker's notebooks and photographic records should make it possible to reconstruct every detail of the original situation in which materials were obtained, and when the results of a "dig" are published they should be comparable point for point with the results of any similar excavation. Delicate tools are used as necessary to minimize the disturbance of buried objects, all loose dirt from each excavated section is screened through a fine wire mesh to make sure that nothing has been overlooked, and everything that may be of cultural significance is photographed *in situ,* preserved and stored, no matter how small, trivial, inartistic, or damaged it may be. Plant remains, animal bones, human skeletal parts, and other things may be sent to specialists whose analyses will help the archeologist to piece together the full story of the extinct culture under study.

## C. MARKING TIME

Every archeologist is keenly sensitive to cultural variations that have taken place at various points of time while his site was occupied by living men. Unless he is careful to take note of successive changes he cannot hope to make an adequate reconstruction of the culture history of the place he is investigating. It is in connection with this vital aspect of his work that the previously described techniques of excavation must now be considered. The practice of digging down from the surface by carefully observed stages, may be said to be determined by an interest in **stratigraphy.** Under ideal natural conditions, where there has been no disturbance, layers of soil accumulate one above the other and study of their deposition is known as stratigraphy. In archeology stratigraphy often provides the most ready key to chronology, for objects found in the deepest undisturbed levels are the oldest, and those found in the topmost strata are the most recent. Unfortunately, disturbances caused by flooding, animal intrusion, volcanic eruption, or some other means are all too common, and the archeologist must learn not to rely uncritically on stratigraphic evidence when it comes to dating his material.

If excavated specimens are of great antiquity a geologist may establish their approximate dates by studying the soil in which they were located; if bones of extinct animals are found associated with artifacts a paleontologist may provide a clue to their age; and if cultural objects are discovered in conjunction with ancient plants a paleobotanist may ascertain how old they are. At the opposite extreme, if artifacts are of recent age they may be dated by comparison with historically known materials. Between these extremes the archeologist is often hard put to establish reliable dates and time sequences, but even so he still has several resources at his command. By consulting field reports of other excavations he is sometimes able to cross-date objects of uncertain age by close comparison with similar things found in places where dates have already been fixed. Should this approach fail the archeologist may try to derive chronological information from comparative studies based on spatial distribution (**diffusion**), or stylistic changes (**typology**).

Things made at one spot are very likely to spread or diffuse to other areas. Archeologists often plot on a map the reported frequencies in which identical objects have been found throughout a wide stretch of territory. If it turns out that there is a very heavy concentration in one place and less frequent occurrence elsewhere, it may be argued that the artifact in question originated where it is most common and diffused to other regions through such agencies as simple borrowing, trade, migration, or war. If this assumption is correct, it follows that the object is oldest in the place where it originated. Such reasoning is far from infallible and beginners are warned that professional archeologists do not rely unduly on the indirect evidence of diffusion for setting up comparative timetables.

As to typology, it may be said to depend on the possibility of working out a time sequence during which variations took place in the style of a particular artifact. Once in a while it can be shown that some forms of manufacture or decoration are older than others. A homely example might be made of the shifts from horse-drawn carriages, to old-fashioned automobile bodies, to modern stream-lined cars. Or else, one might trace the development of automobile tires from very thin, to balloon, to tubeless blowout-proof types. In circumstances where typological sequences have been established for archeological materials, a study of stylistic changes may throw light on comparative dates. No reputable archeologist employs one technique to the exclusion of the others. Wherever possible he uses a variety of approaches and feels safest when the results of several methods of analysis point to the same conclusion.

Occasionally, a chronological device makes possible accurate dating under special circumstances or in a particular region. Throughout the Southwestern United States, especially, archeologists make wide use of **dendrochronology.** This is a system based on the observed fact that where rainfall is highly irregular the trees produce different kinds of annual rings. When there is much moisture in a given year the rings that are laid down are thick and resemble wide bands, but when there is drought the rings are thin and appear close together. Dendrochronology was developed about thirty years ago by Dr. A. E. Douglass, an astronomer from the University of Arizona. By cutting down successively older trees, Dr. Douglass was able to plot the order in which narrow or wide bands occurred. Since all the trees in a given locality showed the same pattern, he found it possible to build up a master plot which went back in time until it overlapped tree ring specimens found in prehistoric places. Today, when an archeologist in the Southwest secures a bit of wood or even a piece of charcoal from a site, its tree ring pattern is diagrammed and moved along the master chart until the two plots match. By this means the earliest and latest rings on the specimen can be accurately dated, and the last ring will give the year when the tree was cut down (Fig. 59). At present Dr. Douglass' master plot runs from our own day back to about the start of the Christian era.

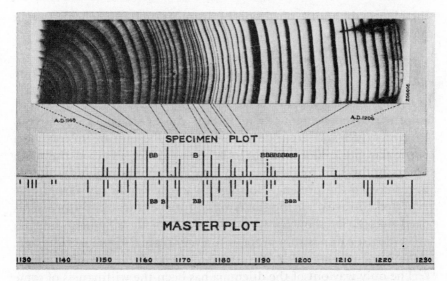

SPECIMEN PLOT

MASTER PLOT

Fig. 59. Dating by dendrochronology. A tree-ring specimen is plotted on graph paper, and matched with the master plot compiled by Dr. Douglass. In this fashion the first and last years registered on the specimen are dated with reasonable accuracy.

The most recent aid to archeological dating is known as the **carbon-14** method. It is based on the circumstance that all living things maintain a fixed equilibrium of substances containing $C^{14}$, a radioactive form of carbon. As soon as death comes there is no replacement of $C^{14}$ and its atoms begin to break up at the rate of 15.6 disintegrations per minute per gram of carbon. After $5,568 \pm 30$ years, the carbon-14 atoms reach their half-life, following which their disintegrations are slowed down to half-speed, 7.8 per minute per gram. By determining the exact amount of $C^{14}$ left in each gram of organic substance, as well as the rate of its disintegration, scientists can figure out the time when the material ceased to live. This technique was devised by Dr. W. F. Libby, a physicist from the University of Chicago, and several colleagues. While the method is unquestionably sound, the conclusions are sometimes uncertain when applied to archeological specimens. Greater accuracy will certainly be achieved as more experience is gained, but at its best the technique will be of limited value in archeology, because it requires fairly large quantities of organic materials that perished no earlier than 20,000 to 30,000 years ago. Beyond that time span, which marks the identifiable range of carbon-14 disintegration, the scheme cannot possibly work.

## D. MAIN GOALS OF ARCHEOLOGY

From what has already been said it may be seen that archeology is torn between two equally important aims. One major objective is to gain a full and accurate knowledge of the culture history of a particular site or locality, the other is to throw light on the main events in the sum total of man's cultural accomplishments from the beginning to the present. No single place or region can possibly be expected to reveal all the stages of cultural evolution, no two spots need necessarily show an identical course of development, and no archeologist can possibly probe into every corner of the world. How, then, is the whole march of culture to be traced?

The only way out of the dilemma has been the willingness of some archeologists to fit together the information contained in a vast number of detailed, local reports. By this method a synthesis has been made and a tentative record of man's cultural progress has been prepared. Most of the story must rest on the occurrence of imperishable artifacts and that is why the stages of universal culture are described in terms of raw materials that were used for making things.

What is known as "the doctrine of the three ages," stone, copper-bronze, and iron, was first publicized, though not originated, by Christian J. Thomsen, curator of the Danish National Museum in Copenhagen from 1816 to 1865. Archeologists are thoroughly agreed that Thomsen's scheme is too elementary and over-simplified to describe the whole march of culture, but within the limits that it goes it has never been proved false. Man, especially in the Old World, did proceed from a reliance on stone to the use of copper-bronze and iron in that order. Throughout the mid-nineteenth century Thomsen's little scheme was vehemently attacked and as stoutly defended. Never was it destroyed, but it was literally broken up. As archeological specimens came to be accumulated in prodigious quantities, the artifacts of stone were recognized to have been made by such differing techniques that it was meaningless to lump them together as products of a single age of stone. French and British archeologists early insisted on a need for separating the **Old Stone Age (Paleolithic)** from the **New Stone Age (Neolithic)**, and this distinction gained currency in 1865 when it was adopted by Sir John Lubbock, later Lord Avebury, in his book, *Prehistoric Times*. Soon after, between 1867 and 1883, the famed French archeologist, Gabriel de Mortillet, proposed a further separation of the Paleolithic into five periods, and most of the names he assigned to these phases are still in common use. Additional refinements have been made in all of the three ages, and problems of terminology, classification, sequence, chronology, techniques, distribution, and interpretation are being actively debated at present.

All of these academic disputes are directed toward a single goal, to provide an accurate and fully detailed account of cultural development. Since man is known to have originated in the Old World the beginnings of culture must there be sought. Moreover, because *Homo sapiens* branched off from a Primate stem, efforts have been made to discover the source of his cultural behavior by observations of the most highly evolved of non-human Primates. This approach calls for experiments with living great apes. Anthropologists do not feel qualified to conduct these experiments, but they eagerly await the findings of those who are trained for such work.

## E. APES, TOOLS, AND CULTURE

Under test conditions it has repeatedly been demonstrated that apes are not limited in their actions to biologically predetermined channels.[1] This is proved in its simplest form by placing something desirable out of reach of a confined animal and leaving a simple stick or rake nearby. An ape quickly gets the idea of picking up the implement and using it to obtain the reward. If it does nothing else, this elementary experiment shows that simians can behave in nonbiologically determined ways, since there is nothing in their genetic inheritance to guide them to the correct use of man-provided objects. On occasion an experimental animal engages in a form of elementary biocultural behavior which his anatomy makes difficult or impossible for man. An ape may place a long pole, furnished by an experimenter, under a suspended banana. Then it climbs up rapidly to

---

[1] Young chimpanzees are the commonest subjects for testing because they are less surly, more co-operative, and generally more responsive to human attention than most other Primates.

The experiments described below are fully reported in W. Köhler, *The Mentality of Apes*, rev. ed., New York, 1925.

seize the fruit before the pole falls to the ground (Fig. 60A). Except
that this strikes humans as a more difficult feat it does not vary
greatly from the first-mentioned kind of simple problem-solving.

Probing a bit more deeply into the same kinds of questions is a
series of tests of a more complicated nature. In these, experimenters
again place food high out of reach, but leave available several boxes
of differing shapes and sizes. To win its reward an animal must pile
two or more boxes under its objective, then climb on them to grasp
what it wants. A bit more complexity may be introduced into the
situation by providing an insufficient number of boxes and some
sticks. In these cases an ape must remember to secure a stick *before*
it starts to climb up on the box pile (Fig. 60B). Such problems call
for a fairly intricate bit of advance thinking, but apes have proved
capable of making satisfactory solutions. Sometimes, too, simians
have shown a capacity for planning ahead to the solution of a problem that requires cooperation between two animals. Experimenters
have devised pairs of weighted boxes containing food that can be
drawn within reach only if two caged animals pull simultaneously
on attached ropes. Again the apes have proved equal to the task, and
there is even a motion picture record of an eager chimpanzee deliberately going to the back of a cage to lead forward an indifferent
partner so that together they may pull close the desired reward.[2]

More important for our purposes are experiments that show
chimpanzees capable of at least the rudiments of manufacturing. If
an ape is given nothing but flexible straws too weak to bring an
object toward it, it may bend the straws over until they are solid
enough for moving things. Other tests have demonstrated that apes
can learn to fit a solid stick into one with a hollow socket, in order
to form an elongated implement capable of reaching whatever is
wanted. Still more satisfactory evidence of a rudimentary ability to
manufacture a simple tool has been obtained from tests in which
apes were given a solid stick too wide to penetrate a hollow one.
This problem was solved by chewing on the wide bit of wood until
it was slender enough to be jammed into the socket.

One of the most revealing and sometimes amusing series of experiments was intended to find out if apes could plan ahead in non-

[2] See M. P. Crawford, "The Cooperative Solving of Problems by Young Chimpanzees," *Comparative Psychology Monographs,* Vol. 14, No. 2, 1937, especially p. 59. Unless
otherwise stated, the remaining experiments are based on W. Köhler, *op. cit.*

A

B

Fig. 60. Experiments with apes. A. A chimpanzee uses its biological climbing skill to climb a pole and seize a reward before the pole falls to the ground. B. A geometric pattern of behavior. An ape has taken the stick from one place, the boxes from others, and placed them under the reward. To be successful it must also have enough foresight to take along the stick before mounting the boxes. C. The Chimp-o-mat in action. A chimpanzee is buying a raisin with a special token for which it has worked.

C

biologically inherited ways under difficult conditions. A vending machine, appropriately called a **Chimp-O-Mat,** was constructed in such fashion that by inserting a token comparable to a poker chip a raisin could be "bought." Experimenters showed the animals to be tested how to do a bit of work, operating a weight-lifting lever or pulling a sliding tray, by means of which a food token was earned. This was inserted into the Chimp-O-Mat and a raisin "purchased" and eaten.[3] Chimpanzees promptly caught the idea and were soon busily working for tokens and buying raisins (Fig. 60C). Rewards were made available for learning to select a particular one out of a number of identical containers, and for making other visual discriminations. Sometimes the Chimp-O-Mat was deliberately rendered out-of-order, but the apes continued to work for tokens, with somewhat diminished eagerness, in anticipation of going on a buying spree when the machine resumed operation. Chimpanzees also learned to discriminate valid discs from counterfeits.

Summarized briefly, experiments with apes have convincingly shown that they can handle external objects as utensils, combine for use such different things as boxes and sticks, make simple tools, recognize the symbolic values assigned to tokens, and plan ahead by accumulating food discs even when their usefulness lies in the future. Tests yielding roughly comparable results have been carried out with a wide assortment of animals, not necessarily Primates, and the conclusion is inescapable that tool handling and making as well as planning ahead are not exclusive prerogatives of man. Equally well established are the negative facts that in not a single instance was the experimental situation devised by a non-human, and never did any other animal invent (as distinguished from recognizing) a symbolic value or switch it about. Their inability to engage fully in the process of symbolization rules out the possibility of true speech among infra-humans, and without speech there can be no culture.

### F. THE MISSING SYMBOL

Every now and then persons more devoted to science than comfort have taken into their homes baby apes, treated them with the same

---

[3] The short account given here is based on a combination of two reports, which may be found in J. B. Wolfe, "Effectiveness of token-rewards for chimpanzees," *Comparative Psychological Monographs,* Vol. 12, No. 5, 1936; and J. T. Cowles, "Food-tokens as incentives for learning by chimpanzees," *idem,* Vol. 14, No. 5, 1937.

care lavished on human infants, and tested them in every conceivable way. They have found their little charges capable of learning much that human children are expected to know and do before they begin to speak. Sometimes little Primates prove to be on a par with their *sapiens* fellows, occasionally they exceed them, and once in a while they fail to equal them. Now and then an over-indulgent "parent" is carried away by enthusiasm and claims to have taught an ape to speak, but careful investigation always reveals that the utterances are limited to a word or so, that they are not always clear to an unbiased observer, and that they are frequently used out of context as well as in their proper place.

A painstakingly thorough experiment of this general sort was reported a little over twenty years ago by Professor and Mrs. W. N. Kellogg, psychologists at the University of Indiana.[4] They took into their home and for nine months reared with their small son, Donald, a baby female chimpanzee named Gua (Fig. 61). With great care they gave identical treatment to the ape and their own infant, and both youngsters were subjected to various tests. Among other things Gua learned to wear clothes, sit in a high chair, eat with a spoon, and respond to a number of spoken commands. Throughout the experiment's duration, ape and child ran neck and neck on most tests, but at the end of nine months Donald began to speak and to forge ahead rapidly, while Gua was unable to make further progress. Thereupon the Kelloggs returned her to a cage.

Although many of the psychological data published in 1933 are out-of-date, a few positive conclusions may be drawn that cannot be challenged today. The Kelloggs never claimed that Gua had learned to speak, and therein lies the key to the building or absence of culture. Lacking the ability to speak Gua was utterly incapable of communicating to other apes a single item of her experiences in Indiana. She had no means of handing on any of her special knowledge either to her generation of chimpanzees or to any offspring that she might have borne. Whatever she had learned had, inevitably, to die with her. Had she been enabled to reconstruct the physical setting of the Kellogg home, she might conceivably have acted out some of her activities there and invoked imitation. Had this been the case, which is, of course, entirely fantastic, she might thus have transmitted part

4 W. N. and L. A. Kellogg, *The Ape and the Child,* New York and London, 1933.

of her knowledge to other Primates, but this is a difficult and limited way of giving information.

To bring the main issue into sharp focus one has only to imagine Gua's situation in reverse. If a human being had lived for nine

Fig. 61. The ape and the child. Donald Kellogg is shown walking with Gua, who is dressed in human style. Although the young chimpanzee learned a great deal at the Kellogg home, she was unable, lacking true, symbolic speech, to share her knowledge with anyone else.

months among apes the chances are that he would bore his listeners to tears with petty details. Through the use of speech he could reconstruct every detail of his unusual experience, and with the aid of translations anything that he had learned could, theoretically, be made a part of human knowledge throughout the world. His words could be carried even to people who never saw or heard him in person, and who had never seen an ape. Sharing experiences with others, contributing to the sum total of human knowledge, and transmitting ideas and information to succeeding generations are things that many normal human beings can easily do; but so long as they lack the ability to invent symbolic values and to assign some of them to sounds (speech), no other animals are capable of doing likewise. Whatever a non-human creature learns must perish with it unless it can be bio-genetically transmitted; whatever man learns can be spread about and handed on indefinitely and nonbiologically. The chances are nil that culture could have originated without speech, and it is equally certain that without it there could have been no adding on or stockpiling of knowledge which is at the very base of culture growth.

## G. CULTURAL ORIGINS

There is one further conclusion to be drawn from the information provided by experiments with apes. When hominids came into being they were anatomically so similar to the Pongidae that it is safe to assume that they could do whatever the big apes could, except for a few things specifically associated with arboreal life. Furthermore, whoever the first men were they had, presumably, at least twice the cranial capacity of their nearest animal relatives. Mentally, therefore, they could doubtless equal or exceed any simian achievement. All this means that even if science never learns whether the first hominids could speak, we may still be sure that they were capable of using nonbiologically inherited tools, crudely fashioning some kinds of implements, and freely planning ahead for the future. The earliest of men were, it follows, at least on the threshold of culture.

There are countless legitimate doubts about the time and place of man's cultural origins, but these are dissipated no later than 500,000 years ago, in mid-Pleistocene times. Evidence that *Sinanthropus pekinensis* regularly used fire and made stone tools can only be interpreted to mean that he had already broken out of the limitations of bio-physico-chemical existence, and had taken the first authentic steps into the world of culture.

SELECTED REFERENCES

Daniel, Glyn E., *A Hundred Years of Archaeology,* London, 1950.

Douglass, Andrew E., "The Secret of the Southwest Solved by the Talkative Tree-rings," *National Geographic Magazine,* Vol. 54, 1929, pp. 737-770.

Kellogg, W. N. and L. A., *The Ape and the Child,* New York, 1933.

Kenyon, K. M., *Beginning in Archaeology,* London, 1952.

Köhler, W., *The Mentality of Apes,* New York, 1925.

Libby, Willard F., *Radiocarbon Dating,* Chicago, 1952.

Stallings, William S., Jr., "Dating Prehistoric Ruins by Tree-rings," *Laboratory of Anthropology, General Series,* Bull. 8, Santa Fe, 1939.

Taylor, Walter W., "A Study of Archeology," *American Anthropological Association, Memoir,* No. 69, Menasha, 1948.

CHAPTER 11

# Lower and Middle Paleolithic Culture in the Old World

## A. STICKS AND STONES

By the time Primates had fully evolved, habits of using hard substances for adding to the strength of the hands, of employing pointed objects for piercing or digging, and of utilizing sharp things as aids in cutting, were probably already formed. As for hominids it seems certain that they have to some degree been users of tools from the start. Assumption of the bipedal, upright posture on the ground emancipated the front limbs from holding or supporting functions and permitted the unrestricted manipulation of implements. Besides giving extra powers to hominid hands and arms, the use of tools also served to protect sensitive body members from injury or excessive wear. As his later history shows, *Homo sapiens* came to rely ever increasingly on extrabiological resources for meeting bio-physico-chemical demands. Archeologists cannot tell with assurance what materials were put to use by the earliest forms of man, but wood, animal bone, and stone are thought to have had priority. Just how extensively wood and bone were utilized in the dim past cannot be ascertained because only under exceptional conditions are they preserved for thousands and thousands of years. Stones are satisfactorily durable, but until humans had learned to fashion them in accord with definite patterns they are hard to identify as tools.

There are some scholars who hold that any hominid use of a lithic object causes markings that are entirely different from natural ones. They claim that if one picks up something hard and uses it, let us say, as a hammer, scars and scratches will be made on the face of the tool that could not be duplicated by nature. Modern archeologists tend to laugh such claims out of court. Almost no one today maintains that he can unfailingly recognize man-used, but not necessarily

Fig. 62. Survival of an eolithic usage. An Australian aborigine, using a sharp but unworked stone for cutting into a tree.

man-made, implements. Just the same, a number of students firmly believe that if all the circumstances of discovery are known, bits of utilized stone could be identified (Fig. 62).

## B. THE EOLITHIC CONTROVERSY

Between so-called tools that are doubtfully associated with human use and objects of unquestioned human make come a variety of stones usually classified as **eoliths** ("dawn stones"). They are supposed to be the results of the very start or dawn of man's efforts to manufacture things. They are very crude and while some claim that they are valid specimens of early workmanship, others say that they have acquired their shapes and markings through natural agencies.

Opposed to the full acceptance of eoliths are arguments based on appearance and chronology. Eoliths are usually so shapeless that they do not seem to have resulted from any consistent adherence to a pattern of manufacture. Truth to tell, just about every kind of stone that has been termed an eolith has been matched by a duplicate made at random by nature. On the score of time, proponents of the eolithic theory claim that some of their specimens are over a million years old, reaching back even to Pliocene times. To this, opponents quickly retort that no hominids are known with certainty to have been in existence so long ago. Early in the present century two Englishmen, Sir Ray Lankester and J. Reid Moir, were finding and publishing reports of presumed eoliths which were, in their opinion, genuinely man-made. Best known of their claims are those dealing with a type of stone called a **rostro-carinate,** a beak-shaped lump of flint from which small bits have somehow been chipped. When attention was drawn to the uneven shapes of the rostro-carinates and other eoliths, Reid Moir replied, in effect, that perfection in turning out regularly formed instruments was hardly to be expected of the earliest of workmen.

Even those who most seriously question anyone's ability to detect the initial stone tools made by men, must still admit that the manufacturing process had to have had a start sometime. Quite properly, the current trend of archeological opinion shies away from the acceptance of eoliths, but it is realized that a day may come when improved scientific techniques will make possible the detection of the first kinds of artifacts consciously made by human beings.

## C. INTRODUCTION TO WESTERN EUROPE'S OLD STONE AGE

For the earliest of his recognizable tools man seems to have pre-ferred as raw material fine-grained, crypto-crystalline stones such as flint and other varieties of quartz, basalt, diorite, and volcanic glass or obsidian. These have the advantages of being hard but brittle and, if skillfully struck with a piece of rock (hammerstone) or a billet of wood, they can be broken into even segments that have very sharp edges. When stones of these kinds are deliberately worked into tools they develop definite markings that experts have learned to recog-nize. The first widely-employed technique of manufacture, which prevailed all through the **Old Stone Age,** comprised two steps. First, with the form of the finished product already in mind, a workman selected a suitable chunk of stone as a nodule or core. Then, the core was trimmed by the removal of fairly large flakes or smallish chips either by striking them off (percussion), or else by pressing them off (pressure-flaking). Two different kinds of instruments could be produced by variations of the same procedure. If the removal of lesser bits was continued until the original nodule had itself been worked into a desired shape it turned out to be a core tool; but if good-sized flakes were detached and made to serve as implements, they became flake tools (Fig. 63). Both styles of artifacts were widely made in early **Paleolithic** times.

To shape flint, commonest of the stones first fashioned into tools in Western Europe, blows were struck on a flat spot on the core, which is known as a striking platform. When a carefully directed blow hit the striking platform, a flake was detached whose inner sur-face below the place of contact ordinarily shows a convex swelling, or bulb of percussion, together with a number of ripples (Fig. 63). There are many variations and fine points of stone-working methods that trouble professional archeologists, but never do they lack the skill to differentiate a truly man-manufactured tool from a random bit of stone.

Nevertheless, when claims of authenticity were advanced for the first-discovered products of human craftsmanship they aroused a storm of controversy. Apart from doubts raised by technical ques-tions much reluctance was based on religious grounds. The oldest implements assigned to man were found with the remains of extinct

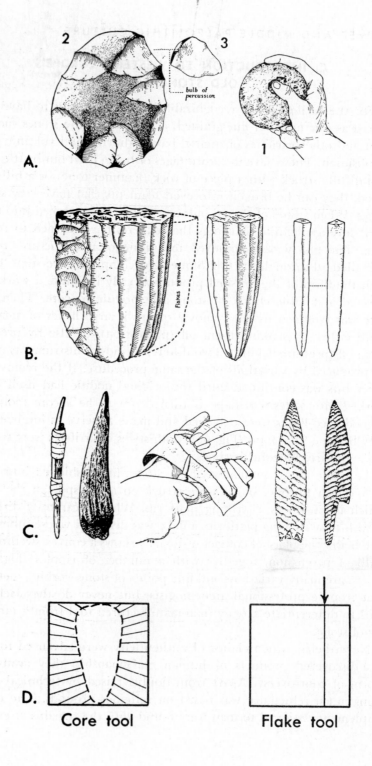

**A.**

*bulb of percussion*

*1*

*2*

*3*

**B.**

Striking Platform

Flakes removed

**C.**

**D.**

Core tool                                  Flake tool

animals in deposits of soil that vastly antedated the traditional time of human creation. Few Western Europeans over a century ago were willing to accept evidence of such great antiquity for man. Regardless of the stubbornness and amused contempt of his contemporaries, an amateur archeologist named Jacques Boucher de Crêvecoeur de Perthes, a French customs official, went right on collecting regularly chipped flint objects from old gravel deposits of the river Somme. He began to astonish the world with his findings in 1837, and when some of his worst critics searched ancient gravel beds in the hope of refuting him they found to their amazement that they were actually discovering additional evidence in support of his viewpoint. The tide of critical opinion changed completely in 1859, the very year when publication of Darwin's theory of evolution gave a modern turn to studies of the biology of man. A small commission of eminent British scientists visited Boucher de Perthes in 1859, scrupulously examined his collections, and proclaimed that he had discovered indisputably man-made stone tools of great age in the Somme River gravels. From the day when it was so announced in 1859, this conclusion has never been seriously challenged in scholarly circles.

Since this part of the science of man is to be devoted to tracing the march of culture, the question of time must be taken into account. With respect to Western Europe it calls for at least a nodding acquaintance with the main facts of Pleistocene geology, because the record of man's cultural development in that portion of the world is fitted into a sequence of Pleistocene events. The most dramatic of these are the great fluctuations of winter and summer conditions that followed one another between 1,000,000 and 20,000 years ago. During much of this time great fields of ice started from four points: in the British Isles, around the Baltic Sea, and among the mountains of the Alps and the Pyrenees. Glaciers spread over most of Europe

Fig. 63. Paleolithic stone-working techniques (after Nelson). A. The three basic elements of the percussion method. 1. A hammer-stone held in the hand. 2. An original core from which (3) flakes are struck off. B. Upper Paleolithic flake production. Long, narrow blades were detached from a previously prepared core. C. Pressure flaking. Two widely used tools are at the left, and specimens of pressure flaked Solutrian tools are at the right. D. How core and flake tools were made. (Left). Manufacture of a core tool must begin with an advance blueprint in the mind of the worker (dotted outline), after which chips are removed as necessary. A flake tool (right) begins with the removal of a flake, which is then converted to a tool.

and with their advance they brought extremely long and bitterly cold periods of weather known as Ice Ages. After many centuries the temperature would rise, stupendous masses of snow and ice would melt, and the glaciers would shrink or retreat back to their starting points. These comings and goings have been best studied in the vicinity of the Alps where it has been established that at least four, and possibly five, glacial advances took place in the Pleistocene. The four main progressions or stadia have been named in chronological and alphabetical order, **Günz, Mindel, Riss,** and **Würm.** In between the forward movements of the vast fields of ice, temperate to tropical conditions prevailed and these are known as Interglacial or Interstadial periods. At no time, even when glaciation was most extensive, did the glaciers join to form a solid cover of snow and ice over all of Europe. Some areas or corridors remained unglaciated all through the Pleistocene, but even these places were doubtless subject to extraordinarily protracted cold spells.

The first forms of man to have existed in Western Europe are supposed to have arrived toward the start of mid-Pleistocene times. In terms of glacial movements this may refer to the Günz-Mindel Interglacial, but Interglacial phases are hard to tell apart and some authorities believe that man did not reach Western Europe until the second, or Mindel-Riss Interstadium. There are even a few arch-conservatives who would date the event as late as the Riss-Würm. All agree though that the first signs of human occupancy in the area pertain to a time of warm weather. This ties in with the discoveries made by Boucher de Perthes and others. It is felt that had icy conditions been prevalent early man would not have been able to survive outdoors, as the finds suggest, along the banks of streams.

Broadly speaking, the term **Lower Paleolithic** may be applied to the way of life practiced by early man before the onset of the Würm glaciation. Very little is known of the kinds of hominids then alive, but there are suggestions to indicate that they were pre- or non-Neandertaloids, possibly like the creatures represented by the Heidelberg jaw. There is also doubt as to the exact time involved, but in very approximate figures the Lower Paleolithic may be dated between 500,000 and 120,000 B.C. Even in the matter of cultural accomplishments there is not much that can be said with conviction. All perishable materials from this remote era have long since disappeared, and only a few stone tools have survived. These precious bits of evidence have been intensively examined by archeologists, who agree that they should be grouped into two classifications depending on whether they were manufactured from an original core or fashioned from flakes.

## D. LOWER PALEOLITHIC INDUSTRIES IN WESTERN EUROPE

Throughout Western Europe, Lower Paleolithic core tools are most commonly made into big, clumsy, roughly pear-shaped objects, about 10 inches long, and apparently meant to be used while clenched in the fist. They are designated as hand-axes, fist-axes, or coups de poing, even though it is pretty clear that they were not axes in the modern sense. The earliest varieties are known as **Abbevillian** (formerly, they were called **Chellian**), and the later ones are termed **Acheulian.** Characteristic of the Abbevillian industry are fist-axes with heavy butts at one end and rounded or pointed tips at the other. Acheulian hand-axes are smaller, oval or almond in shape, trimmed to a thin edge along the whole circumference, and with a center of gravity near the middle. Both types are made by the removal of many flakes from each side of an original nodule, and that is why Abbevillian and Acheulian fist-axes are known as bifacial. Practically all of the flakes knocked off were wasted, but it is possible that some of the larger ones were themselves used as tools, particularly in the Acheulian phase. Often the flake tools that are the incidental results of core workmanship have one sharp edge and are called side-scrapers; and broad, heavy scrapers are sometimes termed cleavers.

Archeologists who specialize in Lower Paleolithic studies distinguish flake utensils that are by-products of core techniques from tools very deliberately planned to be made of skillfully detached flakes. Best known of the earliest flake industries are the **Clactonian** and **Levalloisian.** Although their relative dates are far from precisely fixed it is customary to regard Clactonian as somewhat prior, overlapping with the earlier stages of Abbevillian-Acheulian; while Levalloisian is associated with later phases. Purposely produced Clactonian flakes are often thick and squat, and seem not to have been designed for use as fist-axes.[1] From their appearance it is judged that they were made by striking a core against a heavy stone that served as an anvil. When necessary, the working edge of a flake was secondarily sharpened by the removal of tiny chips. Most Clactonian tools probably served as choppers, knives, or scrapers, and a fair percentage of the latter are concave, giving the impression that they may have been used to shave down lengths of wood that were to be fashioned into clubs or spears (Fig. 64).

At least by the close of the second Interglacial period in Western Europe some workmen were using the Levalloisian technique of flake production. This called for very careful preliminary shaping of a core in such fashion that when the work was finished, flakes ready for immediate use as tools could be detached with single blows. Prefashioned Levalloisian cores are called from their customary appearance, tortoise cores. The more carefully they were prepared in advance, the more suitable for prompt service were the struck-off flakes. Thus does the Levalloisian method forcibly bring home the truth of the statement that tool manufacture calls for an advance pattern in the mind of the workman. As the new style became perfected Levalloisian craftsmen became capable of trimming tortoise cores in a variety of ways in order to furnish a basis for producing flakes that were pointed or triangular, oval, or rectangular. Whatever their forms all Levalloisian flakes are smooth and unworked on the inner side. Even though some of them resemble flat fist-axes, they

Fig. 64. A Clactonian stone tool (after Oakley). The wooden shaft suggests that the concave lithic implement may have been used as a spoke-shave.

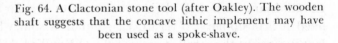

[1] The Clactonian industry is best known from England. Comparable flake implements from France are called **Tayacian**. They are frequently smaller and lighter than their Clactonian equivalents.

can always be distinguished from similar core tools because they are never trimmed on both sides and are, consequently, never bifacial.

## E. LOWER PALEOLITHIC INDUSTRIES IN THE OLD WORLD

Not many years ago most archeologists believed that the divisions and sequences established for the Lower Paleolithic of Western Europe were typical of the entire Old World. This is no longer held to be the case. Discoveries in Africa and Asia have made it clear that in many details the Western European scheme is valid locally but not universally. As a general rule core tools are much alike wherever they may be found, but flake tools are apt to show great variations. On the African continent finds of Lower Paleolithic implements have been made, some of which are very much restricted in distribution, and are not at all like Western European instruments. Still, there are other varieties from these two vast areas that are virtually identical. The suggestion has been offered that one or more African techniques were later adopted in Western Europe, but it is difficult to establish beyond reasonable doubt the priority of the material from Africa. This continent was never subjected to the Pleistocene glaciations that furnish the best dating system known for ancient Europe. It was subject instead to long spells of heavy rainfall (**pluvial periods**). Although the various pluvial periods have not yet been distinguished and matched with glacial advances, it is felt likely that a connection exists and that a correlation of some sort will one day be established.

More distinct from the Lower Paleolithic industries of Western Europe are a number of toolmaking traditions from Eastern and Southeastern Asia. There are some early chopping tools, usually made of pebbles, that may prove to be related to African types, but in Northwestern India, Burma, Java, and China there is neither an Abbevillian-Acheulian core industry, nor a recognizably Levalloisian style of flake manufacture. Instead, the commonest early tools have been described by Harvard's Professor Hallam L. Movius, Jr., as choppers, chopping tools, and hand adzes.[2] Some of the choppers are

2 For further details consult H. L. Movius, Jr., "Early Man and Pleistocene Stratigraphy in Southern and Eastern Asia," *Papers of the Peabody Museum of American Archaeology and Ethnology,* Harvard University, Cambridge, Vol. 19, No. 3, 1944.

A good synopsis and bibliography by the same author may be found in A. L. Kroeber, ed., *Anthropology Today,* Chicago, 1953, pp. 163-92.

like large, crude, core-made scrapers, but others are manufactured from flakes and bear some resemblance to the Clactonian of Western Europe. None of the East Asiatic implements is extensively chipped on both surfaces, and none has the appearance of a bifacial, core-made fist-axe.

Professor Movius has also made a first-hand study of the stone tools found together with the bones of *Sinanthropus pekinensis* at Chou Kou Tien. He has named that industry **Choukoutienian** and has assigned it to the chopper, chopping tool, hand adze complex of East Asia, and not to any of the Lower Paleolithic cultures of Western Europe.

## F. A SUMMARY OF LIFE IN LOWER PALEOLITHIC TIMES

Any effort to present a fully rounded picture of Lower Paleolithic life is pre-doomed to failure because of the meager evidence available. That men of those days lived while the climate was warm is strongly suggested by the occurrence of Abbevillian-Acheulian implements, particularly, in soils containing remains of elephant, rhinoceros, lion, and hippopotamus. Such an association reinforces the interpretation to the same effect based on discoveries of Lower Paleolithic tools in the beds of ancient streams. Throughout most of the world Lower Paleolithic people seem to have camped outdoors, but at Chou Kou Tien, they are known to have lived in caves. Here there is proof that *Sinanthropus pekinensis* made and controlled fire, manufactured tools of stone, hunted deer and cracked their long bones for marrow, possibly hunted human beings and cracked their skulls for brains, and gathered and ate wild hackberries.

For most of the Old World even these few details are lacking. Men and women probably wandered in small bands along the banks of streams, fishing, hunting, and gathering edible plants, seeds, fruits, nuts, roots, and berries. They were at best collectors or gatherers of food provided by nature; they were not food-producers. Nothing is known of any system of symbolic values that might have prevailed, but there are indirect signs of algebraic mentality because of the size of cranial vaults and the ability these folk demonstrated for planning ahead while making tools. Similarly, their capacity for speech cannot be directly proved, but secondary evidence makes it likely that they could talk, because by no other means could traditions and styles of manufacturing have been readily spread and maintained for count-less generations over wide stretches of territory.

Archeologists believe that the Lower Paleolithic people who cus-tomarily lived in the open made only temporary camps. If habitations were put up they must have been too flimsy and impermanent to have survived or to have left identifiable traces on the ground. One can only guess at what use may have been made of perishable mate-rials for building or other purposes. There is much less need for speculation when it comes to Lower Paleolithic artifacts of stone. Taking the entire range into account there are sturdy fist-axes of value for helping kill game or enemies; sharp knives for cutting up slain beasts or severing branches; scrapers capable of working wood or hides; and pointed implements suitable for stabbing or digging operations. Well-made fist-axes may have served as all-purpose tools but the great number of knives, scrapers, points, cleavers, and chop-pers, suggests that there was at least a modest preference for special-ized implements, based on the concept of a particular kind of tool for a specific purpose (Fig. 65).

Even in terms of stone working, by far the best known aspect of

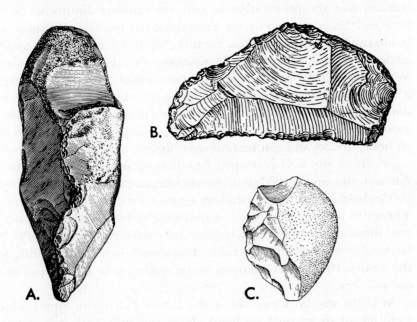

B.

A.

C.

Fig. 65. Typical stone tools of the Lower Paleolithic. A. A crudely made fist-axe, percussion chipped on both faces. B. Flint knife or side-scraper. C. Chopping tool.

Lower Paleolithic life, it is apparent that culture started slowly and remained relatively unchanged in the course of hundreds of thousands of years. True, archeologists know of many variations in the early lithic industries, but all of the manufacturing methods are but modifications of a single approach—the shaping of tools by knocking or pressing smaller fragments from a larger piece of stone. Dependence on one method, most commonly a percussion technique, strictly delimited man's use of the natural resources around him to fine-grained varieties of stone with crypto-crystalline structures, capable of segmenting evenly instead of crumbling to bits when struck or pressed hard. Some workmen were without question more skillful than others, but in a pinch any normal individual could turn out a reasonable facsimile of a satisfactory tool. The quantity of rather poorly made implements is so great that it is fantastic to think of Lower Paleolithic societies as having specialized workmen who devoted themselves full-time to the making of stone products. Every man his own craftsman is much more likely to have been the rule.

Although it is the up-to-date contention that core-made bifacial implements and flake tools have always existed side by side, the fact remains that the preparation of core instruments diminishes with time and disappears before the Paleolithic has run its full course. It is interesting to guess at the meaning of this trend. If we apply modern economic ideas to the situation the termination of core workmanship may be explained on two counts. Making core tools is more costly because it requires bigger blocks of raw material to start with, and nearly all of the struck-off chips are wasted. Furthermore, core tools take longer to produce because they must be worked on both surfaces and can be finished only one at a time. Flake tools, especially of the well-developed Levalloisian style, waste very little raw material, are worked only on one side, and are rapidly produced by single blows after a satisfactory tortoise core has been prepared. There can be little question but that flake techniques won out over core methods of production because they were more economical in terms of raw materials and time. This trend, barely discernible in the Lower Paleolithic, becomes increasingly plain as we approach our own era.

As far as anyone knows all of the Lower Paleolithic implements were meant to be used by hand. They had only little mechanical efficiency of their own, and differences of effective use depended less on the skill with which a utensil was made than on the power and strength of the user. A weak little man holding an excellent fist-axe could not hope to stand up to a big brute of a fellow armed with a third-rate fist-axe. How different from today, when it is a common-place thing for a dainty female with a small revolver to kill a husky 200-pound man. Along similar lines, no Lower Paleolithic tool could be hurled for any great distance, the amount of space covered being dependent once more on the power of the thrower. Judged by what we know of it, Lower Paleolithic culture was only in a very limited degree capable of serving man as a substitute for biology. In this regard hominids were for several hundred millenia not much better off than other Primates of their size and strength. No imaginary observer who might somehow have been enabled to watch how slowly man was building his culture throughout Lower Paleolithic times would have been willing to bet that it would ever amount to much.

## G. MIDDLE PALEOLITHIC CULTURE AND
## NEANDERTAL MAN

The picture of hominid life which is so hazy and dim for the Lower Paleolithic comes into a much clearer and sharper focus in the **Middle Paleolithic.** Although the origins of **Mousterian** culture are still undetermined, it is believed to have flourished in Western Europe from approximately 120,000 B.C. to about 70,000 years ago. It is better known because it is closer to our own time and because its remains are found in caves where materials are likely to accumulate and be kept together. Its products are so often directly associated with Neandertal skeletons that it is hard to escape the conclusion that in Western Europe, at least, Mousterian culture was the way of life of Neandertal man. There the transition from Lower to Middle Paleolithic must be considered in relation to a change of climatic conditions. Toward the end of the Lower Paleolithic the weather shifted from warm to cool to cold. The continuing lowering of temperature is connected with the advance of Würm glaciation. Some of the earlier people may have adjusted their cultures to fit the oncoming Ice Age, but most of them probably died out or moved southward, possibly taking with them the core-biface tradition. Beyond speculations of this sort nothing is known of the fate of Lower Paleolithic man.

Mousterian culture continued to be based on a hunting-fishing-gathering economy and its practitioners never learned to become food-producers. Unrestricted wandering out-of-doors was impossible because of the cold and Neandertal man is known to have had resort to caves. Judged by the location of his cultural left-overs he preferred to live near the threshold of a cave where there was more light and fresh air than in the dank interior. So abundant are the remains of hearths and charred substances that fire must have been commonly used for light, heat, and the preparation of food. Life in heated caves affords testimony of Neandertal man's ability to sustain himself during the frigid Würm period by making cultural instead of biological adjustments. With the help of cultural equipment, too, Middle Paleolithic man was able to hunt down such enormous Ice Age beasts as the mammoth and wooly rhinoceros. He sometimes used their large bones for chopping blocks or anvils, but most of his implements continued to be fashioned from fine-grained stones (Fig. 66A, B). What use was made of skins, furs, or hides, is not certain, but it seems reasonable to guess that some pelts were worn for clothing. Scraps of shells and tiny bones indicate that fish and shell-fish were eaten, but there is little to tell how they were obtained, nor is anything known about the extent to which vegetable products were gathered and utilized.

Neandertal man's stone work is based on established Paleolithic percussion methods. Resemblances or relationships have been noted to core-made, Acheulian bifacial fist-axes, as well as to Clactonian and Levalloisian flake implements. Specialists agree that Mousterian flakes were struck from a prepared discoidal core, and not from a typically Levalloisian tortoise core. Apart from technical details, the great majority of Middle Paleolithic tools are made from flakes that resemble Levalloisian. Besides these, a small, bifacial fist-axe, almost triangular in form, is fairly common and is the only core-made implement regularly used by Neandertal man. For the rest his stone tools consist chiefly of side scrapers and small, triangular points (Fig. 63A). Also found on occasion are rounded objects of flint, whose purpose is undetermined. They may have been intended for hurling one at a time, and it is sometimes thought that they may have been attached in small sets to leather thongs. Instruments of such type, called bolas, are known to have been used by various living tribes to entangle

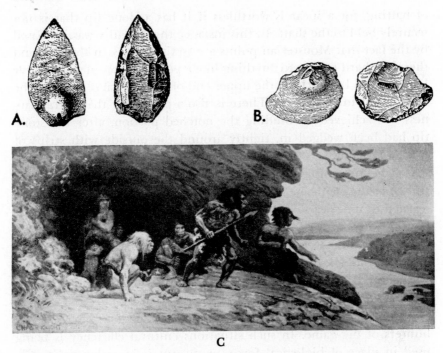

Fig. 66. Specimens of Mousterian culture. A. Back and front sides of a Mousterian point. There is a pronounced bulb of percussion, and the chipping on one face only suggests a connection with the Levallois technique. B. Reverse and front views of a Mousterian scraper. C. An imaginary scene of Mousterian life. Many of the details were supplied by the artist, but Neandertal man is known to have lived at the mouths of caves, and the manner in which a Mousterian point is hafted to a spear shaft is indicated by archeological evidence.

small game, but it is going too far to assume that Middle Paleolithic men similarly employed balls of stone.

A nice problem arises when one tries to consider the possible use of the commonly found small, triangular, Mousterian points. If they were meant to be held in the hand, even of a very strong man, they could have had but doubtful efficiency. Indeed, none of the Middle Paleolithic tools, held in hand, seems to have been capable of striking a deadly blow on a mammoth.[3] To have been effective a Mousterian point must have been attached to a long handle to form a kind of spear. Neandertal man was thus confronted with a difficult problem

[3] It has been surmised that Neandertal man secured much game by trapping. This may be correct, but not one of his presumed traps has survived.

of hafting, for a spear is worthless if it has a stone tip that is not securely held to the shaft. In this instance the difficulty was increased by the fact that Mousterian points are straight across at the base and therefore hard to affix to anything like a pole. The problem was very likely solved by notching the upper end of the shaft and wedging the stone point into the cleft. There is also a possibility that extra firmness was achieved by binding the notched portion, after the stone tip had been wedged in, tightly around the outside with strips of leather (Fig. 66C).

If it be granted, as it well deserves, that Neandertal man successfully met the challenge of a difficult problem of hafting, and that he learned to use spears skillfully, it follows that he had devised a new kind of weapon which incorporates the principle of leverage.[4] Thus, for the first time, were hominids able to add extra-bodily mechanical power to biological strength. One can picture a relatively weak man with a good, long spear, holding at a distance and jabbing to death a stronger man armed with a fist-axe that can be effective only at close range. Spears would give similar advantages to Neandertal hunters of big game. In such situations cultural efficiency is being used in place of biological force, or, to put it in colloquial terms, brain is being substituted for brawn. This is another important trend that is hardly noticeable in the Middle Paleolithic but becomes more and more noteworthy as we approach modern times.

There is one more feature that marks Mousterian culture apart from the Lower Paleolithic. Some Neandertal skeletons have been found deposited in graves that were deliberately dug into the floors of caves. The most amazing of such discoveries was made at La Chapelle-aux-Saints, where a corpse had been laid out in a carefully excavated trench and left surrounded by typical Mousterian implements. To appreciate the meaning of this find it is necessary to know that analogous customs still prevail in a great many primitive societies. Everywhere the habit of putting objects into graves is explained in the same way—they are for the use of the dead in the other world. By analogy, we are forced to conclude that Neandertal man must have had a belief in an after-life. Thanks to what can legitimately be deduced from study of some of his burial practices, we get

---

[4] There is a possibility that Lower Paleolithic man had already made use of a one-piece wooden spear, with a fire-hardened tip.

our first hint of Middle Paleolithic man's religious concepts, and no further proof of Neandertal man's algebraic mentality is needed.

### SELECTED REFERENCES

Burkitt, Miles C., *The Old Stone Age,* Cambridge, England, 1933.
Daniel, Glyn E., *The Three Ages,* Cambridge, England, 1943.
MacCurdy, George G., *Human Origins,* New York, 1924.
Movius, Hallam L., Jr., "Old World Prehistory: Paleolithic," *Anthropology Today* (A. L. Kroeber, ed.), Chicago, 1953, pp. 163-192.
Nelson, Nels C., "Prehistoric Archeology," Boas *et al., General Anthropology,* New York, 1938, pp. 146-237.
Oakley, Kenneth P., *Man the Tool-maker,* rev. ed., London, 1950.
Zeuner, Frederick E., *Dating the Past,* rev. ed., London, 1946.

CHAPTER 12

# Upper Paleolithic and Mesolithic Cultures in Western Europe

## A. PROLOGUE TO THE UPPER PALEOLITHIC

No scholar can tell how long Neandertal man and Mousterian culture persisted after they had reached a peak around 70,000 B.C., but their survival in Western Europe was probably of short duration. They seem to have been crowded out by a succession of important changes that were taking place in nearly every sphere. These were of such significance as to warrant distinguishing the new era, **Upper**

**Paleolithic,** from the Mousterian that had preceded it. Among the innovations heavy emphasis must fall on radically different styles of workmanship and the replacement of Neandertal men by Cro-Magnon varieties. A wide gap culturally and physically is thus indicated between Middle and Upper Paleolithic, and if it is correct to associate the former way of life with Neandertal man, it is equally appropriate to link the latter with *Homo sapiens.*

Wintry blasts greeted Cro-Magnon man when he first showed up in Western Europe. The Würm glaciation had not yet ended, although it might have been wavering. By common agreement Upper Paleolithic culture is thought to have begun no later than the closing phases of the Würm and to have remained in effect until the end of the Pleistocene some 20,000 years ago. Thereafter the Holocene (Recent) period starts and modern climatic conditions are established. No single kind of weather prevailed all through the late stages of the Pleistocene, but extended cold spells alternated with long stretches of warmth. It takes but a moment of reflection to realize that under such conditions Upper Paleolithic life must have varied from time to time and place to place. For purposes of simpli-

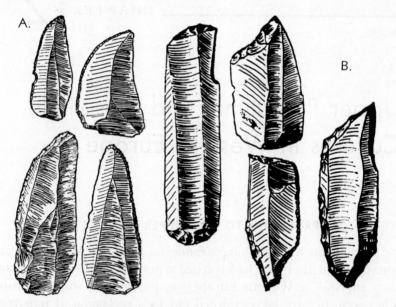

Fig. 67. Upper Paleolithic blade tools. A. Aurignacian types. B. Magdalenian specimens. All Aurignacian and Magdalenian stone work shows a vertical channel and is smooth on the inner surface.

fication three major stages of culture are conventionally recognized and they are named, in order, **Aurignacian, Solutrian,** and **Magdalenian.** Each phase differs from the others in several respects and each may be variously subdivided, but all possess some major characteristics in common. Upper Paleolithic tools of stone are made of fine-grained varieties by percussion or pressure methods (Fig. 67). Hunting-fishing-gathering pursuits continue to form the basis of economic life, and there is no sign of food production, animal domestication, pottery manufacture, or permanent settlement in large communities. Whatever cultural innovations were introduced failed to go beyond the general pattern of the Old Stone Age. A faster tempo of change was inaugurated by *Homo sapiens* but the magnitude of Upper Paleolithic man's achievements must be considered small when compared to what was destined to take place after the end of Pleistocene times.

It was once thought that the original bearers of Upper Paleolithic cultures had penetrated Western Europe from the east, possibly from some point in Asia; and a few manifestations used to be derived from North Africa. Conservative archeologists of today feel that the entire Upper Paleolithic is much too diversified to have come from a single source, and they prefer to treat separately each of the many regional forms that has so far been recognized. Beyond that, there is not much to be said. Local patterns are being carefully studied in respect to their own evolutions, but no overall synthesis is yet available.

## B. AURIGNACIAN ACCOMPLISHMENTS

With the opening of Western Europe's Upper Paleolithic era the "contest" between core and flake tools was resolved in favor of the latter, but the kind of flake utilized differs from anything made before. Essentially, it is parallel-sided, at least twice as long as it is wide, thin, and very sharp along the cutting edges. In this form it is known as a blade (Fig. 67), and comprises the basis for the most common run of Aurignacian and Magdalenian lithic implements. Most of the blades appear to have been detached from a core by a blow on an accurately placed pick, whose point rested on a nodule of stone. Many blades were used exactly as struck off, although some had their working edges secondarily retouched.

Abbé Henri Breuil, one of the foremost authorities on the Upper

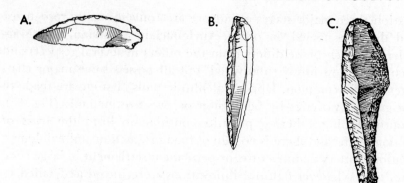

Fig. 68. Representative specimens of Upper Paleolithic industries. A. Châtelperronian blade knife. B. Gravettian knife. C. Font Robert point.

Paleolithic, particularly of France, has suggested dividing the Aurignacian into three major stages on the basis of tool variations; Dr.
Dorothy Garrod proposes a four-fold division; and Dr. Denis Peyrony thinks that there were two distinct traditions, Aurignacian that
worked in bone and Périgordian which used stone, each of which
went through five phases.[1] These differing schemes of classification
indicate how difficult it is to treat of the Aurignacian as a single
period of culture. Nevertheless, authorities agree reasonably well
that the earliest Aurignacian lithic industry was the **Châtelperronian**,
featured by the manufacture of flint blades with one edge straight
and very sharp and the other deliberately blunted and curved to
provide a good grip (Fig. 68A). These instruments made very service-
able knives.

Following the Châtelperronian came the bulk of Aurignacian
stone work. Among the most useful blade tools were end-scrapers,
with the sharp working surface at one end rather than along the side,
giving more leverage to the user; drills and gravers worked to a sharp
point for purposes of boring holes or making fine incisions; burins
with beveled cutting edges that functioned in the manner of chisels;
shouldered points, with long backward-projecting tangs, presumably
meant for insertion into an arrow or javelin shaft; and a variety of
knives.[2]

[1] References to the works in which the authors here cited suggested various schemes
of classification may be found in H. L. Movius, Jr., "Old World Prehistory: Paleolithic,"
*Anthropology Today* (A. L. Kroeber, ed.), Chicago, 1953, pp. 191-192.

[2] For clever illustrations showing most of these forms and suggesting modern parallels, see R. J. Braidwood, *Prehistoric Men*, Chicago, 1948, pp. 62-65.

After the fully developed Aurignacian industries comes a late phase that is sometimes described as the **Gravettian/Font Robert** complex. Blade tools of Gravettian style are somewhat like the earlier Châtelperronian, and may have evolved from them.[3] The principal differences are that Gravettian knives are more perfectly made, and have straight or slightly arched blunted backs instead of fully curved ones (Fig. 68B). When a typically Gravettian implement is made with a backward projection or tang, it is known as a Font Robert point (Fig. 68C).

Fig. 69. Use of a spear-thrower. The drawing depicts the technique used by natives of Northern Australia. The implement has the same effect as lengthening the arm of the user.

Not only do the various stages of Aurignacian work in stone reveal some of the new features introduced by Upper Paleolithic craftsmen but there is ample evidence that man has added to his earlier employment of raw materials a widespread use of bones. Soon after the early Châtelperronian phase there occur in Aurignacian deposits a great number of bone points, split at the base as if to admit a shaft in order to make a hafted spear or a javelin (Fig. 74D). Other kinds of bone points are so common throughout the Aurignacian that Peyrony, let us recall, feels the entire period can be arranged into five parts on the basis of changes in bone work. Besides stone and bone, work-

---

3 Students are reminded that archeologists cannot always tell apart two related kinds of stone tools, unless they know all the circumstances of their discovery.

men of this era learned to handle ivory and reindeer horn, sometimes
using lithic tools for drilling holes in or making javelin points from
less resistant materials. Needles of bone make their first appearance
in the Aurignacian and furnish a bit of indirect proof for the manu-

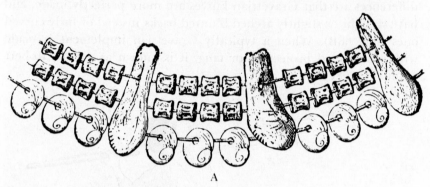

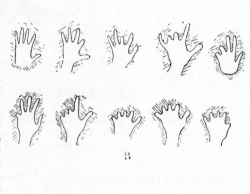

Fig. 70. A. An Upper Paleolithic
necklace (after Verneau and Mac-
Curdy). Each unit is made up of
two sets of four fish vertebrae
each; three gastropod shells; and
one canine tooth of a stag. The
units are rhythmically repeated
at fixed intervals, showing an appreciation of the esthetic principle, "repetition coupled with
diversity." B. Hand imprints from
the Aurignacian era (after Mac-
Curdy, following Cartailhac and
Breuil). Such mutilated hands
are common in various primitive
societies, where fingers are offered as sacrifices. The prepond-
erance of left hands furthers the
notion that fingers were deliberately cut off with the right hand.

facture of some sort of clothing. Among the most important innovations is the spear- or javelin-thrower, usually fashioned of antler
horn. Its appearance is deceptively simple, much like a stick with a
raised hook at one end. When it is to be used, a spear or javelin is
laid flat against the throwing device, with the butt end pressing
against the raised hook (Fig. 69). This has the effect of increasing the
stretch of the user's arm by the length of the spear-thrower, and gives
him more mechanical power than his own body possesses.

In addition to the coming of Cro-Magnon men, the development of lithic blade industries and new kinds of tools, the utilization of additional raw materials, and the gain of mechanical efficiency provided by the use of spear-throwers, the Aurignacian marks a depar-

Fig. 71. An example of Aurignacian sculpture. A female figure, holding a bison horn, is carved of limestone in low relief. This sculpture, from Laussel, Dordogne, France, conforms to an Aurignacian tendency to neglect details of feet and face.

ture from the Mousterian by its flair for ornamentation and other expressions of the fine arts. These range all the way from lines that look like mere doodles, through engravings and sculptures to exceedingly realistic paintings of animals. The catalog is long and cannot possibly be covered here, but one item demands special mention. Figure 70A shows a "necklace" made up of a combination of fish spinal bones, perforated canine teeth of stags, and the drilled shells of gastropods. They are arranged into regular units each one consisting of two sets of four vertebrae, three shells, and a tooth.

A

B

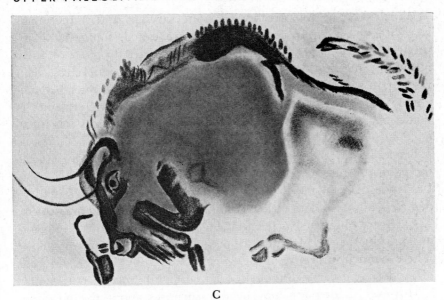

C

Fig. 72. Upper Paleolithic cave paintings. A. Running horse, from the Lascaux cave. Supposedly of Aurignacian age. B. Magdalenian horse and hind, from Altamira. The figure of the horse is drawn over that of the hind, on the same spot. C. A Magdalenian bison from Altamira. In contrast to the splendidly executed outer form of the animal, the heart is crudely depicted by the diamond shaped design.

The same grouping is duplicated over and over, thus showing that even at this early stage of art the concept existed of using fixed units made up of divergent parts and regularly or rhythmically arranged. It is hard to believe that in fashioning such a necklace, crude and unesthetic though it is by present standards, some unknown Aurignacian artist had hit upon the basic principle of repetition coupled with variety that makes up the essence of so much modern art from poetry and music to architecture.

Archeologists have also been intrigued by outlines or impressions of mutilated human hands (Fig. 70B) made on cave walls in Aurignacian times. Their meaning can only be guessed, but hands with one or more finger joints missing immediately bring to mind a well-known primitive custom. Several American Indian tribes regularly expected their men to lop off finger joints while striving to communicate with their deities. It is tempting to consider the possibility that similar practices prevailed during the Upper Paleolithic.

Widely known, too, are several stone carvings and statuettes of large-breasted women (Fig. 71). They are called, somewhat inappropriately, "Venuses." Many a scholar has tried to guess at their meaning, and the most frequently heard explanation refers them vaguely to a "fertility cult." Such an interpretation cannot be completely dismissed, but all that can be said with absolute certainty is that Aurignacian man like his predecessors and successors was interested in sex and reproduction.

Far and away the most exciting examples of Aurignacian art are the paintings recently discovered on the walls of Lascaux cave, near Les Eyzies, Dordogne, France. A variety of large mammals is there depicted, often in motion, like plodding oxen or running horses (Fig. 72A). Every observer has been taken with these splendid and vigorous paintings, some of which are monotone and some in two colors.[4] There is much to admire in these pictures, even by the most rigorous of modern standards, but their original significance is not known.

However inadequate may be our surmises about the meanings of Aurignacian art, it certainly shows that in those days there was a great deal of concern with and aptitude for things non-material and extra-biologic. A further indication along these lines is found in Upper Paleolithic burial practices. They are more elaborate than the ones noted in the account of Mousterian times. A number of deliberate burials have been found, each with some feature to suggest an interest in the fate of the deceased after death. This may be expressed by daubing red clay on skeletal remains or by leaving implements and ornaments in the grave. The high development of fine arts and the burial customs combine to show that *Homo sapiens* was making considerable use of algebraic mentality during the Aurignacian phases of cultural evolution.

## C. THE SOLUTRIAN INTERLUDE

As a result either of the spread of new ideas from places outside of Europe, or by virtue of an actual influx of different kinds of people, there develops in Western Europe a distinct culture complex termed **Solutrian.** One possible source of origin leads to Hungary and another points to North Africa by way of Spain. Wherever it

[4] For a fine study of the Lascaux paintings, consult F. Windels, *The Lascaux Cave Paintings,* New York, 1950.

may have originated and however it may have been carried to Western Europe, the manifestations of Solutrian culture usually follow
the Gravettian/Font Robert subdivision of late Aurignacian. At
this time the extremely frigid weather of the Würm glaciation had
somewhat subsided, and the Solutrians lived under cold but open
steppe conditions. Pitifully little is known of the total range of their
lives, but they were doubtless hunters who slew and ate quantities
of wild horse (Equus *przewalskii*), as well as reindeer and other animals of that day. At the original station of Solutré there is a vast
deposit of earth mixed with partially burned remnants of game,
among which bones of horses are especially conspicuous. Above this
heap were found items of Solutrian style.

Accompanying the remains of Solutrian folk are numbers of Upper
Paleolithic blade tools, but their really distinctive implements, fanci-
fully called laurel- or willow-leafed, stand entirely apart. They are
made from flakes or blades, retouched on one or both surfaces by
pressure. So skillful were the craftsmen that by dint of precisely controlled pressure-chipping they produced symmetrical, ripple-like
ridges across the entire face of an implement and reduced it to remarkable thinness and delicacy (Fig. 73). All Solutrian tools of stone
are pointed, but they may be as small as an inch or as large as a foot
or more. They may also be divided into those that are pointed at

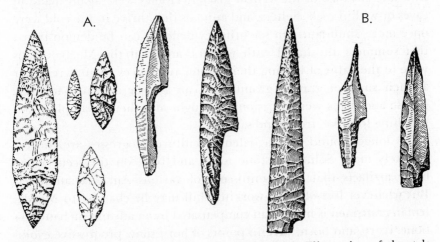

Fig. 73. Solutrian tools from the Upper Paleolithic. A. Flint points of the style
known as laurel leaf. B. Willow leaf points. The notched shoulders are thought
to have facilitated hafting. Solutrian lithic implements show the highest peak of
Old Stone Age workmanship.

both extremes and those that culminate at one end in a tang, presumably for hafting to a javelin shaft. Because they were made with such skill, precision, delicacy, and symmetry, the pressure-flaked stone implements of the Solutrian period reach the greatest heights of Upper Paleolithic workmanship. They were as functional as they were beautiful, and their varied shapes and sizes indicate that they could have served all the purposes of the average tool-kit of their day. The lithic materials were supplemented by a few tools and ornaments of bone, horn, and ivory.

The duration in time and the geographic range of Solutrian culture are both restricted. Cro-Magnon men are known to have been its carriers, but their appearance and disappearance in Western Europe are equally mysterious. Solutrian remains in general are later than Aurignacian, but they soon give way to Magdalenian.

## D. MAGDALENIAN CLOSES OUT THE UPPER PALEOLITHIC

**Magdalenian** culture, last of Western Europe's Upper Paleolithic series, falls in the terminal phase of the Pleistocene. The recession of glacial conditions under which Solutrian man had been lucky enough to live, was followed by the coming of another Ice Age brought about by a late advance of the Würm glacier. Homes were again made in caves or within rock shelters, and animals that thrive in the cold were once more abundant. On scientific evidence it can be demonstrated that summers alternated with winters, and that the Magdalenians were in the habit of leaving their winter residences to hunt reindeer at their summer grazing grounds. It can also be shown that arctic grouse and hares were occasionally caught and there is ample proof of fishing for pike, trout, and salmon.[5]

No longer found as Magdalenian culture progresses are the exquisitely made Solutrian stone tools, and back on the scene come blade artifacts that are reminiscent of various Aurignacian styles. But whatever loss of stone-working skill may be charged to Magdalenian craftsmen is more than compensated by an advance in handling bone, ivory, and horn. Javelin points of horn show progressive evolution, and Abbé Breuil has proposed a classification of Magdalenian

[5] For further details, see J. G. D. Clark, *Prehistoric Europe*, New York, 1952, pp. 26-27, *et passim*.

subdivisions based on variations of plain and barbed harpoons made of reindeer horn. Needles, buttons, awls, and fishhooks of bone are common, and the use of horn spear-throwers, some of which are elaborately ornamented, becomes widespread (Fig. 74).

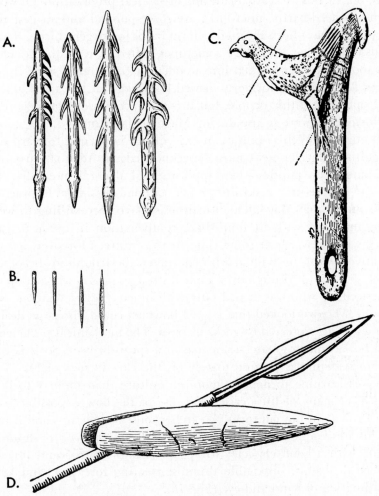

Fig. 74. Upper Paleolithic bone and horn tools (after MacCurdy, following Breuil). A. Several harpoons with double barbs, made of reindeer horn. B. Needles, with circular eyes, and awls of bone. C. An ornamental, horn spear-thrower, from the Magdalenian stage of the Upper Paleolithic. (The portions of C that are outside the dotted lines were reconstructed by Abbé Breuil.) D. Bone point of the Aurignacian period. It is split at the base to accommodate a handle. The manner in which it was fashioned into a spear is suggested in the accompanying drawing (after Braidwood).

Occurring sporadically in deposits of earlier culture but gaining prominence in the Magdalenian are tiny stone implements, suitably called **microliths,** that require mere bits of raw material. Many microliths are so small that they fail to cover an average man's fingernail, but each is carefully made and gives clear proof of human workmanship. Ordinarily, microliths are sharp-pointed and suggest that they might have been inserted to form barbs for larger objects. There is also proof that they were sometimes hafted in rows to provide a saw-tooth effect, or worked into wooden shafts to make stone-tipped darts. Archeologists formerly denied knowledge of bows and arrows to Upper Paleolithic people, but it is now pretty well conceded that such weapons were in use during Magdalenian times.[6]

If one accepts this opinion an exceedingly important forward step in cultural development must be acknowledged. Adequate use of a bow and arrow implies a new application of algebraic mentality, for no one can become a skillful archer without considerable practice. This means that Magdalenian man must have been willing to work long and hard without immediate compensation in order to gain worthwhile rewards at some time in the future. Moreover, a comparatively weak individual who had taken the trouble to become a crack shot could triumph over a much stronger person who had never practiced, or who was armed only with older types of weapon. Nor should it be overlooked that a good bowman could discharge deadly arrows while protected by rocks or trees. The mechanical proficiency of a bow is much greater than that of a spear-thrower. So it is that *Homo sapiens* was coming to rely on the effectiveness of his tools, and was learning to depend more on culture than biology to help him meet many of life's crises. Yet, use of the bow is possible only to a Primate of human form. An archer must be able to stand firmly on his hind legs, and he must have at least a powerful shoulder girdle with a good clavicle; strong but flexible wrists and fingers; prehensile hands; opposable thumbs; rotating forearms; and keen coordination of hand and eye (Fig. 75).

Magdalenian interest in the nonbiologic is attested by the care taken with burials. Graves are more regularly and frequently dug than ever before, there is much use of red ochre, and bodies are often ornamented with shell necklaces or accompanied by numerous tools. Only the most unreasonable of skeptics would try to deny that the

6 See *ibid.,* pp. 30-31.

Fig. 75. Pygmy Negro boys learning to shoot bows and arrows. Only upright posture, Primate anatomy, and preliminary practice make possible the proper use of these weapons.

Magdalenians had some concept of religion, at least to the extent of belief in an afterlife.

Until the discovery of the Lascaux paintings it used to be thought certain that Magdalenian artists were far and away the best of the Upper Paleolithic. Even now the claim is by no means unwarranted. There are countless ornaments, carvings, engravings, sculptures, clay figures, and paintings from this era, a good percentage of which are of breath-taking excellence. Many techniques, styles, subjects, and color schemes were employed, but the highest critical acclaim is generally reserved for polychrome paintings cleverly shaded to give an illusion of depth or solidity. Two of the very finest examples are reindeer figures at Font-de-Gaume near Les Eyzies, France, and the bison (Fig. 72C) depicted on the roof of the world-famous Altamira cave, near Santander in Spain.

Archeologists are seldom content to discuss Magdalenian art in purely esthetic terms. The mere fact that some of the very best specimens are found in dim recesses of inaccessible caverns makes it unlikely that such works were produced only for their own sake or to be admired by the general public. Once more one is tempted to have recourse to analogy with known primitive customs. Many peoples believe that ritual acts of slaying representations of animals will lead, on the principle of **mimetic** or **imitation magic,** to great success on an actual hunt. Religious interpretations of this kind are supported, in part, by Magdalenian portrayals of wounded animals, or realistically drawn beasts with crudely figured hearts shown outside the body (Fig. 72C). Also found is a tendency to paint one creature right over another (Fig. 72B). Such a custom, too, plays a part in some primitive religions. Once a spot has acquired a sacred character it is not likely to be readily changed, and wherever such a belief prevails it is not surprising to find paintings superimposed on one another. There is always a possibility that archeological interpretations based on analogy with existing primitive procedures may be wrong, but there is scarcely a writer who touches on the subject of Magdalenian art without suggesting that there may be religious overtones.

With the end of the Pleistocene and the termination of Magdalenian culture in Western Europe, modern times begin. Some there are who like to speculate on the post-Pleistocene fate of the Magdalenians. A formerly popular theory, not entirely devoid of supporters today, makes much of some parallels with contemporary Eskimo ways of life. Backers of this hypothesis argue that as the glaciers withdrew for the last time Magdalenian hunters followed their usual game northward, where they became or mingled with the Eskimo. Unfortunately, there is too little evidence to permit uncritical acceptance of so plausible a bit of speculation.

## E. INTRODUCTION TO THE MESOLITHIC OF WESTERN EUROPE

Between the end of the Upper Paleolithic and the start of the Neolithic (roughly from 20,000 to 6000 B.C.), there is a spread of about fourteen millenia during which man's cultural progress is but slightly understood. Until the turn of the present century this phase, currently known as **Mesolithic** or **Middle Stone Age,** was rather contemptuously dismissed as a kind of Dark Age. Part of the low regard was due to ignorance of what man had then accomplished, and part of it was based on the patent fact that some of the highest attainments of the Upper Paleolithic were lost. No stone work in the Mesolithic reaches the perfection of Solutrian pressure-flaking, and there is no continuation of the splendid artistic creations of the Aurignacian and Magdalenian periods.

In all fairness to the human beings of Mesolithic times in Western Europe it must be recognized that they were living in an era of drastic environmental changes. The huge glaciers of the Pleistocene were shrinking as they moved northward, leaving enormous fields of melting ice that ultimately raised water levels throughout the region. When much of the water finally drained into the sea the land was relieved of its heavy burden and began, in its turn, to rise. These fluctuations of land and water levels, and the establishment of new equilibria between them, were greatly influenced by the mounting temperatures that continued in force even after they had initiated the melting of glaciers.[7] Animals biologically adjusted to Ice Age weather could not survive the increasingly warm climate and became extinct or migrated far to the north. In place of mammoth, reindeer, bison, arctic hare, and wild horse, came the brown bear, wild pig, elk, beaver, and red deer. At first the new fauna showed adaptations

---

[7] Melting glaciers usually deposit in lakes twin soil layers or varves annually. During warm weather a band of sand or silt forms and is overlaid the next winter by clay. The number of varves in a glacial lake bed thus gives a clue to its age. This method of dating has been well developed in Scandanavia.

to tundra and steppe conditions, but forest types gained in prominence as the Mesolithic grew older. Only *Homo sapiens* met the challenges of drastic environmental changes by adjusting his culture instead of his biology.

Study of postglacial forest development is a fascinating sideline of Mesolithic archeology. Retreating ice sheets and climbing temperatures opened the way for the spread of extensive forests, particularly in the vicinity of the Baltic. Different kinds of trees became characteristic at various times as the weather shifted. A technique of pollen analysis, centered on microscopic quantitative and qualitative analysis of pollen grains entombed in natural deposits of earth, minerals, or peat, yields precise information about the sorts of trees that once prevailed. It is now clear that post-glacial Scandinavia, at least, went through three major phases. The first, **Pre-Boreal,** has willows, birches, and pines, that are adapted to relative cold; the second, **Boreal,** shows the former mixed with warmer varieties such as alder, oak, and elm; and the third, **Atlantic,** features the disappearance of birch and pine except very far north or on mountains where cold weather persisted.

Certainly, over a long span of time during which took place so many alterations of climate, fauna, and flora, no one form of culture could have been universally appropriate. For the Mesolithic, even more than for the Upper Paleolithic, it is necessary to deal with local or regional patterns instead of with one generalized way of life. People who hunted game in forests must inevitably have differed from coastal folk who caught fish and gathered shell-fish; and what was suitable for northern Denmark might have been unfit for southern France. Understandably enough, specialists differentiate a good many particular Mesolithic cultures, but we shall deal only with a few samples.

Efforts have been made to derive some of the Mesolithic cultures from specific Upper Paleolithic manifestations, but most of them are far-fetched. Satisfactorily proved connections may some day be demonstrated, because it is unlikely that all Upper Paleolithic cultures and their carriers were completely exterminated as soon as the Pleistocene closed. There must have been Upper Paleolithic survivors who persisted into the Mesolithic, but their tracks are hard to follow.

On the whole Mesolithic culture did not advance from hunting, fishing, and the gathering of food, to its control and production.

Nevertheless, some efforts at greater efficiency did take place in this sphere of human activity. One of the outstanding specialists in Mesolithic archeology has expressed the opinion that, with the exception of one or two places only, use of the bow displaced the harpoon on land.[8] Similarly, many changes making for better utility were wrought by Mesolithic people on implements that might have carried over from Upper Paleolithic times, but only a few basic innovations were devised. These may not be extensive but they suffice to show that culture was making a degree of progress during the Mesolithic and was neither stagnant nor degenerate.

## F. MESOLITHIC CULTURES IN SOUTHWESTERN EUROPE

Credit for finding the first overlap of Upper Paleolithic and Mesolithic cultures goes to E. Piette, who began in 1887 to excavate a French site called Mas d'Azil. Above five soil layers containing Magdalenian objects he found a sixth holding new types of artifacts which he called **Azilian.** They included small, flat, crudely barbed harpoons of staghorn, perforated near the base; an assortment of microlithic tools made from blades of flint; and about 200 smooth, water-worn pebbles, painted with red ochre in a miscellaneous variety of linear and geometric designs (Fig. 76A).

From the start it was plain that Azilian culture was later in time than Magdalenian, but not as well advanced in material ability or artistic skill. Much conjecture was stimulated by the painted pebbles, which promptly became hallmarks of Azilian culture. Strenuous but unsuccessful efforts were made to interpret the designs as forming a crude alphabet, and the pebbles themselves as religious tokens or an unknown kind of currency. Speculations of this kind are out of fashion in these days, and the puzzle of the painted pebbles remains frankly unsolved.

Very little has survived of other aspects of Azilian culture, yet discovery of its typical remains throughout Southern France and far to the east proves it to have been quite long-lived. Among the Azilian microliths are numbers of so-called micro-burins. They have slanting edges and sharp points and are thought to have been by-products of a technique by which they were struck from a long, previously pre-

---

[8] J. G. D. Clark, *op. cit.*, p. 35. This volume contains much valuable information about Upper Paleolithic and Mesolithic economy.

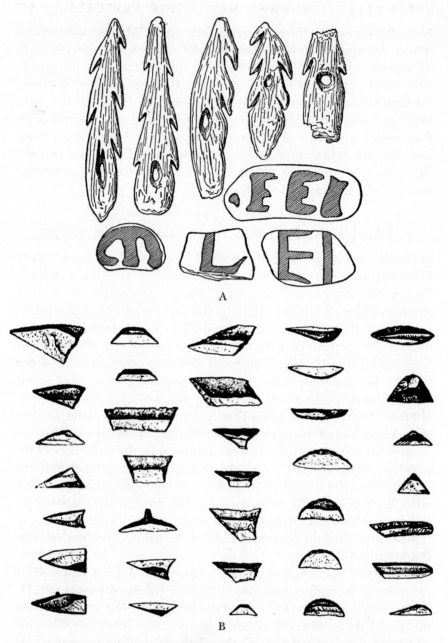

Fig. 76. Mesolithic artifacts (after MacCurdy). A. Azilian perforated stag-horn harpoon heads and painted pebbles (following Hoernes). B. Tardenoisian microliths (after de Mortillet).

pared blade. They do resemble tiny burins or engraving implements but in the modern view they might have been rejects, or else they might have served entirely different purposes from true burins. At several stations in Southwestern Europe Azilian culture blends with **Tardenoisian** (Fig. 76B), which is featured by extensive use of microliths made in all sorts of geometric forms such as crescents, triangles, semicircles, and rhomboids. There is not much to distinguish Tardenoisian from Azilian, except that the former has no painted pebbles and makes greater use of trapezoid and chisel-ended microliths.

## G. AXE-WIELDERS OF THE NORTH

Much more is known of Mesolithic life in northwestern than southwestern Europe, and the probability is strong that some Upper Paleolithic people from Spain or France moved northward in post-Pleistocene times. Changing environmental conditions are here so well marked as to provide archeologists with a good dating system. Besides the vegetation shifts already mentioned, it appears that during the Pre-Boreal phase the Baltic formed one arm of the great Yoldia Sea, but as various sectors of Scandinavia were uplifted, it was converted to a slightly brackish lake (Ancylus) until salt water again transgressed and transformed Ancylus Lake to the Littorina Sea. Most intimately adjusted to the changing times were a group of axe-using peoples in Denmark and the vicinity, whose main implements were hefty enough to cope with the growing forests. The first phase of their culture is called **Lyngby,** and is distinguished by the employment of reindeer antlers. Axes were manufactured by cutting brow tines obliquely; adzes were similarly made; and hafts were fashioned to accommodate a stone axehead (Fig. 77).

Some aspects of Lyngby culture were probably incorporated into the succeeding **Maglemose** phase, which has left more ample remains. People following the Maglemose way of life hunted elk, red deer, and wild pig; caught many pike and other fish from inland waters; did a considerable amount of fowling; and collected edible plants and shell-fish. They made stone tools that vary from microliths in many shapes to heavy core-built axes (roughly rectangular, and not to be confused with generally pear-shaped Lower Paleolithic fist-axes), adzes, picks, and chisels or tranchets. They also made harpoons and barbless fishhooks of antler and bone, as well as assorted items of wood. Among the most interesting of their remains are a number of large paddle-rudders that point to a knowledge of some sort of water transport, most likely in the form of dugout canoes. No doubt they had the resources to deal with forest life and some think it was in

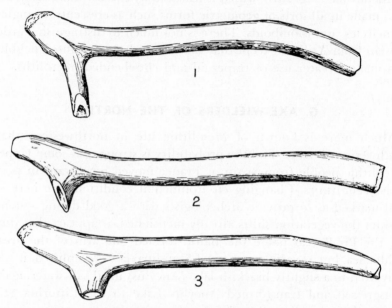

Fig. 77. Three forms of Lyngby axes. All are made from reindeer antlers. Number 1 is in the shape of an axe; 2 is an adze; and 3 is a haft.

connection with hunting that they achieved their greatest cultural triumph, domestication of the dog. There is a question as to whether they originated the idea or borrowed it from outsiders, but this marks the first instance in our outline of cultural progress where man was beginning to use another animal for purposes other than food or as a source of raw materials.

It is important not to confuse domestication with mere taming. A completely domesticated animal must not only be so tame that it will not attack people or run away, but it should also be dependent on man for some of its food, as opposed to foraging on its own, and it should be capable of breeding under conditions of captivity. If a beast has been thoroughly domesticated its entire anatomy may change, in which event paleontologists can usually tell a domesticated creature from its wild relatives. It has been thoroughly established that dogs were the first beasts to have been brought under domestication, and that their ancestors were wolves. There is no way of telling by what steps the Maglemose folk brought about the dog's domestication, nor are the uses to which it was put at all clear.[9] Even so, its mere presence stands out as an important event in the march of Mesolithic cultures.

When the Littorina Sea was formed, according to several experts, some of the Maglemose hunters apparently moved there and settled permanently on its shores, supporting themselves by catching fish and gathering shell-fish. Their culture at this stage is called **Ertebolle** and is often, but not in every instance, represented by huge mounds of food debris known as **kitchen middens.** Kitchen middens consist of discarded shells, bones, earth, lost or rejected tools, and other odds and ends densely packed together and sometimes containing skeletal remains. Those who lived at the seashore long enough to build great heaps of debris were probably permanent residents, for the kitchen mounds show enough fire hearths to suggest that the inhabitants stuck it out even during inclement seasons. Material remains of Ertebolle culture run closely parallel to those of the Maglemose, except for the addition of a small chisel of stone (petit tranchet) that must have been hafted, bone combs and bracelets, and pottery vessels. The invention of pottery is an exceedingly important attainment, but Ertebolle is so recent a phase of Mesolithic culture, dated around 5000 B.C., that nearly everyone agrees that the concept was not original but probably came from some area where at that time Neolithic culture was already well advanced. A description of pottery-making and its implications will, therefore, be reserved until the New Stone Age is discussed. Borrowed or not, Ertebolle pottery manufacturing was not greatly skilled. Vessels were formed of black clay mixed with coarse grit, that took on a gray-brown color when fired. They were so poorly made that they often cracked open. Only oval saucers and wide-mouthed jars with conical, pointed bases seem to have been made, and the most common style of decoration was limited to a series of fingernail impressions along the rim (Fig. 78).

After the forests and coasts of Northern Europe had been settled by Maglemose and Ertebolle axe-wielders, respectively, there came

9 The theory has been advanced, by analogy with known areas where livestock are kept for social or religious purposes, that animal domestication may not have started as a practical measure. This is an interesting but unproved hypothesis.

Fig. 78. Mesolithic pottery from Ertebolle. It is crudely made, impressed designs may be found on the rims, and the bases are usually conical.

into the area bands of microlith users. Perforce, they took what land remained unoccupied, most of which was sandy soil. On this they built small settlements with houses of reeds plastered with mud, sometimes digging subterranean foundations. Their culture lacks the distinctive, large implements of bone, stone, or antler, that characterize much of the Mesolithic and they were unable to make pottery. They seem to have had a sort of shadowy Tardenoisian culture and are thought to have offered but little opposition to the Neolithic invaders who were soon to displace them.

### SELECTED REFERENCES

Braidwood, Robert J., *Prehistoric Men,* Chicago, 1948.
Burkitt, Miles C., *Our Early Ancestors,* Cambridge, England, 1926.
Clark, J. Grahame D., *The Mesolithic Settlement of Northern Europe,* Cambridge, England, 1936.
———, *Prehistoric Europe,* New York, 1952.
Obermaier, Hugo, *Fossil Man in Spain,* New Haven, 1924.
Windels, Fernand, *The Lascaux Cave Paintings,* New York, 1950.

CHAPTER 13

# Neolithic Contributions to Culture

## A. PRELIMINARY REMARKS

By 6000 B.C. *Homo sapiens* had gone through a long and diversified cultural apprenticeship. Throughout the hundreds of millenia of the Old and Middle Stone Ages the species had shown itself capable of adjusting its ways of life to extreme environmental differences without any outstanding biological alterations. It had devised a great profusion of tools made in a variety of ways from wood, fine-grained stones, ivory, horn, bone, and other cold materials. It had made homes in caves, under rock-shelters, in the open, in forested land, and at the seacoast. Fire was everywhere utilized and ingenious methods of obtaining food from nature had been developed. Religious practices are pretty certain to have been begun, and fine arts occasionally reached amazing heights. Before the conclusion of the Mesolithic the potential power of the human body had been greatly increased through the agency of such extra-corporeal things as bows and arrows, sturdily hafted tools, boats or canoes, and, perhaps, the domesticated dog. Also during the Middle Stone Age the making of pottery introduced a new industry and led to an expanding utilization of natural resources. Pottery-making may not have been invented by any Mesolithic people, yet some of them showed that they were at least capable of recognizing its value and mastering techniques of production. Despite the record of their achievements Old and Middle Stone Age cultures advanced at a painfully slow pace, and cannot help but appear remote and drab to those who live in the second half of the twentieth century A.D. This picture, as we shall soon see, changes with dramatic suddenness when man enters the **New Stone Age.**

It is a pity that the term **Neolithic** has gained such currency as a label to describe the new ways of life. There is no denying that fresh methods of treating stone played an important role, but far more significant was the shift from hunting, fishing, and gathering to the humanly controlled production of food based on agriculture and the breeding of large domesticated mammals. These essential discoveries brought in their train a host of secondary adjustments and inventions all of which jointly form the foundations of modern life. As a matter of fact a number of societies have lived on into recent times with patterns of culture that do not always measure up to the full Neolithic. To cite only two instances, the American Indians were, with only two or three outstanding exceptions, culturally Neolithic or less in 1492 A.D.; and the Australian aborigines barely attained that level before they were brought into steady contact with Europeans in the nineteenth century.

The survival of ancient forms of culture in some parts of the world long after they had become outmoded elsewhere, poses an interesting question about the situation 8000 years ago. Surely, there were many

Mesolithic and even continuing Paleolithic communities that persisted in their old customs because they were unaware of or lacked the desire or means to take up the new fashions. Viewed in universal terms a previously unknown situation appears to have arisen in the Neolithic. For the first time in human history there must have been groups of hunters and food collectors who looked with envy on prosperous agriculturalists, particularly in late fall or winter when game was scarce and wild botanical products were unavailable. These are the very seasons of the year when farmers and keepers of livestock are likely, except under the most wretched of conditions, to have food surpluses. A marked distinction was probably felt at such times between "have" and "have not" societies, and it seems reasonable to believe that large-scale raids or wars, as distinguished from sporadic assaults or occasional murders, had their beginning in Neolithic times. By way of proof it may be noted that in the New Stone Age settlements fortified by ditches and ramparts are commonplace.

The uneven distribution of Neolithic advances raises a cardinal point of theory. In tracing the march of culture we are dealing not with universal stages through which all communities must have passed, but rather with a synthesis that puts into an orderly sequence the cultural high-water levels reached here and there by various groups of people. No one race, tribe, nation, society, or corner of the globe showed the way at all times. Instead, numerous kinds of humans made basic contributions at different times and places. Around 6000 B.C. many spots now regarded as "backward" were exerting vigorous cultural leadership and, conversely, such a "forward" area as Western Europe was then far behind the times.

A word of explanation is required to make clear why our descriptions of Paleolithic and Mesolithic cultures were centered on events in Europe. It was not meant to imply that Europe during the Pleistocene had either the earliest or the best forms of culture. The one and only reason why European data were emphasized is because the sequence of man's earliest efforts to develop culture has been most intensively studied on that continent. When it comes to describing Neolithic progress, however, it becomes necessary to shift the scene. Not Europe but the **Eastern Mediterranean Zone** best reveals the manner in which *Homo sapiens* made his way into the New Stone Age. This zone extends from Egypt's Nile River in northeastern Africa to the valleys of the Euphrates and Tigris Rivers of Western

Asia (see end papers). In general terms the Eastern Mediterranean Zone incorporates what is often called "The Fertile Crescent." This is the region, so far as archeologists know, where Neolithic culture was born and from which it was diffused to many other parts of the Old World. That it did not spring into existence full-blown is readily acknowledged, but its immediate ancestry has never been ascertained.

## B. THE LITHIC REVOLUTION

Because Neolithic has become a time-sanctioned term for the new ways of life that started around 6000 B.C., it is appropriate to begin its study with a description of stone usages. Even during the antecedent Mesolithic of northwestern Europe attempts had been made to handle stone in ways that were unknown to Paleolithic man. Large blocks were sometimes roughly shaped by percussion flaking, after which grooves might be pecked in them by repeated blows with a hard, sharp boulder. The pecked-out channels could then be used for hafting. Less often, trenches were cut into one stone by sawing back and forth in the same spot with a tougher one. Most valuable of the new methods, though, was a process of rubbing a bit of stone repeatedly over an abrasive substance such as sandstone, rough fibers, or plain sand. This technique, most commonly known as grinding or polishing, produces a tool that has a smooth, highly burnished surface (Fig. 79).

While cases are known for the Mesolithic where rubbing techniques were used in shaping tools of wood, bone, and sometimes stone, it is not until the Neolithic that grinding or polishing systematically displaces the older percussion and pressure methods of dealing with stone. Introduction of the new process is of deep significance because it greatly increased man's ability to use hitherto valueless raw materials. No longer was it necessary to seek out flint, quartz, or other fine-grained stones of crypto-crystalline structure. Almost any kind of stone, regardless of grain or internal composition, can be ground into a tool. Even granites which crumble when subjected to percussion or pressure flaking can be rubbed into a desired shape. Polishing has the further advantage of producing sturdier working edges than the older methods, which turned out implements that often split or cracked after a few hard blows. When a pressure- or percussion-made tool is damaged it can seldom be repaired and is likely to be discarded and replaced, but the working edge of a polished stone instrument can be re-sharpened or repaired by re-rubbing, pretty much on the same principle that is used to fix a metal tool on a

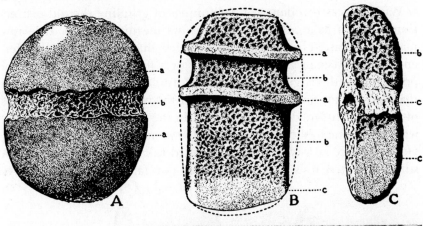

Fig. 79. Lithic techniques of the New Stone Age. A. Club head or hammer. B. Axe head. C. Banner-stone. The *a* surfaces are natural; *b* surfaces are pecked; and *c* surfaces are rubbed or polished. D. An Australian aborigine grinding a Neolithic implement.

D

grindstone. In the long run, therefore, Neolithic implements turned out to be more durable and economical than their parallels from the earlier ages. They enabled man to cut and shape timbers more efficiently, and they may well deserve credit for providing the means of establishing carpentry as a more important craft than ever before.

With increased reliance on techniques of grinding the old distinction between flake and core tools grows meaningless. So little raw material is wasted by the Neolithic process that it makes small difference if a craftsman starts with a core or a flake. Nor did the use of polishing methods greatly affect the forms or sizes of lithic objects that had already gained wide favor. For the most part the same kinds of utensils continued to be made, but in the course of time Neolithic workmen came to show a preference for what is called a celt (Fig. 80). Only a glance at a typical celt is needed to convince one that when suitably hafted it is the prototype of our familiar hatchet or axe

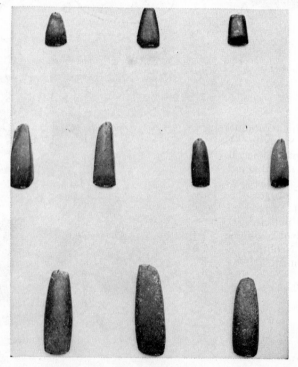

Fig. 80. Neolithic celts from the Swiss Lake-Dwellings. They represent the most common lithic tools of the New Stone Age. All are rubbed smooth, and some have bevelled edges. None was used without a handle.

blade. Abandonment of tools designed to be held in the bare hand or fist is a very revealing feature of the Neolithic. The mechanical advantages of handles had become thoroughly recognized and the principle of hafting was firmly established.

Despite the almost undifferentiated use of stones made possible by Neolithic workmanship there was a differing value put on various kinds of lithic materials. It is probable that mining for particular varieties of stone went on earlier, but not until the New Stone Age is there evidence of large-scale mining activity, with such devices as sunken shafts and connecting galleries. One of the best known centers of flint quarrying was located at **Grand Pressigny**, France. Here there was a prodigious deposit of high-grade flint, resembling amber or beeswax in color. Grand Pressigny flint is so distinctive and so readily identified that its distribution is easy to follow. Examples have been found as far off as Italy, Switzerland, and Belgium, and it was doubtless a prized article of Neolithic commerce. Amber, sea shells, and semiprecious stones were also widely traded.

## C. FROM MUD TO SPODE

Neolithic man learned to increase his material resources not only by contriving a means of utilizing coarse-grained stones, but also by coming to understand how to convert wet clay, which had hitherto been nothing but a nuisance in the form of sticky mud, into fine dishes and outlets for artistic expression. Invention of pottery-making must be ranked as one of man's greatest cultural triumphs. No better appreciation of the value of mental foresight can be had than if one tries to imagine the first person who saw in his mind's eye the possibility of turning clay into the kinds of ceramic vessels that have culminated in the Lenox, Wedgewood, and Spode products of our day. To become a successful potter is no easy matter, and ever so many anonymous craftsmen have made contributions that helped carry the art to perfection. Professor V. Gordon Childe, one of the greatest living archeologists, regards pot-making as the beginning of science and perhaps man's first conscious utilization of a chemical change.[1]

Some of the basic complexities of this skill come to light even in a brief account of some of the steps involved. To begin with, a suitable deposit of clay containing silicate of aluminum must be located. The

[1] V. G. Childe, *Man Makes Himself,* London, 1936, p. 101.

clay must then be mixed with water to form a paste that is plastic but not too sticky, and kneaded until it is perfectly uniform inside and out. To the clay paste must be added a small percentage of temper, which is any coarse gritty substance like chopped-up bits of straw, grains of sand, fragments of crushed shell, or minutely crumbled pieces of stone. At a later stage, while a vessel is being fired, steam or other gaseous by-products escape through tiny outlets provided by the temper and so prevent the clay body from cracking. A potter must make a neat calculation of the exact amount of tempering matter to add in order to get the desired effect without making the finished vessel too coarse. After the clay, water, and temper have been well worked together comes the difficult task of shaping the pot. Early Neolithic workers were inclined to mold small objects like cups by hand, somewhat in the fashion of sculpture. Larger vessels were customarily made by coiling, a process whereby a potter first rolls out "ropes" or coils of clay, and then fits one above the other until the shape wanted has been achieved. The coil junctures may be allowed to show or they may be obliterated by squeezing and rubbing. A preliminary outdoor drying follows, after which the pot must be fired. At a temperature of about 1100 degrees, Fahrenheit, the clay loses its plasticity and bakes into a hard, waterproof, solid material that will retain its form in any environment until smashed.

This synopsis really tells only a small part of the full story. Omitted are the problems of handles, legs, or covers, and the entire question of baking arrangements (kilns), and ways of controlling firing temperatures. Early forms of decoration were simple, ordinarily consisting of impressions made on the pre-fired vessel while the clay was still soft and plastic. Little cuts could be made with a fingernail, bits could be pinched or pulled out with the fingers, lines might be scratched with a stick or comb, and designs could be formed by pressing rope, a roughened paddle, or a stamp, against the yielding body. Any impression made by these methods would become hardened and permanently fixed during the process of firing. Later, presumably, designs were quite commonly painted on pottery, often with the help of a preliminary slip. A slip is a very fine clay wash, sometimes tinted, which is evenly applied over a pot before it is baked. It serves the double purpose of helping to obliterate surface irregularities and of providing a smooth background for painting (Fig. 81B, C).

Fig. 81. Neolithic pottery styles. A. Stroke ornamented ware from the Danube basin. B and C. Painted vessels, black and red on cream, from the montana region of Peru and Ecuador.

A long time elapsed before pottery-making reached a high degree of perfection, but pottery's usefulness for storage, cooking and serving food, as well as its artistic potential were recognized early. Broken fragments, known as potsherds, are always conspicuous in Neolithic remains. This provides a totally different kind of value that has become attached to ceramics. Although objects of pottery are notoriously fragile and easily broken, the resulting sherds are practically indestructible. They do not decompose in the ground, they are unattractive to hungry animals, they are worthless to their owners, and valueless to treasure seekers or grave robbers. Consequently, bits of broken pots are left behind when a settlement is abandoned and remain in place for untold centuries. Modern archeologists are eternally grateful to the unknown discoverer of the potter's craft. They find potsherds so variable in form, composition, manner of manufacture, decoration, and color that they use them as indicators of cultural stability or change. Highly specialized techniques of ceramic analysis make possible such scientifically accurate determinations of clays, coloring substances, tempering materials, and firing temperatures and methods that archeologists can often tell where a given kind of pottery originated. Thanks to this information they are provided with a clue to the study of migration, trade, and cultural diffusion, and in some cases pottery styles furnish an excellent basis for cross-dating.

## D. FOOD PRODUCTION AND FREEDOM FROM WANT

It was farming that made the biggest difference between Mesolithic and Neolithic patterns of culture, and farming could never have been started were it not for man's ability to plan ahead and to have confidence in his predictions for the future. At the very least a farmer must, long before he can expect any benefit from his efforts, be willing to expend time and labor in clearing a bit of land, breaking ground, planting seeds, and removing weeds. Only those who are far-sighted enough to work hard in the hope of gaining future compensation can ever become successful farmers. Although the rewards may be long delayed they are apt, except in unusually bad years, to be very generous when they finally come in. Agricultural communities generally find it possible to raise more than they collectively need, thus developing a surplus which can be stored and used for purposes other than the satisfaction of biological hunger.

Man's control of his food supply took place gradually through a series of steps each of which might have been trivial in itself, but whose cumulative effect was tremendous. A good number of wild plants were potentially capable of being cultivated, but at the dawn of the Neolithic in the Eastern Mediterranean Zone wheat and barley were the first to be raised through human agency. They are known to have been present in the area in the form of natural grasses, and farming began when human beings learned to select for cultivation the seeds of those plants that were most productive and nutritious. Once the concept of domesticating and controlling the growth of wheat and barley came to be understood, it was extended to include other grains, cereals, fruits, berries, and nuts.

Closely affiliated with the idea of farming is the notion of animal domestication. Contemporary anthropologists do not accept the priority of **pastoralism,** but are of the opinion that the raising of plants and the rearing of livestock took place at about the same time. Throughout the Eastern Mediterranean Zone mixed farming, as it is called, is found in very early Neolithic settlements. Cattle, sheep, goats, and pigs, in addition to dogs, were the first beasts to have been brought under domestication, and wild forms of all these species are known to have lived somewhere within the extensive region of supposed Neolithic origins. With the help of surplus agricultural products farmers were able to feed livestock, in exchange for which they acquired a reliable supply of meat, milk, hides and other raw materials, and creatures that could be trained to do much of their work for them. Through the judicious selection of animals for slaughter, coupled with careful supervision of breeding, Neolithic man found himself with another potential surplus in addition to what could be saved from his crops.

There is no reason to think that New Stone Age people gave up hunting, fishing, and gathering just as soon as they had acquired the arts of farming and keeping livestock. On the contrary, there is abundant archeological proof to show that the advantages of the new activities were simply added to the older ones. Hence Neolithic societies, unlike those with Paleolithic or Mesolithic cultures, grew less and less dependent for their welfare on the vagaries of nature. Food shortages and periods of want must have diminished when man became a successful food-producer.

## E. SPINNING AND WEAVING

Domestication of plants and animals stimulated and called into being other practices, not necessarily directly concerned with the production of food. Devices for housing, feeding, tethering, and leading or guiding beasts, as well as the manufacture of agricultural tools would be of this order. A less direct by-product that arose in the Neolithic was the **textile** industry, which necessitated the spinning of thread and the weaving of cloth. Each of the major aspects of domestication played a part in this development. Flax was grown because its fibers could be drawn out and spun into long threads from which linen was made; and the wool of sheep was similarly converted into cloth. In neither case was the matter left to chance, for flax was deliberately cultivated as a non-food crop, and wool-bearing animals were systematically bred to produce a heavy fleece.

The essentials of **weaving** as established in Neolithic days have continued to serve mankind throughout the ages. Whenever and wherever cloth is to be made a suitable thread must first be spun. This is accomplished by twisting fibers together and connecting them into a long skein with the help of a spindle. A spindle is a simple contrivance which need be no more than a slender, rounded stick capable of being twirled, to which yarn may be attached. Ordinarily, the spindle stick is set into a slightly heavier circular disc or spindle whorl which acts as a flywheel to control the twirling action. After a thread has been spun little more is needed than a frame or loom with at least one bar in horizontal position. To this are tied at regular intervals threads that hang vertically downward and are known as

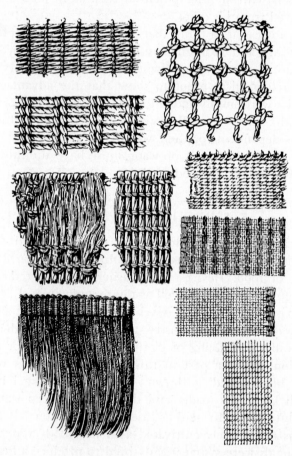

Fig. 82. Examples of Neolithic cloth weaving (after MacCurdy). There is a surprising variety of techniques, each of which is expertly employed. All the cloth is woven from flax, and all the specimens were obtained from Swiss Lake-Dwellings.

the warp. Cloth is then woven by introducing a movable element (woof or weft) which is passed horizontally over or under one or more warp strands at a time (Fig. 82). Designs are produced by the coloring of threads and the pattern in which the warp strings are raised or depressed as the weft moves across them. Even the most complicated, automatic, power-driven looms of our era operate on an elaboration of the original plan that was figured out by some un-known Neolithic genius.

Much basketry is produced along the same principles as cloth weaving. When twined or woven objects are to be made stiff vegetal fibers are fixed in position, without need for a loom, to serve as the warp, and similar elements are passed over and under them in the manner of a weft. There is, though, another basketry technique that is more like sewing than weaving. This is the coiling method, in ac-cord with which a worker prepares rings of fibers and then stitches them in position, one above another. Specimens of both processes are known from Neolithic remains.

## F. ROUND AND ROUND

Long before the Neolithic period reached a close the principle of the **wheel,** which converts straight-line to rotary power, was dis-covered. Very likely its quality of eliminating friction was early recog-nized as suited for improving means of transportation, but its use was doubtless preceded by drags, sledges, or rollers (Fig. 83). How long the clumsier devices persisted is unknown, but the chances are slim that wheels played a great part in transport throughout the Neolithic. When wheels first came to be attached to vehicles they were fashioned from heavy, round sections of tree-trunks. Only later did they evolve into the standard arrangement of hubs, spokes, and rims. In spite of its slow development discovery of the basic concept of rotary power must rank as a major accomplishment. Wheels were soon found to have value in connection with the crafts of pot-tery and spinning. There is little evidence of the employment of a potter's wheel in the New Stone Age, but round spindle whor's occur in such profusion that they testify to the use of circular discs, really small wheels, in the preparation of thread for weaving.

To appreciate the full and ultimate significance of the wheel one must consider its importance to modern industry. Not only are

Fig. 83. A dog-drawn travois. Bundles were tied on the frame close to the animal. Although this photograph shows a travois used by the Blackfoot Indians,
comparable devices may well have been used elsewhere prior to the full development of wheeled vehicles.

wheels placed on all sorts of vehicles from perambulators to airplanes,
but they are also of prime importance to the operation of contrivances
as varied as watches, record-players, and electric generators. The Neolithic inventor of the wheel could not have foreseen the consequences,
but the idea of using rotary power has furnished one of the most valuable technological concepts of our day.

## G. A SUMMARY OF THE GENERAL PATTERN OF
## NEOLITHIC LIFE

As they developed in the Eastern Mediterranean Zone, Neolithic
settlements came to differ radically from those communities remaining at the hunting, fishing, and collecting stage. Nor were the differences limited to changes in the material realm. Great advances
in technology never fail to be accompanied by equally important
shifts of social organization and religion. Farmers, particularly in
the early stages of their reliance on agriculture, are not always unwilling to migrate, but surely no human being in his right senses will
sow a crop and then voluntarily move away while someone else reaps

the harvest. Soil exhaustion, lack of moisture, a heavy growth of weeds, insect pests, or the need of new grazing grounds for livestock may induce farmers to move, but assuredly their wanderings are negligible compared with those of the earlier Stone Age folk.

Besides their greater permanence agricultural communities can support denser populations. Not until Neolithic times do archeologists find signs of settlements large enough to be called towns or villages, and with correspondingly big refuse mounds to suggest long occupancy. People who live by hunting and gathering cannot possibly congregate into permanent groups of large size. The very magnitude and stability of Neolithic communities could not fail to have raised some serious social problems. Large numbers of people simply do not live long in close proximity without a well developed social organization. More elaborate and systematic rules for controlling the conduct of individuals toward each other invariably arise, and there must be some to make regulations and others to enforce them. Full-fledged ethical systems are thus established.

As to religion, there is little of tangible nature to guide conjecture but certain implications are fairly evident. People invariably seek aid and comfort from their deities and it stands to reason that societies which depend on farming and raising animals will not want exactly the same sort of help that hunters and gatherers seek. There is also a profound difference in the degree of reliance on supernatural or religious aid between the two groups. When pre-Neolithic man was faced with a food shortage he could do little about it except pray for assistance. Even with the great scientific advances of our day there is not much that can be done to increase the numbers of wild animals or the amounts of natural vegetation. Neolithic man was not quite so helpless. Many factors remained over which he had no control, but when threatened by a food shortage he might not only seek supernatural aid but he might in addition increase his own diligence. If, for example, it was a matter of drought that bothered him he could pray for rain, but he could also seek to improve the situation by building irrigation canals or transporting water from a distant source. No one pretends to know how often Neolithic man followed one course or the other, and no one can tell which he found more satisfactory, but the fact remains that the people of the New Stone Age were more the masters of their fate than those who lived by Paleolithic or Mesolithic forms of culture. Actual relics show that the bull was an early object of Neolithic worship. Head and horns represent the whole beast, and the first identifiable religious personages are figured with horned headdresses. Two celts placed butt to butt (double axe) stand for conventionalized horns, and in this form (Fig. 84) they are widespread throughout the Eastern Mediterranean Zone.

Fig. 84. Ceremonial use of double axes in the Eastern Mediterranean Zone (after Hall). All the figures are from Egypt, except the one at the extreme right, which is Cretan. These examples demonstrate the link of double axes with the horns of a bull, a powerful beast that was once greatly venerated.

Neolithic communities are thought by Professor Childe to have been pretty self-sufficient, and as communities they probably were; but the same cannot be said of individuals. It is no great strain on the imagination to think of a Mesolithic or Paleolithic man who could carry out all the occupations demanded for a male by his culture, one who could manufacture his own tools, hunt, fish, make shelters, build fires, and the like. It is quite another matter to try to picture a Neolithic person who could by himself make all his own polished stone tools, build his house and outbuildings, breed and care for animals, manufacture pottery, weave cloth, and fashion baskets, all in addition to raising crops. Undoubtedly there was a division of labor between the sexes and between young and old, as well as co-operation among fellow villagers, but it is almost as certain that incipient classes of specialists were emerging in the persons of those who could turn out better baskets, pots, or cloth than their neighbors. Full-time specialization could not arise until some folk regularly accumulated large enough surpluses of food to barter or trade them, in one form or another, for manufactured items. And as specialization increased there would have to be further social regulations to control the orderly exchange of goods. Archeologists have no way of measuring the extent to which new social forms accompanied the advanced technology of the New Stone Age, but it is certain that by 6000 B.C. the good old days of simple biological behavior

had, in some regions, been left far behind, and yet, the full complexities of modern life were just starting.

There is much that is solid and enduring to Neolithic man's accomplishments. The crops that he first brought under cultivation are
still of prime importance; the animals that he succeeded in domesticating remain among the most valuable ever brought under human
control; and the techniques of pottery-making, basketry, and weaving
that he worked out continue to form the basis of much modern
industry. Only his stone tools have become completely outmoded.
It is no exaggeration to say that Neolithic culture in the Eastern
Mediterranean Zone so nearly resembled our own that even the most
up-to-date of farmers would require only a short space of time if he
were somehow forced to adjust himself to the life of a New Stone Age
community.

## H. NEOLITHIC CULTURES OF THE OLD WORLD

Within the Eastern Mediterranean Zone one of the oldest food-
producing communities was at **Merimde,**[2] not far from the Western
border of the Nile delta in Egypt. Merimde reveals indications of
a village with signs of flimsy huts scattered over a space of about six
or seven acres. A fairly high level of social organization is inferred
from the fact that the dwellings were laid out in regular rows or
streets. Ample tool and food remains show that the ancient inhabitants continued to live by hunting, fishing, fowling, and gathering,
but there also occur bones of domesticated cattle, sheep, goats, and
pigs. Remnants of wheat and barley, together with the floors on
which grain was threshed are found, as well as sickles, hoes, grinding-
stones for milling flour, and storage bins. Pottery, cloth-weaving, and
basketry are all in evidence, too, at Merimde.

**Hassuna,** in the upper valley of the Tigris in Northern Mesopotamia (Iraq), is a Western Asiatic site that contains the remains of a
very early Neolithic village, made up of mud houses.[3] The inhabitants of Hassuna were conversant with the usual run of early New
Stone Age materials, in addition to which they made painted pottery,

---

[2] **Fayum** is another ancient example of Neolithic life in the same vicinity.

[3] A very recent publication makes a prior claim to Neolithic culture for an Iraq
site at **Jarmo,** where were discovered polished stone work and traces of wheat, barley,
and peas. See R. J. Braidwood, "The Near East and the Foundations for Civilization,"
*Condon Lectures,* Eugene, Oregon, 1952, pp. 26-31.

fashioned little clay figurines of women, and practiced the custom of burying some of their dead in large pottery urns.

The origins of Merimde and Hassuna go back to about 6000 B.C., but within two or three millenia apparently independent Neolithic advances were being made in India, China, other parts of Asia, and at a few places in North Africa. India added the zebu (humped cattle) to the large mammals domesticated in the Eastern Mediterranean Zone, and nearby places in southeastern Asia are credited with having brought under domestication the water buffalo and chickens. Later, other regions of Asia added to the list the horse, camel, and cat. To the record of important crops India contributed cotton, and either India or China was the first to grow rice. Not all of these additions are early, but they are thought to have become known before the Neolithic terminated. For the rest, Afro-Asiatic New Stone Age cultures differ only in detail from those already mentioned.

Between the Eastern Mediterranean Zone and the heart of Europe the valley of the Danube River furnishes the shortest and easiest passageway. After the New Stone Age had become somewhat mature the Danube Basin proved to be an attractive locality for settlement by some of the expanding populations of the Eastern Mediterranean. This had not been the case earlier. At the very beginning of the Neolithic, the European climate was so warm and moist that forest growth made it hard for farmers to get a start. Later on, the Danubian corridor came to have areas of less timber and more loess. Loess is a fine, yellowish-brown soil, well suited for agriculture because it retains water, and it is often blown into a spot from places that are drying out. Along the Danube it is in the loess lands that archeologists find the first traces of Neolithic settlements north of the Alps. How far Central Europe lagged behind the Eastern Mediterranean Zone in those days is indicated by the fact that none of the Danubian sites is dated earlier than 3000 B.C.[4]

At about the same time groups of Neolithic folk, sometimes referred to as "Westerners," were settling in and around parts of France, Belgium, Britain, Switzerland, and Italy. Although they were farmers they relied heavily on large herds of domesticated cattle. Some of their equipment has given rise to a theory that they were offshoots of earlier North African centers, such as Merimde. In Eu-

[4] Specialists divide Neolithic culture in the basin of the Danube into Danubian I, II, and III. For details consult V. G. Childe, *The Danube in Prehistory*, Oxford, 1929.

rope they built rectangular houses of wood on platforms raised off the ground by stout posts (pile dwellings). In Switzerland and Italy many of their homes seem to have extended out into lakes, with wooden causeways or platforms leading to shore. Even the Swiss **Lake Dwellers,** however, who are believed surely to have lived over water, maintained farms on land where they raised millet, lentils, poppies, oats, and apples, in addition to more than one variety of wheat, barley, and flax. They made use of about 170 kinds of plants, mostly wild forms, including grapes, strawberries, pears, parsnips, carrots, and walnuts. Owing to the fortunate circumstance that the bulk of their remains was buried in mud, a good deal of perishable material was preserved that would probably have disintegrated if kept dry. Thus, specimens of their cloth and basketry, in addition to pottery, have been recovered. Their textile skill was great (Fig. 82), extending even to the art of embroidery.

During a winter drought that affected Central Europe in 1920-21, water levels were reduced to such an extent that several unsuspected Lake Dwelling remains were exposed. A Swiss archeologist, Dr. Paul Vouga, diligently studied the relics and tried to arrange them in chronological order.[5] His system depended largely on variations of a distinctive type of staghorn socket, fixed to receive a stone blade. Still other kinds of antler or horn sleeves have been found at a number of stations, and there was apparently much use of bone for tool making.

A different sort of late Neolithic culture has a distribution along the seacoasts and through much of Northern Europe. Because it features constructions made of giant stones it is sometimes spoken of as **Megalithic,** and there are some who would trace its source to Egypt. Quite a few of the structures contain burials and are commonly known as **passage graves** because a corridor leads to the place of interment. Other Megalithic chambers were made of vertical blocks of stone capped with a huge horizontal slab to form what is known as a **dolmen.**[6]

[5] See G. G. MacCurdy, *Human Origins,* New York, 1924, Vol. 2, pp. 67-71.

[6] Also pertaining to Megalithic culture are solitary upright columns, **menhirs;** pillars arranged in circles, **cromlechs;** or single slabs set in long rows, **alinements.** A very famous example of an alinement is to be found near Carnac, in Northern France. Nothing definite is known of the uses that the big, upended stones served, but a feeling persists that they had religious significance. England's mysterious Stonehenge is often cited as an outstanding example of Megalithic construction. For further details consult G. G. MacCurdy, *op. cit.,* pp. 28-35, 109-129.

Several vital but unsolved problems of great theoretical significance vex the archeologists who specialize in the New Stone Age. How many of the new traits must a site reveal to be classified as Neolithic? Is the mere occurrence of polished stone tools or pottery enough? Does the presence of a single domesticated crop suffice? If one of these features is not sufficient to warrant Neolithic classification, then how many? In what combination? Other troublesome questions concern dates and origins. Were the New Stone Age traits invented only once in a given spot and diffused elsewhere, or were they independently originated in several places at different times? When and where was each feature first invented, and by whom? By what agencies, specifically, were the new customs spread about? When does the Neolithic come to an end?

These questions are posed not to bewilder the reader, but to suggest some of the leads that remain to be explored by future investigators.

### SELECTED REFERENCES

Braidwood, Robert J., "The Near East and the Foundations for Civilization," *Condon Lectures,* Eugene, Oregon, 1952.
Childe, V. Gordon, *Man Makes Himself,* London, 1936, chap. 5.
——, *The Danube in Prehistory,* Oxford, 1929.
——,*What Happened in History,* Penguin, 1943.
Martin, Paul S., Quimby, George I., and Collier, Donald, *Indians Before Columbus,* Chicago, 1947, chap. 7.
Mason, Otis T., "Aboriginal American Basketry," *Annual Report for 1902, Smithsonian Institution,* Washington, 1904.
O'Neale, Lila M., "Archaeological Explorations in Peru: Textiles of Early Nazca Period," *Field Museum of Natural History, Anthropology Memoirs,* Vol. 2, no. 3, Chicago, 1937.
Weltfish, Gene, *The Origins of Art,* Indianapolis, 1953.

# CHAPTER 14

# Cultural Consequences of Metallurgy

## A. PRELUDE TO METALLURGY

For all its near approach to modern patterns of living the Neolithic failed to make the grade. If one central factor were to be singled out to account for the failure it would have to be ignorance of metallurgy. This is not the equivalent of ignorance of metal. A good number of Stone Age peoples used gold, silver, lead, and copper from time to time, but they dealt with them in their cold condition pretty much as though they were unusual varieties of stone. Not until man discovered that metals undergo marked changes when liquefied did he develop true metallurgy. Only then were previously unsuspected secrets unlocked for further exploration and exploitation.

The first metal to come under man's control in molten form was copper, and all signs point to the Eastern Mediterranean Zone as the place where the event occurred. A round figure of 4000 B.C. gives a good approximation of the time when the earliest Age of Metal began. There is marked disagreement among scholars as to whether copper was used in anything like a pure form long enough to warrant recognition of a **Copper Age.** Most archeologists believe that copper so rarely occurs without admixture of other metals or minerals that metallurgists from the start were accustomed to using adulterated copper. Whether by accident or design it was not long before it was found that a combination of copper and tin made **bronze,** a more satisfactory substance because it is harder and melts at a lower temperature. Thereafter, bronze rapidly replaced pure copper as an important resource for manufacturing. By way of compromise we shall call the first Age of Metal Copper-Bronze. It lasted from about 4000 B.C. to about 1500 B.C. when some metallurgists, again in the Eastern Mediterranean Zone, found out that iron, soon compounded to **steel,** had many advantages over bronze. Thereupon was inaugurated an **Iron Age** that endured from around 1500 B.C. to the start of the Christian era. After the latter date it is no longer necessary to study the march of culture only by means of archeology, since written documents become abundantly available. Archeologists can and do contribute much to an understanding of later developments, but in dealing with historic events their functions are greatly modified.

Before taking up the details of life in the Metal Ages it is necessary to repeat that human culture is additive and grows by the accretion of knowledge. Those societies that were among the earliest to learn the arts of metallurgy did not discard the many contributions of the Stone Ages. The new stages of culture grew out of the preceding ones but did not break with them. Cold materials of long familiarity, such as wood, stone, bone, ivory, and horn, continued to be important; hunting, fowling, fishing, and food collection, remained significant; pottery-making, basketry, and the weaving of cloth became increasingly widespread; and farming and stock breeding still formed the essence of the economy. Progress was made partly by the improvement of older devices like the wheel, partly by the expansion of activities like crop raising, and partly by the introduction of entirely new practices.

As we trace the march of culture in the Metal Ages we are again making a synthesis of high water marks. No single society encompassed within itself all the innovations and improvements of the new era. Only a few groups in restricted portions of the Old World took the forward strides, and the bulk of mankind remained at Neolithic, Mesolithic, or Paleolithic levels. This is much like saying that only a few contemporary nations are learning to deal with atomic energy, or like making the simple observation that in any of our cities it may be possible to see moving about at the same time pedestrians, bicycles, automobiles, and airplanes.

As was true in earlier stages the attainment of different forms of material culture and the establishment of a new technology did not make up the sum total of Metal Age accomplishments. Far-reaching

changes accompanied the introduction of metallurgy in the less obvious fields of social and religious organization. In combination all the
fresh ideas and customs paved the way for our present scheme of life,
which is firmly grounded on Metal Age antecedents.

## B. GOING THE NEOLITHIC ONE BETTER

Among the major Neolithic discoveries was the concept of the
wheel. Yet, this concept received little practical application until the
start of the Copper-Bronze Age. Among other uses the wheel was
then applied to the manufacture of pottery. A lump of prepared clay
would be thrown on the center of a revolving disc, and as it spun
the potter manipulated it until it took the shape he had in mind.
Not only did the new method greatly speed up the operation of pot
formation, but the action of the wheel resulted in a vessel of far
greater symmetry than could be achieved free hand. By the same
means a greater perfection of design was made possible. To produce
a perfectly even, circular line that runs clear around a piece of pottery, is next to impossible if the vessel must be turned by hand a
little at a time. But one need only hold a stylus, comb, or brush
steadily in place while a potter's wheel makes a complete revolution
in order to achieve a perfect circle.

There is also an important sociological correlate of wheel-made
pottery that has no bearing on sheer mechanics or technology.
Throughout the world the manufacture of hand-made pottery is the
task of women, but wherever the wheel is used pottery becomes,
almost without exception, a masculine occupation. The reason for
this state of affairs is not known, but it is certainly not due to any
biological difference between the sexes.

An even more significant application of wheels was developed in
conjunction with vehicles. Ponderous two- and four-wheeled carts
are known to have been in use before 3000 B.C. Judged by clay
models discovered in the ruins of Tepe Gawra, Syria, the wheels
appear to have been made of several heavy wooden sections, fastened
with copper nails and held together with a rim of leather. The whole
contrivance turned with the axle to which it was secured. Only
gradually, after the Metal Ages were well under way, were light but
strong wheels made with spokes and rims of metal. Even so, wide-

spread use of wheeled vehicles could not come about until strong animals had been trained to pull them.

That domesticated beasts had been employed to share some of man's labors in the Neolithic is a safe assumption. Nevertheless, no draught animals could have been put to work before the invention of suitable means of harnessing, and few signs of such a discovery appear prior to the Metal Ages. Oxen were certainly among the first creatures set to the pulling of carts or wagons, but they must have proved too slow for many purposes. Asiatic asses and horses were found better suited and were commonly utilized from 2000 B.C. on. Horses do not seem to have been domesticated until the latter half of the Neolithic at best, and they remained unimportant until the Copper-Bronze Age. Horseback-riding as a regular custom came late and may have followed driving by as much as a millenium.

Use of strong animals for pulling was not invariably restricted to vehicles. Comparable utilization of their motive power had already taken place as early as 3000 B.C. when plowing became widespread in the Eastern Mediterranean Zone. Again it had been necessary for suitable accessories to be first devised. Yokes were originally adapted to oxen, and later to horses. Plows of wood must have preceded metal ones, but no specimens of premetallic plows have survived. As the custom of plowing made headway another interesting sociological transfer took place. When small fields are worked with a hoe the task falls to women in practically all primitive societies, but when large farms have to be plowed it becomes a masculine duty. In this case the greater biological strength of men may be a factor.

These are only a few of the ways in which the people of the Copper-Bronze Age expanded notions that had originated in the Neolithic. The examples also show how closely one invention may be interlocked with others and how frequently technological shifts affect social organization. Further improvements and additions were made in every sphere of human existence. In agriculture so many items were added to the crops under cultivation that just about all the plants grown in the Old World before the discovery of America were being raised by Copper-Bronze Age farmers. There was also a new use made of grains, fruits, and cereals, in the form of fermented beverages. It is perfectly possible that barley beer was known in the New Stone Age, but not before the Copper-Bronze period does proof exist that the drinking of beer and date and grape wines had become a fixed custom.

## C. THE MYSTERY AND MASTERY OF METALLURGY

Above and beyond their elaboration of Neolithic concepts the Copper-Bronze Age folk opened new cultural outlets by learning to exploit a previously undeveloped natural resource. Let us begin with some of the advantages gained from man's mastery of molten copper, the first metallic substance to come under his full control. When copper is heated to the melting point it can be poured into a container, and upon cooling it becomes a solid in the shape of the container. The most exciting aspect of this simple fact is that the process is reversible, so that the same chunk of copper can repeatedly be made to go from solid to liquid to solid. Practically speaking, this means that man found out that he could rapidly and economically change the shape of a copper object without wasting any of the precious raw material. Once the basic principle had been grasped it became no trick at all to convert something in the shape of an X to Y or Z to A. This could not be done with wood, stone, bone, ivory, or horn.

Knowledge of this basic physico-chemical reaction soon gave rise to the technique of **casting** or **molding**, whereby a receptacle is first prepared in the desired shape and size from stone, pottery, or some other heat-resistant material. After that a sufficient quantity of molten copper is poured into the mold and allowed to cool and harden. If proper advance precautions have been taken to prevent sticking, it is then an easy matter to turn the solid product out of the mold and to give it such minor finishing touches as may be needed. Usually, no more is required than a bit of hammering or rubbing.

Casting made possible the first steps leading to mass production, for a well-made mold can be used repeatedly and a number of molds can be filled and their contents allowed to harden almost simultaneously (Fig. 85). There is, furthermore, a basic distinction between the skill and intelligence needed to design and prepare molds and what is necessary for filling and emptying them. Thus do we get a glimpse of an embryonic system that was destined to culminate in the modern distinction between skilled technicians who design machines and laborers who work on assembly lines.

Another method of handling molten metal was developed by 3000 B.C., although it was probably not known as early as simple casting.

Fig. 85. Molds used for casting Bronze Age tools. Four saw-blades at a time could be cast in the form at the left, thus making possible mass production.

This is the ingenious **lost-wax** or **cireperdue** process. A wax model must first be made, correct in all the particulars wanted for the final product. Then the wax model is carefully covered with clay in which an entrance hole and outlet are provided. Next, the whole thing is subjected to firing, whereupon the wax melts and runs out and the clay hardens to pottery. After that, the outlet is closed and liquid metal is poured into the space vacated by the wax. As soon as cooling has occurred the baked clay is broken open and the metallic object comes forth as an exact duplicate of the original wax model. Although the ciréperdue technique is much more complicated than casting, it is better for making rounded objects or things that would otherwise have to be made in two parts and fitted together.

Awareness of the reversible nature of liquid and solid copper also makes possible a great saving of raw material. Cold objects can be fashioned only by striking, cutting, pressing or rubbing bits from a larger unit, and whatever comes off is usually wasted. Not so with metals like copper or bronze. Any bits or scraps left over from manufacturing something can be melted together and used afresh. There need be no wastage of chips, flakes, or shavings, no matter how small each particular fragment may be.

Another great advantage of copper is that it is malleable and can be pounded into sheets. True enough, certain kinds of bark can be similarly treated, but sheets of bark are woefully fragile when compared to sheets of metal. Again, copper heated short of its melting point can be forced through the hole of a die and drawn into wire. Strings and ropes of wool or vegetal fibres were undoubtedly used in earlier days, but wire is infinitely superior in strength and durability.

For another thing copper can be coiled into springs that may be held taut or released at will. Only very rarely can spring coils be made with any of the common cold materials. Also, metal can be made with narrower and sharper points without danger of breaking, as in the case of pins and needles. It was necessary to combine the qualities of coiling and sharp pointing before the first safety pin, known archeologically as a **fibula,** could come into being. Once the trick was learned man went in for an amazing degree of elaboration. Fibulae were made in great numbers and in all sorts of sizes and shapes (Fig. 86). Quantities of brooches and clasps were manufactured on similar principles.

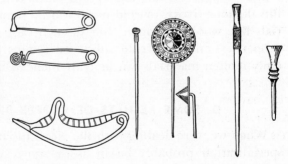

Fig. 86. Pins and safety pins or fibulae. These forms appeared for the first time in the Bronze Age, but some of them continued in use to the Iron Age and beyond.

Among the early uses to which metal was put was the production of weapons and agricultural implements that call for sharp yet sturdy and durable cutting edges. The superiority of metallic blades for such purposes was promptly grasped and copper celts, knives, daggers, swords, scythes and sickles were produced in abundance. Methods of hafting remained to be worked out. An interesting series of metal celts can be arranged to illustrate various solutions to the problem (Fig. 87A). Early celts are flat and very much like those of polished stone. These were presumably wedged into the cleft of a handle, and may have been secondarily tied in place. Others have raised sides that form a constricted channel into which a shaft can be tightly forced. Still others combine this feature with a horizontal bar or stop-ridge, designed to keep a handle from slipping too far down. Most elaborate of all are **palstaves,** in which the sides rise and meet each other to form a hollow socket. Some palstaves even have a ring added at the side to make doubly sure of a tight haft by wedging and tieing.

Despite the wide range of new possibilities that the qualities of liquefied copper put at man's disposal, its softness made the continued use of pure copper impractical. That is why it was soon displaced by a combination of copper and tin. This step was based on yet another advantage of metallurgy, because by melting together two or more metals a blend or **alloy** can be made that has different qualities from any of the contributing materials. Bronze, the first alloy to come into wide use, added hardness and toughness to copper without detracting from its attractive properties. Very early specimens reveal great uncertainty as to the best proportions of tin to copper; but later a formula of about 10 to 15 per cent of tin and 85 to 90 per cent of copper became almost universal. One must not forget that bits of stone, ivory, or cold metal can be pounded into softer materials like wood or leather, but in such cases there is no fusion of properties, and each cold substance retains its distinctive nature. Only molten materials can be truly blended into alloys.

## D. SOME RESULTS OF COPPER-BRONZE USE

When we were dealing with the Neolithic it was pointed out that specialization probably began as the range of arts and crafts increased. During the succeeding Copper-Bronze Age there is no longer any uncertainty about the growth of specialists. Among other things it was not long before whatever sources of free metallic copper may have existed on or near the earth's surface were exhausted. It then became necessary to mine copper ore. To do this called for prospectors trained to recognize hidden cuprous deposits, miners to extract

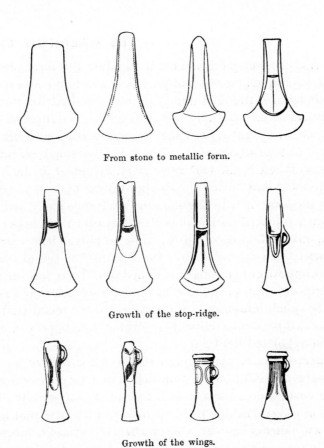

From stone to metallic form.

Growth of the stop-ridge.

Growth of the wings.

A

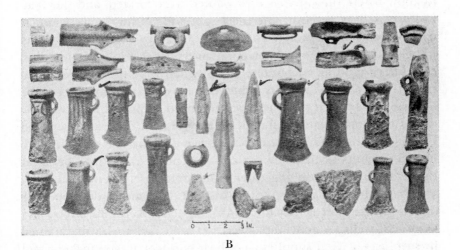

B

Fig. 87. Stages of celt development. The forms run from flat shapes to ringed palstaves. A. The stages in logical order. B. Actual Bronze Age specimens.

the ore, and smelters and refiners to separate the pure metal from its associated impurities. Even after these operations it was no trifling matter to acquire the skill and equipment needed for metallurgy. No individual could possibly carry out all the activities by himself, and anyone who wanted to make or acquire copper things had no choice but to depend on others. That is how personal self-sufficiency, which was highest in the Old Stone Ages, dwindled in the Neolithic and came to an end during the Copper-Bronze era.

Much the same is true of community self-sufficiency, particularly after bronze replaced pure copper. It so happens that copper and tin deposits very seldom occur in the same locality. Hence, practically every society that advanced into the Bronze Age found itself compelled to import either copper, tin, or both. Thus was initiated an export-import business, and thus did community self-sufficiency reach a close. So much importance was attached to the metal trade that it always tended to become either a government monopoly or a private enterprise regulated by the state.

In order to secure the supplies required for bronze work many things were necessary, chief of which was a surplus of something valuable that could be exchanged for tin or copper. By 3000 B.C. methods of mixed farming had improved to such an extent that well-favored settlements had the wherewithal to engage in long-distance trade. There then arose a new impetus to knowledge. Importers had to know where the supplies they wanted were located, and they had to learn ways of reaching the exact spot and getting home again. If trips were to be overland an elementary knowledge of geography was essential. One had to know what rivers, lakes, forests, mountains, or deserts would be encountered, and which were the best routes to take. If travel was to be by water the art of navigation had to be understood. In each case there was the need of providing a suitable means of transportation, animal-drawn vehicles or boats propelled by oars or sails. It is no mere coincidence that the rise of such intellectual pursuits as map-making and astronomy came into being at the very time when the ingredients for bronze were being sought.

But intellectuals are also specialists and they cannot develop their skills to the utmost if they must work regularly to produce food and other essentials. Among the specialists who had to be maintained by surpluses of vital supplies were boat-builders, wagon-makers, and drivers or travelers who regularly made long-distance journeys.

Still other important consequences resulted from the establishment of export-import trade. No one would risk sending a load of valuable goods for the purchase of expensive raw materials unless his investments were protected. In minimum terms this meant that voyagers conveying costly cargoes had to have armed guards. Here begins the tie-up between business and the military which is still of such great concern today.

Before many decades had elapsed it was found to be inefficient to send heavy loads back and forth to complete a single transaction. Instead of relying on elementary barter, systems resembling coinage were devised, by means of which a great deal of value could be encompassed in a small item. Bars of silver were first used for this purpose. Their worth depended on weight and there was much worry over sharp practices of adulteration and short-weighting. Later, when small coins replaced clumsy bars of precious metal, traders accepted them only if they were confident of the stability of the governments that issued them. From the beginning coinage was recognized to be a public rather than a private function, and that is one of the ways in which economics and politics became linked.

As commerce continued to expand there was a strongly felt need for systems of weights and measures. Every dealer had to know how large a return he could expect for a given amount of goods. The principle of so much of this for so much of that, which underlies all trade, cannot operate without standardized units of values, weights, and measures. And standardization along these lines cannot develop without mathematics. This was not the only practical application of mathematics in the early Metal Ages. Measures of distance were essential to geography, and the arts of astronomy and navigation also have mathematical foundations.

With the rise of big business came a further need for precise notation. Records of all sorts had to be accurately kept to prevent chaos, and neither maps nor charts could be prepared without a means of writing. Ownership and identifying marks were indicated by impressions made with **seals.** Some were flat, some cylindrical, and both sorts were pictorial and carved out of hard material. Seals, like signet rings, had only restricted meanings pertaining to the person of the user, and could not express all the details of a transaction. For the rest it was necessary to have true writing, based on a **phonetic alphabet.** A phonetic alphabet implies that certain graphic symbols stand for particular sounds, thus making it possible to put into writing whatever meaningful sounds a given spoken language utilizes. In Mesopotamia, with perhaps a parallel development in Egypt, true writing is found prior to 3000 B.C. The earliest Mesopotamian records were made by cutting wedge-shaped characters into soft clay tablets (Fig. 88). Because of the wedge-shaped characters this writing

Fig. 88. Model of a Mesopotamian clay tablet (after Chiera). A sharp-pointed stylus is thought to have been used for incising the cuneiform writing at the top. The scene below was made by pressing a seal into the soft clay of the tablet before it was baked.

is called **cuneiform.** When the clay tablets were baked the cuneiform inscriptions became permanently fixed. Thousands of complete or fragmentary tablets containing cuneiform writing have been dug up by archeologists from ancient settlements in Western Asia, and there are specialists who can read many of the antique scripts. Their translations reveal that an overwhelming proportion of the earliest written documents dealt with business, and far smaller percentages were concerned with politics and religion.

One of the fascinating aspects of archeology is to observe how a number of apparently unrelated traits may be combined to help form a new device. An extraordinary instance of the process is to be found in the formation of a **calendar.** Whether based on movements of the sun, moon, stars, or the planet Venus, all calendars depend on some knowledge of astronomy coupled with mathematics. To keep accurate track of the passage of time, based on measurable activities of heavenly bodies, it is necessary to be able to write. So, in a sense, the calendar may be regarded as a combination of astronomy, mathematics, and writing. Its earliest uses, too, were composite, ranging from religious interest in the heavens to the commercial importance of knowing the length of time involved in completing a business transaction.

Learning to write and read was a long and laborious process which ordinary folk did not try to master. To serve them there arose a specialized group of **scribes,** who exchanged their skill for the necessities of life. Scribes worked for illiterate individuals, as well as for the state and its rulers, temples and their administrators, and business men. For the latter they drew up agreements which were signed with the seals of contracting parties in the presence of witnesses. Contracts were binding and there were courts of law to see that their terms were carried out. The equivalents of our phrases, "Put it in writing," and "I'll sue you," were everyday features of Mesopotamian Copper-Bronze Age life.

A few additional comments may help to bring about a fuller appreciation of the significance of writing. Its introduction speeds up the building of culture because it helps to prevent loss of ideas and so contributes to the formation of an ever growing stockpile of human knowledge. What is put down in writing acquires permanence and stands an excellent chance of being more accurately preserved than can be done by word of mouth. Whatever is written can easily outlast the lifetime of the author; with the help of translation and copying it can be spread throughout the world; and when signed with an official seal it has greater authenticity than a verbal message. For the student of culture growth, too, the development of writing is of the utmost importance. With the help of written statements one can learn the full range of ideas, values, symbol systems, and abstract concepts that once prevailed in an extinct society. Archeologists working in historic periods are no longer confronted with the need of trying painfully to deduce these intangibles from material remains, and the record of the past emerges in greater detail and clarity than ever.

Even so brief a synopsis as has been given in this chapter serves to bring out the complexities of Copper-Bronze Age life. Mention has been made, no matter how scantily, of miners, prospectors, smelters, metallurgists, traders, travelers, drivers, sailors, geographers, astronomers, mathematicians, soldiers, scribes, lawyers, rulers, and priests; to say nothing of agriculturalists, stock breeders, potters, weavers, and small merchants. No one of the specialists could have been a full-time farmer, and no full-time farmer could have doubled as a true specialist. Social distinctions based on wealth and occupation, as well as on sex and age, are everywhere in evidence, and differences between rural and urban folk come into prominence. Everyone who lived in a Copper-Bronze sort of community was directly and deeply affected by the new technology and its consequences, but metal was so scarce and expensive that only a fraction of the populace regularly used things of copper and bronze; others had an occasional metallic object or two; and the average person's material culture continued to be no more than Neolithic.

## Selected References

Breasted, James H., *The Conquest of Civilization,* New York and London, chaps. 1-5.

Chiera, Edward, *They Wrote on Clay,* Chicago, 1938.

Childe, V. Gordon, *Man Makes Himself,* London, 1936, chaps. 6 and 7.

Cline, Walter, "Mining and Metallurgy in Negro Africa," *General Series in Anthropology,* No. 5, Menasha, 1937.

Delaporte, Louis J., *Mesopotamia,* London and New York, 1925.

Kroeber, Alfred L., *Anthropology,* rev. ed., New York, 1948, chaps. 12, 13, and 17.

# CHAPTER 15

# Metal Age Cultures of the Old World

## A. COPPER-BRONZE CULTURE IN WESTERN ASIA

A sage who was conversant with the entire world as it was known in the fourth and third millenia B.C. (4000-2000 B.C.) would have been sure of the fact that the latest advances of culture were to be found in the neighborhoods of Mesopotamia, Egypt, and the Indus River valley of Northwestern India. By comparison with these centers the rest of Africa and Asia was certainly backward; Europe, any wise man of that time would have said, was too far behind ever to count for much; and as for the Americas—what were they? Anyone nowadays who is disturbed by the lack of progress in the undeveloped regions of the world should find solace in the errors of past judgments. Inasmuch as the Western world got its start toward dominance in the Copper-Bronze Age by diffusion from the Eastern Mediterranean Zone, especially from Mesopotamia, we shall present an account of that area before touching lightly on its neighbors.

At various places in Mesopotamia, not far from Mosul, archeologists have uncovered remains of what seems to have been an extensive Age of Copper (Chalcolithic). Above these materials are objects showing a transition to the use of bronze. The excavations indicate that the full Copper-Bronze way of life in Iraq began in the north, probably above Bagdad. In those days Southern Mesopotamia was too wet and swampy for human habitation, but shortly after 3500 B.C. some of the waters receded and in due time the region came to be known as **Sumer** and was settled by people called **Sumerians.** Everything about

257

their origin is obscure, but the fortunate circumstance that they wrote on clay, coupled with the diligence of archeologists and other scholars, has led to the decipherment of their language and a detailed knowledge of how they lived.

Before long Sumer was divided into city-states, including Biblical Ur, Nippur, Lagash, and others. Each had its own territory, whose boundaries were jealously guarded and sometimes fought over in large-scale wars by soldiers armed with metal weapons. Every city-state had its own ruler and local deity. The rulers were intimately associated with their respective municipal gods, and in some cases came to be identified with them. Many later notions of the divine right of kings can be traced back to Sumerian concepts. Theoretically, the deity owned all the land within his city and the ruler and lesser officials were supposed to administer it on his behalf. Each god dwelt within an elaborate temple in whose name a great deal of business was transacted. Not until Christ drove the money-changers out of the temple was it considered wrong to mix religion and profits.

Sumerian scribes also had temple connections. They wrote and kept accounts in cuneiform which evolved afterward into the Phoenician script from which our own alphabet was ultimately derived. Similarly, they kept track of weights and measures in a way that provides a basis for some of our methods of reckoning. Sumerians used a sexagesimal system, based on units of 60, a number which can be evenly divided by 1, itself, and 2, 3, 4, 5, 6, 10, 12, 15, 20, and 30. Whenever we tell time by seconds, minutes, and hours; sentence offenders to 30, 60, or 90 days; or navigate with a compass marked into 360 degrees; we are unconsciously borrowing from the ancient Sumerians who long ago disappeared from history.

It was the same Sumerians who first applied precise mathematical calculations to astronomy. They identified and named most of the planets, worked out their movements, tried to predict eclipses, and hitched navigation to the stars. In each of these spheres we have built modern science on a Sumerian groundwork. Of course they made serious errors when judged by present standards, and there is no denying that much of their information was applied to the discredited pursuits of fortune-telling and astrology, but there is also a lasting quality to many of their accomplishments.

Without question the Sumerian achievements in material culture are most impressive. They made tremendous forward strides in farming techniques, animal domestication, pottery manufacture, weaving, metallurgy, and architecture. Wood and stone have always been scarce in Southern Mesopotamia, but for erecting buildings they used mud and clay skillfully, packing it into wooden forms to make sun-dried brick, and baking it in kilns to produce true, waterproof bricks. It is the Sumerian use of temper that gave rise to the Biblical admonition that brick cannot be made without straw. In Mesopotamia, too, it is believed, was invented the principle of the arch, whereby a curved, self-supporting structure can be constructed. As is to be expected the finest buildings were temples, homes of rulers, and public monuments often situated atop massive artificial mounds of earth. Architects prepared blueprints for the erection of great buildings, some of which were several stories high. Commoners had to be content with living on the flats in small, squarish huts of reeds, thatch, and mud. There is proof of town planning, and public drains for which professional builders were held responsible were in use in the cities.

While the Sumerians were the pioneers of advanced culture in Southern Mesopotamia, they were not the sole inhabitants of the area. Shortly after 3000 B.C. **Semitic** names begin to show up frequently in the records, although prior to that date the Semites were found chiefly in the north.[1] Around 2300 B.C. a Semitic ruler named **Sargon** overran and united all of Mesopotamia. The invaders absorbed the elements of Sumerian culture and their priests even learned the rival tongue for use in their own rituals. Surviving bilingual texts that were used in sacerdotal schools show that this is an early example of religious conservatism, whereby one language is used in daily life and a more ancient one is retained for worship.

Sargon's empire did not long endure following his death and for several centuries no one power dominated the whole of Mesopotamia. Then, about 1700 B.C., **Hammurabi** rose to prominence and again put the Semites in control. He is rightly famous on several counts. When he made his capital at Babylon he had its city god, **Marduk,** elevated to the highest theological position in the country, thus putting Marduk before all other gods and instituting a Semitic trend to monotheism. He also ordered a compilation and codification of existing laws in the area. When completed, the results were known

[1] Anthropologists identify Semites by language only and not by race or religion. Both Arabs and Hebrews speak Semitic tongues and are Semites.

as the **Code of Hammurabi,** which tradition says was handed to him by the sun-god, **Shamash.** This code contains almost all of the precepts later set forth in the Ten Commandments, and also establishes such principles as "an eye for an eye, and a tooth for a tooth." Hammurabi likewise is credited with having set up legal procedures which are, in several respects, ancestral to our own. Witnesses were sworn, perjury was punished, judicial decisions were enforced, and appeals could be made from lower to higher courts.

Within the span of the Copper-Bronze Age in Mesopotamia there developed a cult centered around heavenly deities, whose worship was universal rather than local. A very popular pair consisted of **Ishtar,** the planet Venus, and her husband-lover, **Tammuz,** god of vegetation. Annually, Tammuz went to the underground world of the dead, from which he was restored to life the next spring through the efforts of Ishtar. Their story became the source of the Greek tales of Venus and Adonis and, in the opinion of sober scholars, the cult of Tammuz played a direct part in the origins of Christianity.

## B. THE COPPER-BRONZE AGE IN EGYPT

Egypt's Copper-Bronze culture presumably evolved at the same time and along the same general lines as Mesopotamia's, but there are fewer facts available to explain the steps by which Egypt advanced from the Neolithic, and in later years Egypt became more isolated from world events. The two countries were surely in touch with one another in Copper-Bronze days and ideas diffused back and forth. Even so, they continued unlike in countless respects. Egyptian rulers were more directly deified and Egyptian writing differed in being **hieroglyphic.** This means that it consisted of rows of pictorial symbols that stood for objects, ideas, or sounds. From the beginning Egypt also had a system of cursive writing, which used lines that were joined into a connected script. It was inscribed with ink on wood, papyrus, or pottery. In its more formal aspect the cursive writing was called **hieratic** and was used by priests, whereas in its lay form it was known as **demotic.** Like the Sumerian, Egyptian writing came to have all the elements of a phonetic alphabet, but the two systems used completely different sounds and signs and Egyptian was not taken over by any of the European languages.

Again like Mesopotamia, Egypt accumulated a vast body of astronomical lore and an associated store of mathematical knowledge. Although the Egyptians developed a decimal system of reckoning they did not advance as far into higher mathematics. Egypt, however, formulated a 365-day solar calendar which, it is pretty well agreed, is the direct forerunner of ours.

Specialists and craftsmen closely parallel to those of Mesopotamia arose in Egypt, but the things they produced are quite distinctive. In addition Egyptian artisans originated the manufacture of glass and the faïence method of decoration. There was a good deal of foreign trade with the same consequences as in Iraq; and similar social divisions are to be found between poor and rich, urban and rural dwellers, specialized workmen and farmers, rulers and subjects, and priests and laymen.

One outstanding difference is the Egyptian emphasis on the cult of the dead. As early as 3000 B.C. all of Egypt was united under a ruler named **Menes.** Some of his family's tombs have been excavated and their contents are extraordinarily rich. From the time of Menes, efforts were made to preserve the physical remains of royal personages at least, and to the same complex of beliefs belong the customs of mummification, pyramid building, and obelisk construction. As the wealth and power of the rulers grew their funeral monuments increased in grandeur until a climax was reached in the **Great Pyramid of Cheops,** dated around 2600 B.C., which measures 755 feet on a side and towers to a height of 481 feet.

## C. HARAPPA CULTURE IN INDIA

Less than thirty-five years ago, scholars knew of no Copper-Bronze Age culture that was either as old or as brilliant as those of the Eastern Mediterranean Zone. Beginning in 1922 a series of excavations was started in Northwestern India that brought forth astounding evidence of a mature Copper-Bronze culture, which may have existed as early as about 3000 B.C. Its remnants were found in or near the valley of the Indus River and are particularly impressive at the sites called **Mohenjo-Daro** and **Harappa,** in the district of Sind (Fig. 89). From the latter the remains are often referred to as the **Harappa Culture.** The two great centers give proof of a highly urbanized way of life that lasted for considerably more than a thousand years. Each city was successively rebuilt a number of times, yet their building arrangements, methods of construction, and artifacts show remarkable uniformity throughout all the centuries of their occupation.

Both cities contain structures of truly baked brick laid out along regular streets, through which ran covered drains for carrying away household refuse. Some of the homes had rooms for bathing and had water flowing into them. The residents practiced in their own distinctive way, all of the essential industries and arts known in the Copper-Bronze Age anywhere. They traded with Mesopotamia, but were neither culturally nor politically dominated by Western Asia. Indeed, they were so completely independent that their pictographic form of writing still remains their very own, for the simple reason that it has never been deciphered. About 400 characters, superficially reminiscent of Egyptian hieroglyphs, have been identified, but what they mean is an unsolved mystery.

To provide the city folk with food there must have been a large supplementary population of farmers. Barley was the principal cereal and was eaten solid or drunk as beer; wheat was raised, stored, and milled to flour for making bread; and cotton was cultivated and woven into cloth. Humped cattle were under domestication, and so also were humpless cattle, water buffaloes, sheep, goats, pigs, dogs, horses, and asses. Less certainly domesticated, but probably under human control, were the elephant and camel. Besides what was locally available Harappa Culture abounds in materials that could have been procured only through a well-organized export-import trade.

There is a curious lack of recognizable cemeteries or religious structures at Mohenjo-Daro and Harappa and it was formerly thought that there were no extensive fortifications, but later excavations indicate that some of the buildings may have been citadels. One architectural feature at Mohenjo-Daro has attracted much notice. It is a large bath or swimming pool, about 40 feet by 24 feet, with a well-paved floor of brick, and a decided slope toward a drain in one corner (Fig. 89). That it was built to hold water may be taken for granted, but the purpose that it was meant to serve is a matter for conjecture.

Prior to the exciting discovery of Harappa Culture the start of anything in India resembling modern life used to be dated at 1500 B.C. and attributed to a migration of Indo-European speakers

(Aryans).[2] Now it is known that there had been a brilliant Copper-Bronze culture in the Indus valley centuries earlier than the time of the Aryan invasion. The question then turns to the unexplained extinction of Harappa Culture. Some archeologists believe that it

Fig. 89. Remains of Harappa culture at Mohenjo-Daro. Ruins of the Great Bath are in the center foreground.

faded out in pre-Aryan days from internal or local causes, but others argue that Harappa Culture was terminated by the invaders of Indo-European speech. The latter viewpoint does not seem to be entirely upheld by such evidence as is now on hand.

For one reason or another very little is known of the varieties of mankind that were responsible for the formation of the earliest Copper-Bronze cultures. About all that can be said without quibbling is that they were members of *Homo sapiens,* that the Caucasoid stock played a major part, and that the Mediterranean race was strongly represented. The Negroid stock probably played a contributory role, but the presence of Mongoloids is not attested, with the possible exception of the first Chinese Metal Age. China's Copper-Bronze phase can be dated from the Shang dynasty (about 1500-1100 B.C.), and many wonderful remains have been found at the Shang capital of **Anyang.** There is abundant evidence of a mature

2 As in the case of Semitic, anthropologists regard "Aryan" as purely a linguistic term. There is no such thing as an "Aryan race," for many varieties of mankind speak Aryan tongues. See p. 130.

Copper-Bronze culture at Anyang, but its late date sets it apart from the events we are tracing, and its connections with the Eastern Mediterranean Zone are entirely obscure.

## D. COPPER-BRONZE CULTURE REACHES EUROPE

One of the incidental results of the Copper-Bronze Age was a remarkable increase of the human population. As people spread out from the more crowded centers of the Eastern Mediterranean Zone it was inevitable that some of them should go in the direction of Europe. Settlers went early to Crete and Cyprus, moved on to other islands in the Aegean Sea, and came at last to the peninsula of Greece. Influences from the populous areas were also spread by colonists or other migrants to Asia Minor, including the city of Hissarlik, site of Homer's Troy. When it was found that sources of copper and tin were located in Hungary, Bohemia, Cornwall, and Ireland, commercial relations with those regions were begun. Prior to 2000 B.C. the Copper-Bronze Age had begun to reach Central Europe, and slowly it grew and spread to other parts of the continent along the Mediterranean Sea or by way of the Danubian corridor.

Between 1800 and 1400 B.C. Greece received specialized craftsmen from the island of Crete, as well as from places in Asia Minor. The city of **Mycenae** was one of the very first Greek communities to gain renown in those days, and its success was due to the absorption of Cretan and Eastern Mediterranean Zone influences. By 1400 B.C. Mycenae was in a position to reverse the trend and to dominate Crete and send its own exports to Troy, other communities in Asia Minor, the Eastern Mediterranean Zone, and even Italy, Sicily, and the British Isles. Improved methods of land and sea transport helped to speed up communications and trade, and Mycenaean ships are known to have reached a length of 100 feet, capable of carrying about 150 people.

Yet Mycenae itself never attained the splendor of the great Copper-Bronze cities of Africa and Asia. It was highly militaristic and was enclosed by ramparts of huge stones, to the style of which the name **Cyclopean masonry** has been given. Only a small area was enclosed, within which the bodies of great personages were placed in domed structures known as **beehive tombs,** whereas commoners were buried in cemeteries outside the Cyclopean walls. Implements of war predominate among the ruins of Mycenae and much importance was attributed to long rapiers of bronze. Light war chariots drawn by trained horses were greatly prized by the wealthy and powerful, and ordinary soldiers fought on foot with inferior weapons as befitted vassals of their overlords. A great deal of the archeological material corresponds to descriptions found in Homer's epic of the Trojan War and his works are judged to provide a trustworthy reflection of the life of those days.

Mycenae represents the first emergence of Greece or any other European area as a world leader. However, it was doomed to collapse when raided by formerly backward people who ultimately acquired a knowledge of metallurgy and its correlated arts and crafts. By the time that Greek culture was to rise to the great heights of its classical period in art, architecture, literature, and philosophy, a thousand years were to elapse and the new attainments would have little connection with the earlier Mycenaean age.

## E. IRON MAKES ITS ENTRANCE

Somewhere around 1500 B.C. people living in the vicinity of present-day Armenia discovered how to manufacture things of iron. They did all they could to keep their knowledge hidden from others, but they used the new metal for weapons and as their armies made conquests the secret was automatically disclosed. Among the first to exploit the advantages of iron were the **Hittites,** followed soon after by the **Assyrians.** Both the Hittites and the Assyrians found the great and wealthy Copper-Bronze centers of the Eastern Mediterranean Zone extremely tempting targets for attack, and were soon coming down on them "like a wolf on the fold." The successes of the Iron Age invaders were due not only to their fighting ability and superior arms, but also to the internal collapse of the older societies. Assuredly, the Copper-Bronze Age communities carried within their own social systems the seeds of destruction. Throughout their existence objects of bronze remained out of reach of the general populace and wealth tended to become concentrated in the hands of a few. Such was the case, too, with all the associated advances of knowledge and industry. Commoners worked hard, paid heavy taxes and supported the state in many ways, but got pitifully little in return. By and by rulers came to rely not on masses of loyal citizens but on

slaves and mercenaries. No wonder they could not offer strong resistance to invasion and attack.

Within a few centuries after 1500 B.C. every one of the great Copper-Bronze centers in Mesopotamia, Egypt, and India, had collapsed;
and even in far-off China the Shang dynasty was soon to be over-
thrown by the Chou. A kind of Dark Ages followed, but the accomplishments of the early Metal Ages remained to form a platform on
top of which the Iron Age was built. At first the period of transition
gives the impression of moving backward, but in the long run it
appears that cultural progress was still being made as new and more
modern forms of group living emerged.

In strictly technological terms it was not easy for iron to displace
bronze. Above all, it was necessary for new metallurgical skills to be
acquired. Because of its internal composition iron does not readily
lend itself to casting, either in simple molds or by the lost-wax
method; and cast iron is too brittle to be practical. Not until methods of **forging** (repeated pounding while hot) and **tempering** (sudden
alternations of heat and cold) were figured out, could sturdy implements be made of wrought iron. Even so, forging and tempering remained free-hand techniques, requiring a strong operator who could
turn out only one object at a time. Other drawbacks were the
quantities of fuel needed and the tendency of pure iron to rust. On
the other side of the ledger, the new substance was far more abundant than copper, and even more so than tin. It could also be used
by itself, thus making it much cheaper than bronze. Moreover, iron
is tougher than bronze, and mixed with a small amount of inexpen-
sive carbon it becomes still harder as well as rust-resistant. Suffice
it to say that it was not long before the advantages were found to
outweigh the disadvantages, with the consequence that for the first
time iron made possible the everyday use of metallic implements.
Iron was indeed the poor man's metal. With the use of metallic
tools forests and timber could more easily be cut, plowing and culti-
vating practices could be improved, every soldier in an army could
be well-equipped, and cheap household instruments and ornaments
became available to almost everyone.

The late start of the Iron Age provided time for two Copper-
Bronze traits to mature to a point where they could achieve widespread distribution. Writing, thanks to simplification of the phonetic
alphabet, became less of a highly specialized craft. Universal literacy

was far from being attained but many ordinary folk learned to read a bit and to write their names, and small merchants began to find that they could keep their own accounts. Coinage, too, was brought to lower social levels than ever before. Coins of small denomination were minted, making it easier for people of little wealth to buy and sell, undertake to save for the distant future, pay taxes more conveniently than in kind, and so participate to some extent in the money economy of the total community. Without any formal planning the Copper-Bronze Age had turned into an era of aristocrats, and the Iron Age was to witness the rise of the common man.

## F. IRON AGE CULTURES OF CENTRAL EUROPE

The complexities of Iron Age archeology, supplemented as they are by a wealth of historical documentation, are exceedingly difficult to summarize. Instead of trying to treat the entire Old World, therefore, American anthropologists have fallen into the habit of singling out for examples two of the best-known sites in Central Europe. The older is called **Hallstatt,** and was discovered in Austria; and the more recent, **La Tène,** gets its name from a place in Switzerland. It may be assumed that the knowledge of working with iron reached some parts of Europe by 1000 B.C., but it did not become widespread on that continent for a couple of centuries. Hallstatt culture is customarily dated from 800-400 B.C., and La Tène runs from 400 B.C. to 1 A.D.

Most of the originally identified Hallstatt material was found in a huge cemetery that was excavated over a stretch of twenty years starting in 1847. The graveyard is located at the scene of an ancient salt-mining center, close to one of Europe's oldest iron-working areas and not far from a connection with the basin of the Danube River. Burials were about evenly divided between unburnt and cremated, and there are slight indications from the associated grave furnishings that upper class and wealthier folk were the ones who practiced cremation. Early Hallstatt represents a transitional stage of culture, for many objects of bronze as well as iron pertain to it. Despite a later increase of iron materials Hallstatt never in its active years showed such traits as great cities, elaborate architecture, wheel-made pottery, coins, or writing. It is an odd twist of fate that a folk whose graves have long endured should have left so few traces of their regular habitations. A place in France, which had a Hallstatt form of culture, provides evidence that the people lived in rectangular huts made of perishable materials and surrounded by earthen ramparts. Just the same, next to nothing would be known of the Hallstatt were it not for the objects left in cemeteries.

Several types of swords have been recovered. The earliest ones were long, heavy, and made of bronze. Then follow imitations in iron, and shorter swords with the pommel branching into two horns or **antennae.** Daggers were also common (Fig. 90), and there were

Fig. 90. Iron daggers from Hallstatt (after von Sacken and MacCurdy). Both daggers at the right have antennae handles. The third one from the left is made entirely of iron, but the one at the extreme right has a bronze handle. Hallstatt swords were of the same forms as the daggers.

many iron knives with blades that folded into a handle like a modern jackknife. A type of bucket, **situla,** made by riveting together sheets of bronze, occurs frequently, and there was a great variety of pottery, skillfully made by hand and often painted with black or red geometric figures on a yellowish slip. Enamelled bronze (bronze coated with a glassy surface) appears for the first time, and bronze bracelets with inlays of iron were in vogue. Fibulae of bronze or iron were stylish in the mature Hallstatt, and there was a limited use of amber, coral, gold, and glass. A few chariot burials belong to the later Hallstatt phase of culture, with the body of a presumed warrior laid under and between the wheels of his vehicle. The chariots were light, usually four-wheeled, and had their hubs and spokes covered with forged iron.

Attempts that are none too satisfactory have been made to subdivide Hallstatt into successive periods on the basis of variations in burial customs, sword and dagger types, and fibulae and pottery styles. The best division tentatively sets apart an early phase with big swords of bronze or iron and no fibulae, from a later stage featuring short, antennae-handled, iron swords, a fanciful variety of fibulae, and occasional chariot burials. In general terms representations of Hallstatt culture have been found scattered through a wide zone of Central Europe from Hungary to Spain, but the Iron Age did not reach Northern Europe and the British Islands until some centuries later.

The type station of La Tène, the second phase of Central Europe's Iron Age, is situated at the eastern end of Lake Neuchatel, Switzerland. Explorations began there in 1858 and were carried on sporadically for several decades. A period of four centuries, ending on the verge of the Christian era, is thought to span the years that La Tène was occupied. From the nature of the objects recovered Dr. Paul Vouga has been led to the conclusion that the place had been a military establishment, with important trading connections. His opinion was based on the exceptionally large number of iron swords found. The earlier ones resemble the short swords of later Hallstatt, and the more recent ones were made without antennae. Wherever La Tène remains have been discovered in Central or Western Europe, they always show a frequent occurrence of well-made iron swords, lances, javelins and spears. Shields and helmets were also common, and much stress was laid on what we would call military insignia.

Apart from weapons La Tène culture reveals a profusion of coins, originally issued in many places, fibulae of bronze, iron, and gold, and an abundance of bracelets, wheel-made painted pots, glass beads, and objects of enamelled bronze. Made of iron, too, were a large number of tools and utensils, including axes, knives, hammers, saws, and agricultural and fishing devices (Fig. 91). That there was an increase of accumulated wealth is indicated not only by the stocks of coins, but

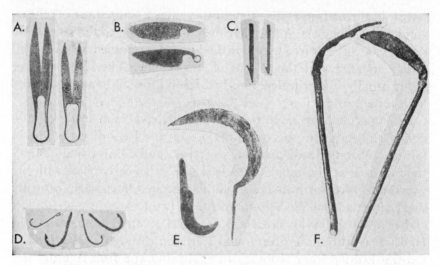

Fig. 91. Iron Age non-military tools (after MacCurdy, following Vouga). A. Scissors. B. Razors. C. Harpoon heads. D. Fish-hooks. E. Sickles. F. Scythes.

also by the first large-scale appearance of locks and keys. Shears and scissors are other objects that came into common use in the La Tène, and there is a wide range of tweezers, razors, ornaments, and trinkets. Burial in the ground was the rule throughout most of the period, but cremation appears before its close. Important men were interred with their chariots, and one famous grave of this sort also contained wine, several varieties of meat, iron spits, and a great carving knife (Fig. 92). Wine seems to have been imported from Italy or Greece, and historic records state that wily Greek traders were quick to realize that they could drive better bargains if they got their customers drunk.

During the 500 years prior to the Christian era the world's most important historical events continued to take place not in Central Europe but in Greece and the Eastern Mediterranean Zone. Darius, the Great, of Persia, had by 500 B.C. subjugated all of Western Asia and was looking for more worlds to conquer. Greece was the only European nation of the day that seemed worth bothering about, and in 491 B.C. Darius sent a huge fleet of six hundred ships against Athens. After unchallenged initial successes the Persians reached Marathon, where they were soundly beaten in 490 B.C. at the hands of a confederation led by Athenian Greeks.

It is beyond the scope of this volume to trace the rise of classical

Fig. 92. Chariot burial. This presumed warrior from the Iron Age was buried under a two-wheeled chariot, with food and implements. The small rectangle in the foreground contained the remains of horse trappings.

Greek culture that followed soon after Marathon. However, for the benefit of those who may look upon the archeologically established Iron Age as something distant and unconnected with modern times it may be well merely to list, with their dates, a small handful of the well-known historic figures who lived in late Hallstatt or La Tène times. Herodotus, father of modern history, died in 425 B.C.; Hippocrates, father of modern medicine, was born in 460 and died around 370; the great playwright, Sophocles, lived from 496 (?) to 406; Socrates' life ran from 469 to 399; the everlastingly famous Aristotle was born in 384 and died in 322 B.C.; the short but important lifetime of Alexander the Great fell between 356 and 323; Cicero lived and died between 106 and 43 B.C.; and Julius Caesar was born in 100 and died in 44 B.C. So did the Iron Age witness the shift of world leadership from the Eastern Mediterranean Zone to Europe, and thus did it bring mankind to the threshold of our era.

### SELECTED REFERENCES

British Museum, *A Guide to the Antiquities of the Bronze Age,* Oxford, 1904.
———, *A Guide to the Antiquities of the Early Iron Age,* Oxford, 1905.
Childe, V. Gordon, *The Bronze Age,* Cambridge, England, 1930.
———, *New Light on the Most Ancient East,* New York, 1934.
Hawkes, Charles F. C., *The Prehistoric Foundations of Europe to the Mycenean Age,* London, 1940.
Mackay, Ernest J. H., *The Indus Civilization,* London, 1935.
Wooley, Sir Charles L., *The Sumerians,* Oxford, 1929.

# CHAPTER 16

# Man and Culture in the New World: Part I

## A. NEW WORLD VERSUS OLD WORLD

Despite the abundance of material already presented, almost nothing has been said about the evolution of man and culture in the extensive territories of the Americas. From the point of view of learning the main steps leading to the formation of *Homo sapiens* and of becoming acquainted with the broad outlines of his cultural progress it may be enough to limit one's self to the Old World, but to arrive at a better understanding of the varieties and complexities of human behavior it is necessary to know something of the New World as well. Not that there is any direct contradiction between the events that took place in the two areas, but there is a profound difference in details. It is only by examining the differences that a student of anthropology can gain an insight into the range of biological and cultural activities that may be found in dissimilar environments. An impartial and comprehensive science of man cannot be formulated if one hemisphere of the globe is left out of consideration.

Because of circumstances that are still inexplicable there was no hominid evolution in the Americas, even though the general pattern of biological development followed much the same course up to the emergence of Primates. Lemurs and tarsiers were well represented in the American Eocene, and at a later date platyrrhine monkeys made their appearance. At this stage the evolution of Primates in the New World seems to have come to a halt. Nowhere in the Americas has anyone ever found a verifiable specimen, fossil or living, of any

catarrhine monkey or ape—always excepting importations from
abroad by Frank Buck and other historic figures. There is also a total
absence of extinct hominids, which lends further support to the
contention that man did not originate in America. Not even Neandertal man, whose remains show up throughout the Old World,
has ever made an appearance in the New. And yet, there were millions of Indians present when Columbus arrived. There seems to be
no way of getting around the conclusion that man entered the New
World from the Old, at some time after he had evolved into *Homo
sapiens*. By then, it will be remembered, culture had progressed so
far in the Eastern hemisphere that it is unlikely that cultural evolution in America should have started from scratch. Instead, the first
migrants are thought to have brought with them a way of life which
corresponds roughly to Upper Paleolithic, or Mesolithic.

Whether or not the first Americans remained in touch with their
homelands in the Old World is a moot question. Archeologists in
this country are reluctant to say that all contact was immediately
broken, yet, as they study the evidence it looks very much as if the
great bulk of later American culture went through an independent
evolution in isolation. For example, a good number of groups moved
into a Neolithic stage, but instead of relying on Old World beasts
we find them domesticating such New World creatures as the alpaca,
llama, and turkey. Even these had only a restricted distribution in
pre-Columbian days, and aboriginal America's limited use of domesticated animals provides one of its sharpest distinctions from the
Neolithic in the Old World.

On several other scores there are such wide contrasts as to
strengthen the belief that almost all of the Neolithic of America was
independently evolved. Take, in this connection, the matter of agriculture. In one spot or another the prehistoric Indians learned to
raise numerous crops, including maize or corn (*Zea mays*); several
varieties of beans; squashes and pumpkins; tomatoes; cocoa; manioc
or cassava; tobacco; white and sweet potatoes; and cotton; only the
last two of which were then known in the Old World. Much the
same may be said of pottery. Neolithic peoples in the New World
manufactured an incredible variety of ceramic objects, but only a
restricted number of their forms and decorations can be matched in
the Eastern hemisphere. Similarly, some American Indians may have
known the principle of the wheel, but at no time before Columbus

was the concept put to practical use and the rare instances of its occurrence are limited to little things that might have been toys.

One of the most startling revelations of American archeology is the astounding cultural advance that was made once or twice by an essentially Neolithic people. Among the Maya Indians of Guatemala and Yucatan who were in practically every regard Neolithic, are to be found an amazing collection of traits which, throughout the Old World, do not appear until the maturer phases of the Copper-Bronze Age. The Maya were grouped into city-states; founded great urban centers with many architecturally splendid structures; organized a complex social system featuring great rulers, commoners, and corps of specialists; and maintained a highly trained body of priests who had a knowledge of writing, mathematics, and astronomy, and who were capable of keeping track of an exceedingly intricate but accurate calendar.

Prior to 1492 there was a Copper-Bronze Age in America, but its effective range did not extend very far beyond the territorial limits of the so-called Inca Indians of Peru and Bolivia. Only the Inca had some craftsmen who regularly used an alloy of copper and tin, but even they did not make large quantities of everyday implements of bronze. A few tribes in Ecuador and Colombia worked with other alloys, but they do not seem to have utilized bronze. One must not jump to the conclusion that America's Copper-Bronze Age was a duplicate of the Old World's. In some regards it was, but neither in writing, mathematics, nor the use of a calendar did the Copper-Bronze Inca equal the attainments of the basically Neolithic Maya.

Thus does the archeological record of America teach us that there is nothing inevitable about the traits of culture that may accompany either the Neolithic or the Copper-Bronze Age. Still, it would be a serious error to go to the extreme of saying that technology, especially metallurgy, has nothing to do with the total march of culture. In America such essentially Neolithic people as the Maya, Aztec, and others, may not have known the use of bronze but they were capable of dealing with molten gold or silver. This indicates that in the New World the early Metal Age is not necessarily synonymous with the Copper-Bronze Age.

By way of another contrast with the Old World the aboriginal metallurgists of America never learned to utilize iron. Whether they would have developed an Iron Age had it not been for European conquest and colonization will never be known. In any event, it is certain that the American Indians were the more readily defeated because they lacked such cultural items as metal weapons, wheeled vehicles, domesticated horses, and gunpowder.

When it is compared with the Old World story the evolution of culture in pre-Columbian America appears greatly compressed in time and scope. In time it extended from about 15,000 or 20,000 B.C. to 1492 A.D., and in scope it ran from a sort of Upper Paleolithic-Mesolithic beginning to the Copper-Bronze Age. Within these limits it reveals much diversity and complexity, and drives home the lesson that culture is a universal phenomenon of mankind.

## B. MAN COMES TO AMERICA

If man did not evolve in the New World he must have entered from the Old. This unequivocal statement of fact, innocent as it seems, has given rise among American archeologists to a series of long-lasting, sometimes acrimonius, and completely unresolved debates. Prominent questions that await definitive answers include: Who were the first people to have come? When did they arrive? Where did they come from? What kind of culture did they bring along? These queries can be broken down into numerous more detailed ones that are still harder to answer, but it will serve our purpose to examine the main four in broad terms.

The problem of who the first Americans may have been is complicated by the fact that archeologists have as yet found no skeletal remains associated with the oldest recognizable artifacts. In other words, there have been discovered ancient specimens of undeniably human workmanship, but there is no way of telling who made them. Since the middle decades of the last century reports have occasionally been made of skeletal remains supposedly pertaining to Pleistocene man, but in nearly every instance the claims were subsequently modified or rejected. Until the time of his death the late Dr. Ales Hrdlicka led a stubborn and usually successful campaign to refuse the label of Pleistocene antiquity to any hominid specimen, particularly if it bore a resemblance to living Indians. Today there is complete willingness to accept as valid Pleistocene human relics, regardless of their appearance, if they can be accurately dated by geological or other scientific methods.[1] Just the same no candidate for the honor of being the first American has been unanimously nominated, to say nothing of having been elected.

If one turns from the unsolved problem of the very earliest arrivals to questions of somewhat later inhabitants, he is a little better off for reliable information. By making a stratigraphic study of successive skull types at Pecos, New Mexico, Professor Hooton was able to demonstrate that the prehistoric residents of that abandoned village were a composite rather than a unified group, and that the earliest strains were longheaded (dolichocephalic) and non-Mongoloid.[2] Much more recently Professor Georg K. Neumann has been making an exhaustive survey of human remains found in archeological deposits, in an effort to reconstruct the racial history of pre-Columbian America. His terminology is original and entirely different from Hooton's, but he also finds that the first known folk were physically varied, longheaded, and non-Mongoloid.[3]

On the basis of present-day knowledge scholars accept the probability that the peopling of the New World began with the arrival of *sapiens* strains. They did not come in a single movement but in an indefinite number of waves of migration that lasted over many centuries. Gradually, the later arrivals tended to occupy the hearts of the continents while the first comers moved to the margins. Last, or nearly so, to come on the scene were the ancestors of the modern Eskimo. As more and more people reached America there was a general but not universal increase of broadheadedness (brachycephaly) and Mongoloid characteristics. The ancient situation is still reflected in the present. Most groups of American Indians are classed as Mongoloid by virtue of skin and eye color, hair form and distribution on the body, and cheekbone configuration, but they are not at all identical and many sub-varieties can be distinguished among the living tribes.

The date of man's entrance into the New World would be entirely open to question if anthropologists had to rely on skeletal

[1] For a discussion of this controversial problem, see, with the citations he makes, T. D. Stewart, "The Development of the Concept of Morphological Dating in Connection with Early Man in America," *Southwestern Journal of Anthropology*, Vol. 5, 1949, pp. 1-16.

[2] E. A. Hooton, *The Indians of Pecos Pueblo*, New Haven, 1930.

[3] G. K. Neumann, "Archeology and Race in the American Indian," *Archeology of Eastern United States* (J. B. Griffin, ed.), Chicago, 1952, pp. 13-34.

fragments. Luckily, some estimates can be made from the occurrence of humanly manufactured artifacts. Several of these have been dated by a combination of techniques, with the result that nearly every one accepts an entrance date of 15,000 to 20,000 B.C. This leads to speculation about the environmental conditions that prevailed at the time, especially in the locality that served as the original gateway.

On the score of place of entry there is comforting agreement. Only a rare dissenter, almost never a trained anthropologist, objects to the contention that man came to America from Northeast Asia, by crossing the Bering Straits into Alaska. A few disturbing details remain to be clarified before high probability can be converted to established fact, but in most respects the hypothesis of a Bering Straits approach is scientifically supported. At the time in question North America was most likely in the closing phases of the Wisconsin glaciation that came at the end of the Pleistocene in the New World. Geological and related studies have shown that neither Northeastern Siberia nor Alaska was then heavily covered with ice, and in addition there were doubtless enough ice-free corridors to have made migration possible. Nor did the Bering Straits provide a serious obstacle. They are narrow enough for the American shore to be seen on clear days from parts of the Northeastern Asiatic coast, they are broken up by islands that limit open water to twenty-five miles or less at a stretch, there may have been a land bridge between the two continents toward the close of the Pleistocene, and there were probably seasons of winter when crossings could have been made on solid ice.

Although the theory of a Bering Straits gateway is most widely accepted, it is not the only one that has been proposed. Migrations across the Atlantic have been postulated on one basis or another from Wales, Western Asia, Egypt and other parts of Africa, or from fabulous places like Atlantis. Not one of these suggestions is backed by trustworthy proof, and none, with the possible exception of a Norse migration around 1000 B.C., is taken seriously by American anthropologists. In a somewhat different category are the hypotheses of ancient trans-Pacific movements to other New World regions than Alaska. Enough evidence has been accumulated to establish the possibility that now and then a boatload of navigators from islands in the South Pacific may have reached a spot on the Western shores of the Americas, but it is highly improbable that they ever arrived in sufficient numbers or early enough to have become ancestors of the American Indians or the founders of their ways of life.[4]

When it comes to the question of what kind of culture the first occupants of America brought with them there is again no clear-cut answer. Whatever they had that was intangible or perishable cannot be recovered, and whatever they have left behind of a durable nature can tell only a partial story at best. Even so, archeologists would be delighted if they could identify all the material remains of the original migrants but, sad to tell, not a single artifact found has ever been dated close to the postulated entrance date. Failing actual specimens recourse has been made to speculative reconstruction. Professor A. L. Kroeber, dean of American anthropologists, has attempted to reconstruct the elements of original New World culture on the basis of items that have been universally reported among the known tribes. Kroeber feels that traits which are common to every one of the Indian groups may well have been retained from the culture that was brought here at the beginning. His list of material items includes stone implements made by pressure or rubbing, bone or horn objects fashioned by polishing, knowledge of hafting, control of fire, making of baskets or nets, use of the spear-thrower or bow, and possession of tamed (domesticated?) dogs.[5] Such a list of traits fits the Old World pattern of cultural evolution at a point that resembles the Mesolithic.

To sum up the material in this section, American anthropologists are pretty well agreed that man came to the New World by crossing the Bering Straits from northeastern Asia to Alaska about 15,000 to 20,000 B.C. Several waves of immigrants followed the first arrivals, bringing in diversified physical features that became increasingly Mongoloid. The Pleistocene's Wisconsin phase was nearly over when the earliest settlers came, and their culture was about on a level with Europe's Mesolithic. After they had taken up residence in the New World they may have received a few influences from the Old, but on the whole most of their later achievements in cultural development seem to have been independently evolved in the Americas.

4 In spite of its author's frank disclaimer, published at the end of his book, some readers of Thor Heyerdahl's Kon-tiki are of the opinion that he proved the possibility of a reverse migration from Peru to Polynesia. Anthropologically, the voyage of the Kon-tiki proved next to nothing. Heyerdahl has since expounded his theories more fully in American Indians in the Pacific, New York, 1953.

5 A. L. Kroeber, Anthropology, New York, 1948, p. 778.

## C. INDIANS BEFORE POTTERY

Between the supposed time of man's initial arrival in America and the earliest date assigned to any recognizably human artifact there is a gap of several millenia. Whatever the reason, the fact remains that the story of cultural evolution in the New World cannot be started much before 12,000 B.C. In the Old World sequence of events this is a recent date, but in America it is part of the remote and dim past. Furthermore, the inventory of original cultural equipment when viewed in the light of actual discoveries is more meager than the hypothetical list of traits inferred by Kroeber.

A few American artifacts have been dated at 12,000 B.C. They consist for the most part of chipped stone points shaped in the form of a lance head (lanceolate). An occasional flint knife, scraper, or graver, has been claimed to have similar antiquity, and the possible use of a spear-thrower has been suggested. On the basis of the lance-shaped projectile points, found together with bones of extinct mammals, it has been argued that the first migrants from Northeastern Asia may have been big-game hunters of Pleistocene mammoths, mastodons, bison, wild camels, and wild horses, who were led to the New World while pursuing their quarry. It is then presumed that these vaguely known hunters gradually spread east and south of Alaska until they had peopled portions of all the Americas.

What are currently thought to be the most likely manifestations of the oldest American culture have been found in just a few places, among the best studied of which are Sandia and Clovis, both in New Mexico. At a limestone cave among the northern Sandia mountains, Professor Frank C. Hibben found signs of three clearly separated occupation layers, the oldest of which contained nineteen Paleolithic implements, now known as **Sandia points.** They are well-made, slightly reminiscent of Solutrian workmanship, and notched at one side to produce a shoulder (Fig. 93 B, C). Also found at the same level, were two bone implements shaped like the stone Sandia points, which may have some reference to spear-throwers; several snub-nosed scrapers, flat on one side and with a thick, carefully flaked end; some nondescript lithic fragments; and a couple of fire hearths full of charcoal. The strong likelihood that the unknown makers of the Sandia points were Pleistocene hunters is couched on the association of their tools with extinct forms of large mammals. Despite a few claims to

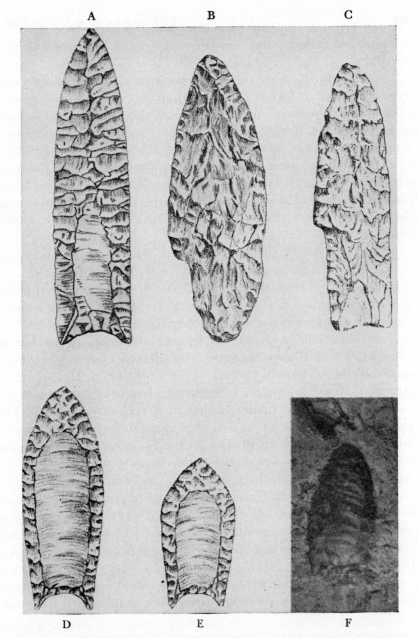

A B C

D E F

Fig. 93. Early American projectile points of stone (after Wormington). A. Clovis fluted point. The central channel is less fully developed than in the Folsom points (D and E), which it resembles. B and C. Sandia points. The notch or shoulder at the left is typical. D and E. Two varieties of Folsom points. Each has all of the details characteristic of the type in general. F. A Folsom point *in situ*. Photographed exactly as it appeared when it was first discovered.

the contrary, Sandia points are believed to have had a very narrow distribution.

A somewhat different case can be made for the **fluted points** that were discovered at Clovis, also in conjunction with bones of extinct mammoths.[6] These are small stone objects, three or four inches long, which are called "fluted" because they have a channel or groove running almost halfway up the length of the face (Fig. 93A). In contrast to the Sandia specimens **Clovis fluted points** have close analogies with lithic artifacts from a number of other sites in the United States but are entirely unknown in the Old World. It has been conjectured that they may be forerunners of the Folsom point to be discussed below.

Around 10,000 B.C. the early culture of the New World begins to emerge with a little more clarity than in the case of the postulated big-game hunters from Sandia and Clovis. By now the larger Pleistocene mammals had begun to die out, except in favorable wooded areas. For this period the term **Paleo-Indian** has been suggested. Although indications of human activity around 10,000 B.C. may be had from archeological sites elsewhere,[7] the clearest evidence to date is furnished by the **Folsom Culture** of the southwestern United States. Recognition and acceptance of Folsom Culture make up one of the most exciting and dramatic chapters of American archeology. The story has so often been told that it need not be repeated in detail.[8] Suffice it to say that from 1926 on, first at Folsom, New Mexico, and later at the Lindenmeier site in Colorado, as well as elsewhere, repeated discoveries have been made of a highly characteristic stone and bone industry which was unquestionably produced by hunters of an ancient form of buffalo, *Bison taylori*. Well over 6000 lithic objects have been recovered, and a quantity of bone artifacts has been excavated, but not a speck of any Folsom Man has ever come to light.

Among the assortment of implements found the **Folsom point** stands out as the most significant artifact of the culture. It is a small,

[6] Excavations were made at Clovis around the mid-1930's, first by Dr. Edgar B. Howard, and later by John L. Cotter. A detailed geological examination was carried out by Dr. Ernest Antevs in 1934.

[7] J. B. Griffin, "Culture Periods in Eastern United States Archeology," *Archeology of Eastern United States* (J. B. Griffin, ed.), Chicago, 1952, pp. 353-54.

[8] A good summary may be found in F. H. H. Roberts, "The Folsom Problem in American Archeology," *Smithsonian Institution*, Annual Report for 1938, Washington, 1939, pp. 531-46.

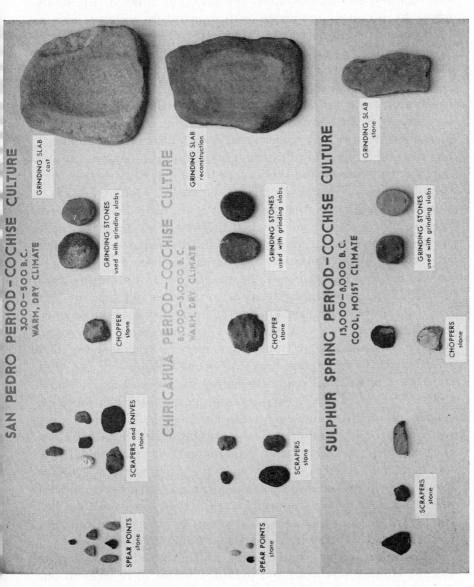

Fig. 94. Stages of Cochise culture. Only the Sulphur Spring period corresponds, approximately, to the antiquity of Folsom culture.

thin, leaf-shaped blade of stone with a slightly rounded tip, deftly flaked by pressure, and made with a markedly concave base so fashioned as to leave a sort of rabbit-eared projection at each end. When the point was just about finished in other respects, a long, thin flake was knocked off lengthwise (Fig. 93 D, E, F), probably with the help of a bone punch. Thus a groove or channel was made about halfway or more up the long face of the artifact. This channel, reminiscent of the Clovis style of manufacture, is the most readily identifiable feature of a true Folsom point. That such implements, representing a high peak of lithic workmanship in America, served as projectile points is readily admitted by all, but whether they were spear heads or arrow tips has never been settled. Moreover, there is still some doubt as to why the grooves were made. Perhaps, as has been surmised, the fluting lessened the weight of the stone point, gave it greater penetrating power, and made it easier to haft. These are reasonable conjectures but they have never been proved.

At about the same dates as those assigned to Folsom culture there were living in the southeastern corner of Arizona and adjacent New Mexico a people whose remains suggest that they were more interested in gathering wild vegetal products than in pursuing game. Archeologists know about them from objects found at several spots, all of of which may be said to represent the **Cochise Culture** (Fig. 94). Only the earliest phase is of comparable antiquity with Folsom.[9] Relative lack of devotion to hunting is inferred from the absence of projectile points, although one must not rule out the possibility that these might have been made of perishable substances that have since disintegrated. On the other hand, reliance on wild seeds, nuts, fruits, and berries is brought out most clearly by the presence of grinding stones such as are known from later times to have been used for preparing plant foods. The principal early tools consist of thin, flat, milling stones, the whole class of which are called metates in American archeology. Whatever was put on a milling stone was crushed or ground with a rubbing stone, mano, which, in the earliest level of Cochise Culture was small and evidently meant to be held in one hand only. Both the metates and manos were made of sandstone.

Strange as it seems archeologists can say almost as much about American culture around 10,000 B.C. as they can about what took

[9] For an account of the three phases that make up Cochise Culture, consult E. B. Sayles and E. Antevs, "The Cochise Culture," *Gila Pueblo, Medallion Papers*, No. 29, 1941.

place in the next few millenia. Even for a period as late as 7000 to 5000 B.C. only occasional glimpses of cultural developments are available. A few things seem fairly certain. The older Pleistocene fauna were pretty thoroughly extinct and recent species of animals were common everywhere. Temperatures were considerably higher than at present. In the Great Plains the heat was accompanied by drought, but far to the east there was enough rainfall to stimulate the growth of grass and forests and to make the area increasingly attractive to settlers. There thus arose in the present territory of the Eastern United States a phase of culture that is sometimes called **Early Archaic,** typified by small groups of wandering Indians who knew neither how to grow crops nor how to make pottery. There is good proof, based on the frequency of stone mortars and pestles, that the Early Archaic people relied more heavily on plant foods than their Paleo-Indian predecessors; and this circumstance has led some writers to propose a connection between Early Archaic in the eastern United States and Cochise Culture in the Southwest. Many habitations were made near water courses and relics of weirs, nets, and hooks point to great interest in fishing. It is not unusual to find Early Archaic bodies buried in circular pits, and occasionally dogs were intentionally interred with humans, together with red ochre and other funeral offerings.

A subsequent period sometimes identified as **Late Archaic** in the eastern United States may be regarded as transitional between Paleolithic and Neolithic. It extends in time from about 3000 to 1000 B.C. and is featured by the introduction of a host of new items that might have been brought in by a fresh wave of short, stocky, broadheaded migrants from Asia. Archeologists dealing with the Late Archaic in this area note for the first time a profusion of notched or stemmed projectile points, polished stone celts, adzes, banner-stones,[10] and weights or plummets. Also found are objects made from human bone, and tubular things of clay or stone that have been tentatively identified as pipes. Copper, used for utilitarian purposes without being liquefied, was imported from the vicinity of the Great Lakes,

[10] In the earlier days of American archeology scholars were puzzled by finds of stone objects with winglike projections extending from a central perforation. Their purpose was unknown, but it was surmised that they might have been carried on staffs like banners. Modern archeologists look on them as weights connected with the use of spearthrowers.

and steatite (soapstone) bowls were carried out as far as the Lower Mississippi Valley.

As was the case in the Old World many groups in America went from a Paleolithic to a Neolithic stage, but some tribes never took up a New Stone Age form of culture. This is true not only of peoples living in extremely cold climates unsuited for crop cultivation, but even of some societies whose lands were later adapted to agriculture by European settlers.[11] Again, as was true of the Old World's Mesolithic, pottery was occasionally produced by noncultivators; [12] and, conversely, instances have been reported of farming populations that had no pottery.[13] Despite such exceptions it seems to have been the customary rule throughout the world for a ceramic industry to accompany agriculture. Within the last millenium before Christ the stage was set in the New World for Neolithic culture and incontrovertible proof of its existence becomes available soon after the start of the present era.

## D. NEOLITHIC HIGHLIGHTS NORTH OF MEXICO: EASTERN UNITED STATES

Without question the first and foremost food crop of the pre-Columbian Americas was maize, which was widely grown in numerous varieties. Because of its importance the question of the domestication of corn has been exhaustively studied for many years, but the story is complex and has not yet been unravelled. Most signs point to a beginning of maize cultivation south of the Rio Grande, and it is there that the greatest Neolithic heights were reached in the New World. North America also had some remarkable farming centers, so many that they cannot all be touched upon in this text. Only two vital areas will be discussed, but together they cover a good stretch of territory and a long range of time.

11 Many nonagricultural tribes are known, but pre-Columbian farming seldom penetrated South America below a line drawn eastward across that continent from Chiloe Island, off the Coast of Chile. Further details are given in J. B. Bird, "The Archeology of Patagonia," *Handbook of South American Indians* (J. H. Steward, ed.), Vol. 1, Washington, 1946, pp. 17-18.

12 A. Serrano, "The Charrua," *idem.*, p. 194. The Eskimo likewise provide an excellent example of a nonagricultural folk who knew how to make pottery.

13 J. B. Bird, "Excavations in Northern Chile," *American Museum of Natural History, Anthropological Papers*, Vol. 38, No. 4, New York, 1943, p. 307. Dr. Bird expresses the caution that the occurrence of agriculture without ceramics, weaving, or basketry may be accidental.

One of the primary regions of pre-Columbian Neolithic development north of Mexico is to be found in the Eastern United States. Anthropologists concerned with this part of the world are accustomed to using terminology derived from the **McKern or Midwestern system** of classification.[14] This is a scheme which proposes that homogeneous sites, or **components,** showing similar cultural items, should be grouped together into a **focus.** Related foci make up an **aspect;** comparable aspects fall into a **phase;** and like phases constitute a **pattern.** East of the Rocky Mountains the Mississippi and Woodland patterns represent Neolithic peaks, but we shall deal only with the Woodland, which begins in the early centuries of the Christian era.

In terms of its basic economy **Early Woodland** may be looked upon as a continuation of the generally nonagricultural Late Archaic. Tubular pipes were ground from stone and positively associated with tobacco smoking; large earthen mounds were constructed over the bodies of the dead; woven cloth made its first appearance; and copper was being used more for ornaments than implements. Pottery-making thus seems to have begun in the northerly ranges of Early Woodland, where the first forms resemble styles known from Northeastern Asia. The possibility of Asiatic diffusion is strengthened by the fact that in both areas the pottery is associated with burial mounds. Use of ceramics may have spread southward but there is some uncertainty about the situation.

Around 600 A.D. or thereabouts the Eastern United States entered on a **Middle Woodland** period, whose cultural climax was reached in the **Hopewell** phase. The most active centers were in Southern Ohio and the Illinois Valley, and a noticeable lag in development is revealed in sites to the southeast and along the Gulf Coast. Hopewell people were farmers who raised the three most basic North American crops—corn, beans, and squash. These were supplemented by game, fish, and wild edible plant products. An ample food supply is attested by the large sizes of permanent settlements, the building of enormous earthworks for socioreligious purposes rather than for practical considerations such as defense, and the rich flourishing of art in forms and styles that were so standardized as to suggest the presence of specialists. Pipes of polished stone are abundant in Hopewell remains and reach an exceptional degree of elaboration. Many

14 W. C. McKern, "The Mid-western Taxonomic Method as an Aid to Archaeological Culture Study," *American Antiquity,* Vol. 4, 1939, pp. 301-13.

are made like a platform, on which there is often carved a realistic effigy of an animal within whose body the bowl is to be found (Fig. 95 A).

Pottery-making was a featured activity. Hopewell vessels were grit-tempered, gray-buff in color, and decorated with bands or rows of incised, impressed, or stamped designs. There are exceptionally fine

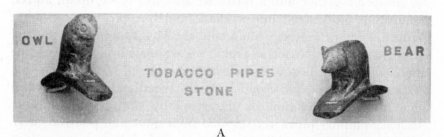

A

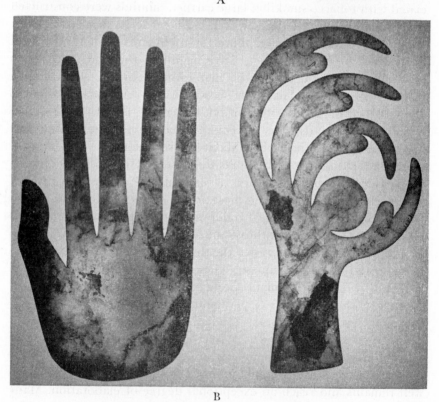

B

Fig. 95. Some artifacts of Hopewell culture. A. Two varieties of platform pipes. B. A human hand and the foot of an eagle, made of mica.

pieces, showing no signs of practical use, that are judged to have served in sacred contexts; good, carefully fashioned wares that show evidence of restricted utility; and ordinary cooking pots that are customarily ornamented with impressions from a cord-wrapped paddle, and are sometimes equipped with feet.

Production of ornaments must have been a major activity. Copper was cleverly handled, without being liquefied, and was made into breastplates, ear-spools, bracelets, armbands, and a great many other forms. Sheets of mica were used whole or cut into complex geometric or realistic figures (Fig. 95 B), and a great profusion of decorative objects was made of pearl, silver, shell, bone, animal teeth, stone, and human skeletal parts. Much of the finest art work is found in graves, and Hopewell culture reveals a variety of burial customs. Corpses were placed sometimes in log tombs and sometimes on platforms; some graves were lined with woven mats and some with sheets of mica; many bodies were buried under cone-shaped mounds of earth; and others were cremated in clay basins.

Hopewell artifacts from the flourishing locations in Ohio and Illinois show that the people had farflung trade connections. Marine shells were brought in from the seacoast, obsidian must have been obtained from regions of volcanic activity, copper came from around the Great Lakes, mica was probably received from Virginia and North Carolina, and there is more than a hint of contact with Mexico. Apparently Hopewell pots were exported widely, for typical specimens have been found over a good part of the Eastern United States.

Somewhere about 1000 A.D. the great Hopewell phase of Middle Woodland underwent decline and was succeeded by a less well-known stage that may be called **Late Woodland**. This probably had only a short, transitory existence before it was absorbed or replaced by an eastward spread of the Mississippi pattern that lasted into historic times. Most authorities at present believe that cultural events in the Eastern United States during the last centuries of American prehistory show a strong parallel with what was happening in the Southwest. There are so many things common to both areas that a connection seems perfectly logical. Sites are known from Texas and Oklahoma whose inhabitants may well have served as intermediaries between the two major Neolithic zones north of Mexico, but numerous puzzling details await clarification.

## E. NEOLITHIC HIGHLIGHTS NORTH OF MEXICO:
## THE SOUTHWEST

The southwestern United States, an extensive region whose center is in the drainage of the San Juan River near the four corners where meet the boundaries of Arizona, New Mexico, Colorado, and Utah, occupies an unique position in American archeology. Much of the territory comprises a high plateau and there are many arid spots where perishable materials may last for amazingly long periods. In addition to an abundance of artifacts, plant and animal remains, and dried out bodies loosely called mummies, the Southwest provides a record of continuous occupation from early prehistoric times to the present; there are living tribes whose customs help in the interpretation of extinct cultures; and tree ring dating often makes possible a more accurate means of timing events than can be established elsewhere. It was in the Southwest that most of the leading American anthropologists did their field work a generation or two ago. While archeologists were busy examining ruins a flood of ethnologists invaded the area to seek information from its Indian inhabitants.

Within the Southwest archeologists were first attracted to the vicinity of the four corners, where some spectacular ruins awaited scientific investigation. After an initial phase of devotion to detailed reports of particular sites, efforts were made to formulate a synthesis that would apply to the whole region. A sequence was established that was marked into three pre-ceramic periods called Basket Maker I, II, and III, followed directly by five fully developed Neolithic stages known as Pueblo I, II, III, IV, and V. Not long after this scheme had been proposed students working at a distance from the four corners began to find material that did not fit into the Basket Maker-Pueblo pattern. It was then decided to rechristen the latter as **Anasazi,** to re-name the various stages, and to restrict their application to the plateau territory of the four corners.[15] At least three other sub-regions have been tentatively recognized for other parts of the Southwest.[16]

[15] The more recent terminology is explained in F. H. H. Roberts, Jr., "Archaeology in the Southwest," *American Antiquity,* Vol. 3, 1937-38, pp. 3-33. A somewhat similar but fuller account occurs in E. H. Morris, "Archaeological Studies in the La Plata District," *Carnegie Institution,* No. 519, Washington, 1939, pp. 8-44.

[16] The most distinctive and by all odds the most accepted of these subdivisions, called **Hohokam,** is centered along the Gila River and its vicinity in Southern Arizona.

Over the years a stupendous body of literature on the subject of southwestern archeology has grown up. It is an exciting topic and the interested reader will do well to consult references given at the close of this chapter. We shall, however, limit our discussion to the Basket Maker-Pueblo, or Anasazi, sequence. Archeologists fully expect that the start of Anasazi will some day be traced back to an antecedent culture of the type indicated by Sandia, Cochise, or Folsom. Meantime, it is assumed that a century or two before the opening of the Christian era the ancestors of the **Basket Maker** (Basket Maker I and II in the earlier system) people began to frequent the plateau country around the four corners. They were long-headed Indians who supplemented the hunting and gathering of food by growing corn and, possibly, squash. They hunted deer and smaller game with spears and spear-throwers (here known as **atlatls**). Their agricultural implements were simple **dibbles** or wooden digging sticks about three or four feet long and beveled or pointed at one end, as well as flat metates and manos of stone. They may have kept turkeys and they certainly had domesticated dogs, whose ancestry has been traced to Asia.

There is little evidence of permanent housing, although the Basket Makers probably erected brush shelters in caves or under overhanging rocks, and they may have built simple lodgings in the open. Most of the information about them comes from storage pits dug into the ground, wherein have been found notched stone projectile points, curved wooden clubs, cigar-shaped pipes of clay or stone, and remnants of a few other artifacts. Storage pits were about two or three feet deep, and only a little larger in diameter (Fig. 96A). Some were plain, but others were walled with upright slabs of stone. They served quite often as burial chambers; [17] there is a possibility that they may have been roofed with mud-covered poles to make pit-houses of a type known in Northern Asia. These people are called Basket Makers because they seem to have had no knowledge of pottery, but knew how to make many things of stiff vegetal materials by coiling

---

Somewhat less clearly distinctive and not as yet so sure to be accepted as a separate cultural entity, is the **Mogollon-Mimbres** manifestation of Southwestern New Mexico and adjacent Southeastern Arizona. Even less distinct and less likely of acceptance as an individual stage is the **Patayan,** whose remains are supposedly distributed along the Colorado River Basin, south of the Grand Canyon of Arizona.

[17] Basket Maker burials were in the flexed position, with knees drawn up to the chin.

A

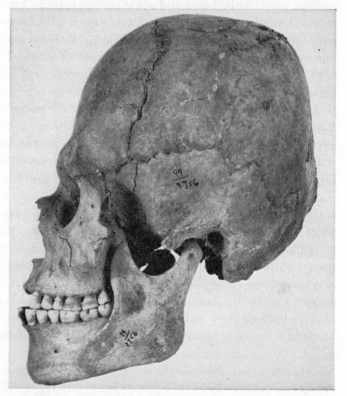

B

Fig. 96. A. Basket Maker storage cist. It is an early type, walled with stone. B. Skull with artificial deformation. Although this skull was found by Dr. Vaillant in Mazapan, Mexico, similar specimens are common in Basket Maker sites.

or weaving. Local plants were used, of which yucca was a favorite. They made a variety of bags, nets, baskets, trays, and jars, as well as several kinds of sandals. In addition, at least three types of cradles were fashioned of wood or bark, and some garments were made from skins.

About 500 A.D. **Modified Basket Maker** culture (formerly Basket Maker III), begins in the same general region as the earlier stage. Throughout this period pit-houses were surely in use and some groups even congregated in what may be called small villages. They seem to have been of two kinds. Some consisted of a score or so of pit-houses placed near one another, but others were stone structures erected above ground and containing about the same number of contiguous square or rectangular rooms. Several of these relatively large buildings had straight lines, but others were in the form of crescents. In either case they are thought to have served as communal dwellings, with individual families occupying only one or two rooms each. During this stage, too, religious chambers known as **kivas**—usually circular, but occasionally squarish—were built underground, apart from the living quarters. The Indians of Modified Basket Maker days were similar in physical type to those who came before, but in later times they may have begun the custom of artificially deforming the back of the head (Fig. 96 B). Modern students of the practice are convinced that while it squeezed the cranium permanently into an unnatural shape, it affected neither the growth of the brain nor the mental ability of the individual.

Although Modified Basket Maker culture continued most of the older ways of life, it also made a number of innovations. Farming seems to have been more intensively carried on, more varieties of corn were grown, and beans were added to the former crops. Bows and arrows gradually replaced atlatls, and more deeply troughed forms of stone metates, small stemmed projectile points, and notched axes were introduced. But the most important novelty was the manufacturing of pottery. The earliest pieces were of a plain, gray color, shaped by coiling within a basket and hardened in the sun without actual firing. Where the idea of pot-making originated among the Modified Basket Makers is not known, but before long numerous styles had developed, all hand-fashioned by coiling. Similar lines of cultural progress appear to have been followed throughout the **Developmental Pueblo** (formerly Pueblo I and II) stage until the

**Great Period** (Pueblo III) began around 1000 A.D. Among other things the Indians of this date began to move out of small villages and to congregate in massive, terraced buildings that contained up to a thousand rooms. The huge pueblos were made of stone masonry and were several stories high.[18] Kivas continued to be built underground, separate from living quarters. They were in several styles, but were usually round and often attained great size. Details of construction provide a hint of religious conservatism because they retained features that go back to earlier pit-houses. In some places kiva walls were decorated with fine, highly artistic murals.

There was a time when archeologists tended to attribute the cultural upsurge of the Great Period to the arrival of a new kind of people, but it is the modern consensus that such a postulate is inaccurate. Some differences in the populace are nevertheless to be noted. Broadheadedness increases, and artificial deformation of the cranium becomes commonplace. This may mean that a few bands of newcomers had arrived, but there is no indication of a wholesale change of population. Physically as well as culturally the Great Period seems to have been an indigenous outgrowth of earlier developments.

Not all of the Indians in the San Juan district moved into the huge terraced structures, and not all of the massive pueblos were identical. Apart from differences in their modes of construction a few of the huge buildings, such as the cliff-houses at Montezuma's Castle in Arizona, were erected among overhanging rocks on ledges high up the walls of steep cliffs; others, like pueblo Bonito in the Chaco Canyon of New Mexico, were located out in the open; and some, like Awatovi near the Hopi villages of Arizona, were built on flat-topped mesas, far above the surrounding plain (Fig. 97).

Many specialized kinds of excellent pottery were produced locally at the various great pueblos, feather-covered garments were made almost everywhere, turquoise and olivella shell were widely used in the manufacture of countless ornaments, agriculture was intensively practiced and now included cotton that was cleverly utilized for weaving, and numbers of sandals, baskets, cradles, and trays continued to be made of vegetal materials. From every point of view the

---

[18] Pueblo, when spelled with a capital refers to a generalized aspect of Anasazi culture. When written with a small letter it signifies a particular structure, community, or tribe.

Fig. 97. Communal pueblos in the Southwest. A. Pueblo Bonito was situated in the open at Chaco Canyon, New Mexico. It was probably built after Pueblo III had begun. B. Montezuma's Castle was located in rock shelters on the sides of a steep cliff near Campe Verde, Arizona. C. Awatovi was perched on a high mesa, close to the modern Hopi pueblos in Arizona.

Great Period marked the highest peak of Anasazi culture, but its brilliance was not long-lasting. By 1300 A.D. signs of decline are apparent throughout the neighborhood of the four corners. The large pueblos were abandoned one after the other and fell into ruin, arts and crafts declined, groups of Indians wandered over the countryside, and a shift of population took place southward, toward the Little Colorado River and the Rio Grande.

Various scholars have attempted to explain the collapse of the Great Period, but no one has been entirely successful. A combination of several factors seems to offer the best explanation to date. First of all, tree ring studies have conclusively established that there was a long drought between 1276 and 1299 A.D., and under such conditions a big, close-packed agricultural community must have been impossible to maintain. Secondly, it has been shown that the dry spell was accompanied by excessive erosion, which led to the cutting of huge arroyos that ate away great stretches of arable soil and made large-scale farming difficult. In the third place, on the basis of an historic breakup at the Hopi pueblo of Oraibi, the writer has argued that congregation into massive population units puts an exceptionally heavy strain on a people's social organization. A weakly-knit social system, coupled with an outbreak of factional bickering, might easily have played a contributory part in the termination of the Great Period. Fourth, incursions of hostile tribes may also have been a disturbing influence.[19]

Whatever its causes of decline may have been, the Great Period ended around 1300 and was followed by a **regressive** stage (Pueblo IV), which later underwent a **renaissance** south of the original Anasazi center. While Pueblo culture never again recaptured its earlier exuberance, it did not fade completely away and many of its former traits were retained. Villages continued to be built in large, communally-inhabited blocks of contiguous rooms, often facing an open court or plaza within which were dug underground kivas, now customarily square and never exceptionally large. Natives living along the Rio Grande learned to make new kinds of glazed pottery, and there was lively trade not only among various local communities but even as far off as the Mississippi Valley. A large number of the

[19] A discussion of this entire problem may be found in M. Titiev, "Old Oraibi," *Papers of the Peabody Museum of American Archaeology and Ethnology,* Harvard University, Vol. 22, Cambridge, 1944, chap. 7.

towns founded after 1300 have persisted into modern times (Pueblo V), having survived the Spanish conquest of the sixteenth century and the westward expansion of the United States. Many Indian villages are still functioning actively and have retained a good measure of their prehistoric culture. It is for this reason that serious anthropologists as well as curious tourists continue to visit the Hopi towns, Zuni, Laguna, Acoma, Santo Domingo, Taos, and other famous pueblos.

## SELECTED REFERENCES

Brew, John O., "Archaeology of Alkali Ridge, Southeastern Utah," *Papers of the Peabody Museum of American Archaeology and Ethnology,* Harvard University, Vol. 21, Cambridge, 1946.

Griffin, James B. (ed.), *Archeology of Eastern United States,* Chicago, 1952.

Haury, Emil W., et al., *The Stratigraphy and Archaeology of Ventana Cave, Arizona,* Tucson and Albuquerque, 1950.

Kidder, Alfred V., *An Introduction to the Study of Southwestern Archaeology,* New Haven, 1924.

Laughlin, William S. (ed.), "Papers on the Physical Anthropology of the American Indians," *The Viking Fund,* New York, 1951.

Martin, Paul S., et al., *Indians before Columbus,* Chicago, 1947.

Neumann, George K., "Archeology and Race in the American Indian," *Archeology of Eastern United States* (J. B. Griffin, ed.), Chicago, 1952, pp. 13-34.

Roberts, Frank H. H., Jr., "Recent Evidence Relating to an Early Indian Occupation in North America," *Proceedings of the Eighth American Scientific Congress,* Vol. 2, 1942, pp. 31-38.

Sayles, E. B., and Antevs, Ernst, "The Cochise Culture," *Medallion Papers,* No. 29, 1941.

Sellards, Elias H., *Early Man in America,* Austin, 1952.

Wissler, Clark, *The American Indian,* rev. ed., New York, 1938.

Wormington, Helen M., "Ancient Man in North America," *Museum of Natural History,* Denver, 1949.

———, "Prehistoric Indians of the Southwest," *Ibid.,* 1947.

# CHAPTER 17

# Man and Culture in the New World: Part II

## A. THE ESSENTIALLY NEOLITHIC MAYA

Generally accepted criteria of Metal Age culture do not readily apply to the pre-Columbian Maya and Aztec. Some Maya artisans hammered ornaments of gold and fashioned "sleigh bells" of copper, and Aztec craftsmen attained the art of casting liquid copper and gold by the lost-wax (cireperdue) method, but experts freely admit that these Indians failed to go beyond a sort of metallurgical infancy because they never manufactured utilitarian implements of metal. Under the circumstances it seems most logical to describe them as essentially Neolithic. On this level they went far beyond the achievements of any of the more northerly American tribes.

Although the origins of Maya culture are lost in obscurity it is conceded that it had become completely Neolithic centuries before that stage was reached in the Eastern and Southwestern United States. The late Dr. Sylvanus G. Morley,[1] leading Maya specialist at the time of his death, was of the opinion that the ancestors of the Maya had acquired knowledge of ceramics and plant cultivation during the first millenium before Christ. He divides the succeeding epochs of Maya culture into an Old Empire ranging from 317 to 987 A.D., and a New Empire that endured in one fashion or another from 987 to 1697. Since, by his own admission, the term "Empire" is misleading—the Maya were never grouped into a large, unified,

[1] Much of this section is summarized from S. G. Morley, *The Ancient Maya*, Stanford, 1946.

political division—we shall speak only of **Early** and **Late Maya** periods.

Early Maya culture (317-987 A.D.) is believed to have started in the lowlands of North-central Peten, in Guatemala, at a time when the region was so densely forested that farmers had repeatedly to clear and burn over the land. Despite this difficulty the Early Maya found it possible to achieve surpluses of food and other goods, thus furnishing the setting in which the more highly specialized features of the culture could flourish. Crops of maize, beans, squash, pumpkins, sweet potatoes, tomatoes, and cassava were raised. In addition, many wild fruits and nuts were gathered and chili peppers, allspice, coriander, and vanilla were cultivated for seasoning and flavoring. Game was hunted in the forests, and the plumage of birds and the skins of deer and jaguar were used for making fine cloaks and sandals. Cocoa was grown in quantity and was made into the universally popular drink of chocolate. Among the most important non-edible plant materials were mahogany and cedar wood for building, liana vines for tying, gourds for containers, tobacco, rubber, and copal resin that was used as incense. From their environment the Early Maya also secured in abundance building stone, lime, and gravel. There is no doubt of their favorable situation, nor of the intelligence with which they took advantage of natural resources, but in the last analysis it was maize that was their staff of life and, figuratively speaking, the basis on which they built their remarkable culture.

Early Maya society was highly organized. There were numerous city-states, each headed by an hereditary ruler, descended in the male line, who was the leading power in civil, religious, and military affairs. He appointed town and village chiefs who, together with priests and special councilors, formed an advisory body. Most of the administrators were related to the ruler and constituted a nobility. Of equal or even higher status were the priests, who were divided into grades on the basis of function. Commoners came next and were the actual builders of the great monuments that were the glory of the Maya. At the bottom of the social scale were slaves, some of whom were born to that condition whereas others came into it as prisoners of war, criminals, or orphans.

Architecture and sculpture, using wood, stone, and clay were among the major arts and crafts, and wooden mallets and polished stone celts were the most important tools. According to Dr. Morley, the years from about 730 to 880 saw the greatest development of all pre-Columbian times in New World sculpture. Pottery was made in huge quantities and in greatly varied styles. No cloth of the Early Maya period has actually been recovered, but from artistic representations it is known that elaborate cotton garments were in wide use. Basketry, too, is known only indirectly. Flint-chipping, the all-around handling of precious and common stones, and work with feathers, all reached high levels, but metallurgy was practically unknown.

In terms of material culture the most amazing accomplishment of the Early Maya is the erection of imposing assemblages of high pyramids, massive stairways, colorful temples, carved monolithic columns (called **stelae**), and ceremonial ball-courts that characterize their cities.[2] Yet, the material achievements are more than matched by the intellectual heights reached in particular by the priesthood. A system of writing was devised, in which carefully made figures (glyphs) stood for ideas or sounds. Neither connected, cursive writing, nor a true phonetic alphabet was developed, but Maya hieroglyphics command special attention because they were part of an essentially Neolithic way of life. Most of the writing was concerned with dates and religion,[3] and here again there is reason for wonder and admiration. The Maya had an original sign for zero, with the help of which the value of a digit changed according to its position, just as we recognize the differences between 5, 50, 500, and 505. Mathematics, in turn, was geared to astronomy, and together with writing they made possible a reliable calendar in which accurate corrections were made for leap years. Not content with a single calendar the Early Maya kept simultaneous track of a sacred year of 260 days, and a secular year of 18 months of 20 days, plus five unlucky days at the end. New Year's Day in the two systems fell together every 52 years, and was the occasion for special ceremonials.

Brilliant though it unquestionably was, the culture of the Early Maya declined in 987. As in the case of the Great Pueblo collapse in the Southwestern United States many reasons have been advanced to explain why all the old cities were abandoned, but no one knows what really happened. At the time that the earlier localities were

2 S. G. Morley, *op. cit.,* pp. 312-381.

3 Most of the Maya dates can be read by experts, but there are two different schemes for relating the system to the Christian calendar. See Morley, *op. cit.,* pp. 259-311 and pp. 457-62.

being evacuated the culture was kept alive and later brought to a genuine renaissance in Northern Yucatan, which had been only marginal in the earlier phase. There was some mingling with peoples from the highlands of Central Mexico and there were some innovations in religion, lesser arts and crafts, metallurgy, and architecture, but basically, Late Maya culture is a continuation of the Early period (Fig. 98).

## B. AZTEC CULTURE

Distinctive though it was, the manner of Late Maya life was not devoid of outside influences and must be seen in the light of what was taking place in the Valley of Mexico, wherein Mexico City is situated. These happenings were part of the record of events in what anthropologists term Meso-America, a major portion of which includes Mexico, Yucatan, and Guatemala. Human habitation and culture in **Meso-America** may reach back to the end of the Pleistocene.[4] Then follow several stages, until about 200 B.C. there starts a **Formative Horizon,** which is roughly contemporaneous with the time when Early Maya culture was beginning to emerge in Guatemala. During the Formative Horizon many people were clustered in large metropolitan communities. Great pyramids, doubtless with religious implications, were constructed, and forward strides were made in writing, astronomy, mathematics, the calendar, pottery-manufacture and other arts and crafts. These developments, together with a tightly-knit social structure, were advanced in the **Classic Horizon** that comes between 400 and 900, at the same time that Early Maya culture was reaching its peak, and were carried still further in the Valley of Mexico during the **Toltec Horizon** (900-1200 A.D.). The Toltec Horizon saw the introduction of metalwork in gold, silver, and copper;[5] worship of the feathered-serpent, **Quetzalcoatl;** new architectural details in the construction of public monuments; use of hieroglyphic writing; and other fine attainments (Figs. 98, 99). During the Toltec Horizon a Mexican-Maya combine ruled Northern Yucatan in Late Maya times. Thereafter, about 1200, the culture of the

[4] The summary of cultural events in Meso-America is based on A. Caso, "New World Culture History: Middle America," *Anthropology Today* (A. L. Kroeber, ed.), Chicago, 1953, pp. 226-37.

[5] It is possible that the arts of metal were transmitted to the Valley of Mexico from outside regions. See, especially, the works of A. Caso dealing with Monte Alban; and S. K. Lothrop, "Archeology of Cocle, Panama," *Memoirs of the Peabody Museum of American Archaeology and Ethnology,* Harvard University, Vol. 7, Cambridge, 1937.

A

B

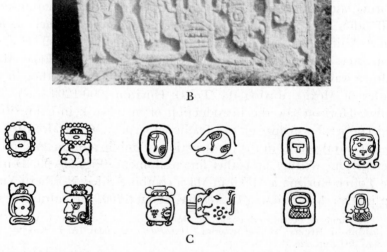

C

Fig. 98. Some aspects of Maya culture. A. A ruined temple at Uxmal, in Yucatan.
B. the lower half of a carved stela in Chichen Itza, Yucatan. It shows the feet of a
warrior, trampling on Ahpuch, the god of death. C. A few examples of Maya
hieroglyphics.

Fig. 99. Examples of Toltec-Aztec craftsmanship. A. Front wall of the Toltec temple to Quetzalcoatl (the feathered serpent) at Teotihucan, Mexico. B. Aztec artisans working (left to right, top) with feathers, gold beads, and stone beads. Below, a male carpenter, and a female weaver.

Toltecs declined and not long afterward the **Aztec** became their cultural heirs. The Aztec made themselves rulers of the Valley of Mexico, brought the older achievements to a head, and were the dominant power against whom the Spanish conquerors struggled to ultimate victory.

Superficially, Aztec culture was closely parallel to that of the Maya. There were similar systems of writing, architecture, economic life, social organization, and calendar manipulation. In each respect some important differences are to be found, but the greatest distinction is one of emphasis. The Aztec were more of a conquering people, ruling their neighbors and demanding tribute. Warfare was given high place and was intimately connected with religion. Aztec gods required much human blood and the chief honor of a warrior was to provide captives for sacrifice. Numberless victims were marched, often with solemn pomp and ceremony, up imposing stairways crowned by temples and shrines. There, high above the throngs gathered for the spectacle, they were stretched backward over sacrificial stones and held by arms and legs while a priest slashed open the chest and pulled out the heart. Sometimes bodies were then rolled down the steps to be flayed, and sometimes the blood of a victim was mixed into cakes which the populace ate.

Trade, both foreign and domestic, was another important Aztec activity, and there was a formal class of merchants who traveled widely over Mexico bringing goods back and forth, and acted secondarily as spies and intelligence agents. Regular, carefully supervised markets were held frequently, and while barter prevailed there was also a medium of exchange in the form of highly prized cocoa beans. In the markets were made available the products of specialized artisans, who devoted their lives to perfecting particular crafts, such as pottery, featherwork, carpentry, the making of mosaics of precious stones, or cloth weaving (Fig. 99B). Metallurgy was known and some remarkable ornaments and luxury items were made, but even for so major an Aztec pursuit as war, wooden swords edged with obsidian were used. By some definitions it would be permissible to class the Aztec in a Metal Age, but the bulk of their culture was indisputably Neolithic.

## C. INCA OF THE COPPER-BRONZE AGE

While the cultures of the Aztec and Maya were flourishing and exchanging some of their ideas and customs, another great New World way of life was being elaborated in South America that had but little contact with Meso-America. This culture is commonly described as **Inca,** although the term applies literally only to the ruler and his family, whereas the general populace are better identified as speakers of the **Quechua** language. The direction of Inca culture differed from that of the Maya and Aztec, and it was the only one of the three cultures to make considerable use of bronze.[6]

At its peak the core of Inca culture was in the capital city of Cuzco, not far from the border of Bolivia high in the Andean mountains of Peru. In the fifteenth century A.D. Cuzco was the center of a remarkable social system that has been described as a benevolent dictatorship. Actually, it was closer to a form of despotism which was benevolent only to a small degree. Almost every act of a commoner's life was rigidly prescribed. Each man and woman who tilled the soil, as most of the people did, was given the use of a stipulated plot of state-owned land, was told where to live, what to grow, what subsidiary crafts to pursue, and how much work he was expected to do at a given age. In addition, each householder was heavily taxed and had to contribute years of military and labor service to the government. Even marriages were supervised by the ruler's officers, and if a population surplus developed at one spot the excess might be shifted to establish or fill out a colony elsewhere. Whatever aspect of the system could be called benevolent arose from the state's desire to keep all ordinary subjects at identical, but reasonable, levels of well-being. To this end if crops in one district were inadequate, sufficient food to compensate for the deficiency would be provided free-of-charge from government warehouses. These handouts were balanced by the gathering up of extra foodstuffs wherever a community exceeded the established quota. Only on regularly held market days were the plain folk given a chance, on a small scale, to buy or sell as they saw fit. Barter was the only form of exchange, for the Inca never invented a system of coinage.

[6] The treatment of Inca culture is drawn in part from J. H. Rowe, "Inca Culture at the Time of the Spanish Conquest," *Handbook of South American Indians* (J. H. Steward, ed.), Washington, 1946, Vol. 2, pp. 183-330.

By virtue of a form of society that was so carefully controlled from above, it was not difficult for Inca rulers to organize ambitious programs of public works and to maintain bodies of carefully trained specialists. Great city structures were built of stone by common laborers under the direction of professional architects, engineers, and master masons. Crowbars and levers of bronze or wood were employed during the process of construction, but hammers of heavy stone were the commonest tools. These, together with water, sand, and ample supplies of "elbow-grease," were used to trim and polish the huge, stone building blocks, often of irregular shape, that had to be tightly fitted in place (Fig. 100). A large variety of palaces, temples, storehouses, forts, and other structures were erected, and a network of roads, superbly engineered, was built regardless of obstacles imposed by steep mountain grades or coastal deserts. Suspension bridges were skillfully placed over streams, and much effort and ability were expended in irrigation works, water-control projects, and the construction of tremendous terraces that made it possible to farm the sides of mountains.

Inca society, in the last analysis, rested on an agricultural foundation. Maize was the staple at lower altitudes and was grown so long ago that some experts believe its cultivation might have originated here. Corn was made into a fermented beverage called **chicha** and intoxication was a regular part of ceremonial life. White potatoes, a grain called quinoa, and several other domesticated plants were of the greatest importance at the higher levels. Throughout the area, in one locality or another, beans, peanuts, chili, tomatoes, avocadoes, lima beans, and many other foods were grown. From every point of view the Andean area must be reckoned as one of the world's greatest sources of plant domestication. Besides raising crops of many foodstuffs Inca farmers also grew cotton and coca, the basis of cocaine, and gathered wild grasses for thatch and cordage. By contrast with the manifold uses made of vegetal products less importance was attached to animals. There was some hunting, but it was strictly regulated; fish were caught but seldom eaten by the average person; and a number of domesticated beasts were kept. Llamas were raised for their wool and flesh and also served as beasts of burden and for sacrifices. Alpacas provided wool, primarily; domesticated ducks were known; and dogs were numerous. Swarms of guinea pigs were allowed to roam through the households, acting as scavengers and

Fig. 100. A street in Cuzco, Peru. Cuzco was the ancient capital of the Incas. The walls are survivals of the excellent stone masonry that was an outstanding aspect of Inca culture.

providing the commonest source of meat available to ordinary folk. As compared with other New World tribes the Inca people had a large list of domesticated animals, but even they made little use of them to supplement human labor and they had no beast trained for pulling.

The Inca manner of combining social and material aspects of culture may be understood from a consideration of the **Yana-kona** and **Aklya-kona.** The Yana-kona comprised a group of young men, taken into the service of the monarch. They were taught to fulfill numerous functions for the state, and some were even trained to hold minor administrative posts. There is also a possibility that they furnished metallurgists who worked for the ruler. Smiths dealt with gold, silver, copper, and bronze, for which tin was mined in Bolivia. Some utilitarian implements like knives, axes, chisels, hoes, and crowbars were made, as well as needles, bells, and an amazing variety of decorative and ornamental objects. Artifacts of gold and silver were reserved for the Emperor and the highest nobility, and Cuzco palaces were filled with delicate figures fashioned from precious metals.

Aklya-kona was a class of young women, chosen for special care and training at an early age. A few were destined for sacrifice, most of them were dedicated to lives of chastity, and some were later given as concubines or wives to nobles or commoners, respectively. Under expert direction some of the Aklya-kona were trained to weave the finest of fabrics for the use of the highest classes. Their skill has probably never been exceeded. They knew almost all of the techniques of weaving that have ever been invented, including methods of making brocades with gold and silver threads, embroidery, feather-ornamented cloth, and tapestries of excellent quality.

Inca genius and ingenuity may be found in almost every aspect of life, yet they never attained the intellectual levels of the Maya and Aztec in the fields of mathematics, astronomy, writing, and the calendar. Not that the Inca lacked all knowledge along these lines. It has been argued, for instance, that they understood the concept of zero, but in the absence of writing such a claim cannot be proved. They are known to have divided the year into twelve lunar months, each marked by a ceremony, but no one can tell how they reckoned the remaining days of a full year. In order to keep track of the multitude of details concerning the people they ruled so carefully the Inca must have had a way of keeping records, but all that archeologists have found are the ingenious objects called **quipus** (Fig. 101). A quipu consists of a central cord to which are attached strings of varied make or color. Each string represents a class of objects, and knots tied along its length indicate numbers. With the help of quipus admin-

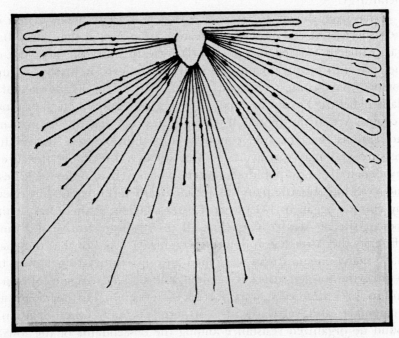

Fig. 101. A Peruvian quipu. Knotted strings served the Incas as accounting devices, and comprised their method of keeping track of statistics.

istrators found it possible to keep track of all kinds of statistics, but the system could work only as long as some people had memorized what each quipu stood for. At best a quipu was useful only as long as its significance was remembered, like a handkerchief tied about one's finger. As a way of recording data permanently it was hopelessly inadequate.

## D. THE END OF PREHISTORY IN THE NEW WORLD

Surely, one can see even from the brief treatment here given that the line of cultural development in the New World ran parallel to the Old in broad outline, but differed in one essential detail after another. In both vast areas there was a similar origin in a hunting and food-collecting stage, featured by the manufacture and use of Paleolithic tools. This was followed by the entrance of some groups into Neolithic levels and culminated in cultures that had acquired metallurgy.

As has been shown, the start of culture was a late phenomenon in the Americas. It was most likely derived from Asia at the outset, but was primarily carried independently forward until the first half of the sixteenth century. Conventionally, American prehistory is supposed to have come to an end in 1492, but a few decades actually elapsed before Europeans made any marked impact on aboriginal customs. When the blow fell, though, it struck hard. The primary motivations that inspired conquest from Europe were desires for treasure and native converts to Christianity. Inevitably this drew invaders to the most populous centers, which were also the wealthiest, and so a kind of battle plan was automatically formulated. The opening episode began in 1519 when Cortez confronted the Aztec at the present site of Mexico City. For all their administrative skill and efficiency the Aztec had followed so aggressive a policy that they had made many enemies who welcomed an opportunity to get even by helping the foreign attackers. A long and bloody struggle followed, but in 1521 the Aztec were forced to succumb. Further south in Guatemala, and eastward in Northern Yucatan, other Spaniards found no organized resistance among the descendants of the Maya, whose culture had disintegrated long ago. With the founding of Merida in 1542 the entire territory of the ancient Maya came under Spanish control. Today, several million full-blooded Aztec and Maya Indians continue to live in Meso-America, but they cannot read the ancient hieroglyphs, calculate the calendars, construct fine monuments, or manufacture the splendid products of the past.

What may have been a mere accident of history paved the way for the conquest of the Inca domain. Huayna Capac, the last great ruler, died suddenly in 1527 without having named a successor. Two half-brothers, his sons by different mothers, promptly engaged in a civil war to determine who should rule. When Pizarro arrived he cleverly took advantage of their bitter struggle, and so managed to defeat them one after the other by 1532.

Shortly after, in 1540, Coronado undertook the first Spanish penetration of the Southwestern United States. He met resistance occasionally, but was soon able to win at least the nominal submission of the natives. There were no great stores of treasure to reward a conqueror, so little effort was made to subjugate the Indians thoroughly and they continued to carry on much of their old culture even though they acknowledged the legal control of Spain. At the same time that Coronado was traveling through the Southwest, De Soto was leading an expedition into the Southeast. Here he found the Mississippi pattern of culture still flourishing, but his coming began to upset the established ways of native life and when the colonization of the Eastern seaboard started the old customs rapidly disintegrated. Much the same was true of the Northeastern United States. The colonists who founded Jamestown in 1607, or who reached Plymouth in 1620, were confronted by tribes whose cultures were going concerns. But when colonial expansion started to move westward aboriginal life quickly changed or vanished.

## E. HOW DIFFUSION OPERATES

Within a hundred years after the discovery by Columbus there was not a region of high American Indian culture that had not been greatly influenced or submerged by Europeans. This century was not, except in rare cases, marked by goodwill or helpfulness on either side. From the standpoint of the Indians the termination of nearly all of their old customs must have been a continuous tragedy. Yet, from a detached anthropological view, there is a lesson in cultural growth to be learned from the situation. At the cost, it must be admitted, of a deplorable amount of bloodshed and grief, each party's culture was enriched by the contact in several respects. Europeans learned to grow potatoes, corn, and tobacco; and Indians learned to raise wheat and oats. Europeans acquired knowledge of rubber and cocaine; and native Americans became acquainted with iron, steel, and wagons. Domesticated ducks and turkeys were introduced to the Old World; and the New found out about horses and cattle. Thus does the process of diffusion operate despite the basic hostility of the peoples concerned.

Much the same is true of the present moment. From some of our bitterest enemies we have learned to use such instruments of war as dive bombers, massive tanks, and powerful submarines. With equal alacrity our opponents have hastened to adopt American contrivances like jeeps. Plainly, diffusion may operate in a climate of hate as well as in a friendly atmosphere. And, it must be stressed, diffusion does not conform to principles of mathematics. Things can be added to both sides of an equation without subtracting from either. When Europeans learned to grow white potatoes they added them to their existing crops without necessarily giving anything up; and when Indians discovered how to grow wheat they were not forced to sacrifice any of their traditional foods in exchange. In such respects each side was a gainer and neither was a loser.

Post-Columbian contacts of Europe and aboriginal America also throw light on the way in which particular cultures grow. To some extent they develop from local inventions, but they also expand by accretions gained through diffusion. Indeed, if one takes a world view existing cultures are found to have a much higher percentage of diffused elements than of independent inventions. If all borrowed items were suddenly to be removed from the established way of life of the United States it would eliminate such cardinal aspects as the English language, Judaism and Christianity, printing, coinage, and the wide range of useful plants that were first domesticated by the Indians of the New World.

Finally, we may note from the cultural interchange that took place after 1492 that all groups of *Homo sapiens* are potentially capable of assimilating each other's cultures. No biological or mental barriers stand in the way. Many New World Indians of our day live by standards that were derived from European sources in historic times. Some people say, without adequate thought or sufficient consideration of the facts, that the aboriginal Americans deserve lowly status because they are degenerate and unable to absorb the finer points of civilization. The opposite may be repeatedly demonstrated. Throughout the Southwestern United States, where sizable native populations are still to be found, the Indians who stubbornly reject the ways of the Caucasoids are apt to be objects of admiration, friendly interest, and benevolent concern. It is precisely those who have shown themselves most capable of absorbing "White" culture who are most likely to be punished, usually in proportion to the extent that they have mastered the patterns of the Caucasoids. Many a native youngster who has been well trained in a particular craft at a government school finds himself baffled on trying to get a job to discover that "Indians need not apply." Culturally imposed obstacles, it must be concluded, do far more to prevent the sharing of a given way of life than any supposed deficiencies of mind or body.

## SELECTED REFERENCES

Bennett, Wendell C., "A Reappraisal of Peruvian Archaeology," *Memoir, Society for American Archaeology,* No. 4, Menasha, 1948.

Caso, Alfonso, "New World Culture History," *Anthropology Today* (A. L. Kroeber, ed.), Chicago, 1953, pp. 226-237.

Hay, Clarence L., *et al.,* (eds.), *The Maya and Their Neighbors,* New York, 1940.

Morley, Sylvanus G., *The Ancient Maya,* Stanford, 1946.

Rowe, John H., "Inca Culture at the Time of the Spanish Conquest," *Handbook of South American Indians* (J. H. Steward, ed.), Washington, Vol. 2, 1946, pp. 183-330.

Steward, Julian H. (ed.), *Handbook of South American Indians,* six volumes, Washington, 1946-1950.

Strong, W. Duncan, and Willey, Gordon R., "Archaeological Notes on the Central Coast," *Columbia Studies, Archaeology and Ethnology,* Vol. 1, No. 1, New York, 1943.

Tax, Sol (ed.), *The Heritage of Conquest,* Glencoe, 1952.

Vaillant, George C., *Aztecs of Mexico,* New York, 1941.

# CHAPTER 18

# Some Laws of Culture Growth

## A. INTRODUCTION

Students who are just becoming acquainted with the science of man frequently ask: "Why, apart from mere curiosity, should we have to learn so many details of man's cultural past?" This is a legitimate question, worthy of a careful answer.

Anthropologists do not find it difficult to justify their interest in the data of archeology, even when the subject leads back to times so remote that few facts are available and all interpretations are dubious. Unless one takes the indefensible position that modern culture sprang ready-made into existence without antecedents, he must be willing to study what came before in order to understand what is going on now. Without such understanding of the past systematic controls for the present can never be established. There is a tendency in some quarters to heap scorn on social scientists because they cannot regulate or direct social processes. Such criticism is not entirely unjustified, but if the situation is ever to be improved social scientists will have to gain an even greater knowledge of the past factors that have brought about current conditions, and it is to archeology that they will have to look for further enlightenment.

On one important point at least archeologists have already made a lasting contribution. Thanks to their findings additional support has been given to the conclusions of physical anthropologists on the score of the basic unity of *Homo sapiens*. No one knows, nor is anyone likely ever to discover the stock or racial affinity of the very first fist-axe maker, potter, weaver, farmer, or metallurgist; nor is it probable that we shall ever learn the identity of the first person to have made use of a spear, bow and arrow, wagon, boat, alphabet, calendar, or coin. But archeologists have shown that no one stock or race can truthfully take credit for having begun all these achievements, and that once they had become part of human culture they came to be handled by all manner of people. Many Caucasoid groups were pioneers in metallurgy, but they were not a whit better than the early Mongoloid artisans of the Shang dynasty of China, the Inca Indian craftsmen of Peru, or latter day Negroid workers with bronze and iron in Africa. From the start the building of culture has been a joint enterprise of mankind, and leadership in the movement has shifted without loss of progress from one region to another and from one hominid subdivision to another.

Archeology has taught us that everywhere on earth human beings have transcended the bio-physico-chemical realm and entered the sphere of culture. It has also brought to light the infinite variety of forms that particular cultures may take and has demonstrated how often a group of people in one locality may develop a way of life that is markedly different from that of their neighbors. It is easy enough to become bewildered by these facts and to come to the erroneous conclusion that the totality of culture is a chaotic hodge-podge which has followed no consistent pattern of development. A discerning student of man, however, must learn to recognize the unity that underlies the mass of differing details. Today it can be proved that a number of consistent trends have been operating from the beginning along regular and therefore predictable lines. Once the existence of these trends has been recognized their past courses can be charted, and if they show steady movement in a given direction it may be forecast that they will continue to go in the same direction in the future.[1] Archeology makes one of its major contributions when it provides the data from which trends may be charted.

All sciences go through a preliminary fact-gathering stage, after which efforts are made to discover which phenomena regularly occur together. Observation of associations or connections that repeatedly go together leads to the establishment of scientific laws which seek to describe the combinations and to explain how, when and why they were formed. Then, laws that are found to have been long operative

---

[1] It is convenient to talk of trends as moving consistently in one direction, but actually trends generally move in zigzag fashion even when they ultimately continue level or go up or down.

in the past are used in forecasting the future. Thus, anyone who has again and again watched blue litmus paper turn red when dipped in acid can predict that on future occasions blue litmus will redden on contact with an acid. The longer and oftener one can observe the operation of a supposed law in the past, the more certainly can he foretell its future course. Under such conditions prediction is no more than a projection into the future of a trend line observed in the past. So it is that those who want to know how culture is likely to act in the future must find out from archeologists how it has behaved in the past. Few social scientists have as yet begun to study universal trends of cultural behavior, and too little information is available about some former cultures, but enough is already known to justify the tentative formulation of a few laws. These formulations are among the most significant of the inferences to be drawn from archeology. Equally important is the fact that the recognizable trends which are expressed as laws can already be shown to operate, not independently, but as integrated parts of one whole pattern of cultural evolution.

## B. THE LAW OF INCREASING RELIANCE ON CULTURE

For all the grave doubts that may beset the student of human origins, it has been firmly established that *Homo sapiens* had reached his present anatomical condition at the very latest by 20,000 B.C., and that he has undergone very little biological change since. At that time, which coincides pretty well with the end of the Old Stone Age, man had made only a little cultural progress but unlike his biology he has since enormously modified his culture. Except in a few instances Paleolithic man could not rely on cultural devices to take the place of or to supplement his biological mechanisms. To sustain individual life and to reproduce the species he was still making most of his responses in accordance with his inherited bio-physico-chemical makeup. He had only limited means for making fit to eat foods that were inedible in their natural state; when he wanted to get to a distant spot in a hurry he had no recourse but to run; when he wanted to shatter something hard he had to depend to a large extent on his physical strength; [2] if he wanted to carry something he had to

[2] In order to keep the argument as unified and simple as possible, it is assumed throughout this discussion that every person has complete access to all the items available in his stage of culture. The reader must recognize that this is not actually the case.

use his own or another human body; when his eyes began to fail he had to reconcile himself to dimming vision; if his lungs sickened when he was young he could not breathe properly, and stood little chance of living to have offspring; and if a woman could not be delivered naturally of a baby, she was doomed to die in childbirth.

Without trying to trace all the intermediate steps that signalize changes in each of these instances, let us consider the same set of items in a contemporary setting. As we do this **the law of increasing reliance on culture** (Fig. 102) should become strikingly clear. Today

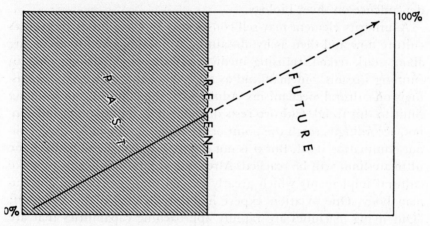

Fig. 102. The law of increasing reliance on culture.

there are many methods of making palatable products that are naturally poisonous or indigestible; those who are in a hurry to get to distant places do not run but use vehicles like automobiles or airplanes; for shattering hard substances there are many power-driven implements or explosives; cargoes are transported by trucks, freight cars, or ships, and not on human backs; eye-glasses give perfect vision to multitudes with defective eyes; artificial respirators keep alive many who could not otherwise breathe, and young men have been lifted out of iron lungs long enough to enable them to beget offspring; and modern obstetricians daily deliver with the aid of instruments and surgery women who would die in childbirth if left only to the workings of biology.

Professor Hooton, among others, has occasionally deplored the existence of the law of increasing reliance on culture on the grounds that it serves to perpetuate in *Homo sapiens* defective genes that might, without the help of cultural props, be eliminated in a struggle for survival.[3] Whether or not the net result is a lowering of mankind's biological efficiency is open to question, but in any event the law is not likely to be reversed. Man has not lived by biology alone for many millenia. At present human fitness is measured by one's adjustments to cultural rather than biological factors. Despite nostalgic longings for "the good old days," or fervently expressed hopes of a return to "the simple life," there is no record of a single society that has actually decreased its reliance on culture and stepped up its dependence on sheer biology.

A minority element may self-consciously forego a bit of its group's culture now and then as by abstaining from all cooked foods, going about stark naked, refusing medical assistance, or bathing only in running streams, but mankind as a whole continues to rely increasingly on cultural mechanisms. Admittedly, there must be an ultimate limit to this trend. Culture rests on biological foundations and cannot, accordingly, reach the point of eliminating human biology without eliminating itself. But it is not easy to foresee when or where the ultimate limit will be reached. Already mankind has begun to make cultural implements which greatly exceed the potentials of the human body. One aviation expert has thus described the situation: "Our flying machines are rapidly approaching capabilities that are penalized rather than aided by the presence of a human pilot." [4]

The law of increasing reliance on culture does not stand apart from other trends of cultural development. Among other things it makes possible man's shift from dependence on brawn (biological strength) to trust in brain (cultural efficiency). Long ago, as in the case of mechanical aids to vision, man began to expect perfection from his cultural equipment rather than from his anatomical structure.

For another thing, the law of increasing reliance on culture helps to level out the non-biological differences between the sexes. When culture is only weakly developed the biological distinctions of male and female loom large, but as cultural substitutions for biology come to be developed women and men can use them with almost equal

3 E. A. Hooton, *Men, Apes, and Morons*, New York, 1937, p. 294.

4 This statement was made by J. H. Kindelberger, and was quoted in *The Ann Arbor News* for June 13, 1952.

efficiency. Throughout the world it will be found that as cultures
advance sex differences tend to diminish, except in matters directly
related to biology. In any society whose history is long known there
is a much wider gap between the roles of men and women in earlier
stages of culture than at later times. Any middle-aged citizen of the
United States can recall cultural activities that were once regarded
as entirely masculine and are now carried on by individuals of either
sex.

## C. THE LAW OF EXPANDING USE OF NATURAL RESOURCES

It would not have been possible for man to have increased the
efficiency of his culture had he not learned to make wider use as time
went on of the raw materials provided by nature. This could have
been accomplished only by a growth of knowledge, for no new ingredients have been added to the composition of the earth since its
formation. Whatever original substances or organisms have occasionally been formed have always been re-combinations or refinements of
older ingredients. Basically, man has had the same physico-chemical
resources available to him from the day when hominids first appeared. Until 20,000 B.C. *Homo sapiens* was able to utilize only a
small fraction of his physical environment, not much more than
the air around him, wild plants and animals, water, and a few substances that could be used while cold. Then, in the Neolithic, grass
and loess lands that had had no particular value in the Old Stone Age
became highly important for grazing and agricultural purposes; wet
clay shifted from the category of a nuisance to that of a valuable
commodity for manufacturing pottery; and previously neglected
fibers took on a new significance as the making of textiles developed.
Later, metallic ores became greatly prized, and in our own day the
rapid march of culture has given previously undreamed of value to
once negligible items like uranium.

To chart the past operation of **the law of expanding use of natural
resources** (Fig. 103) is none too difficult, nor is it hard to foretell that
some materials presently of little worth will some day turn out to
have exceedingly high value. At the same time, it must be recognized,
man's increasing ability to utilize the potentials of his environment
had much to do with increasing the speed of culture growth. Archeologists have demonstrated that Paleolithic man made relatively few

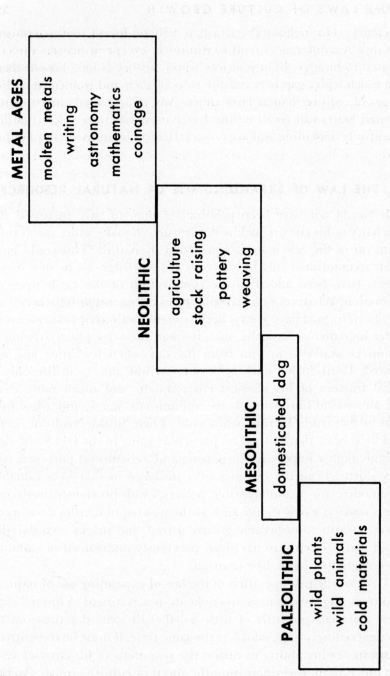

Fig. 103. The law of expanding use of natural resources.

innovations from 500,000 B.C. or earlier to 20,000 B.C. Progress was also comparatively slow in Mesolithic times, between 20,000 B.C. and 6000 B.C. From then on the tempo became faster and faster during the Neolithic and Metal Ages, and our own era is distinguished for its amazing speed of culture change, especially in the realm of technology.

Since cultures grow only a little by means of local invention and very much through the agency of diffusion, quick progress is aided by the speed and frequency of contact between a given society and many others. With the modern perfection of means of communication an item invented in one place can rapidly be spread throughout the world. All societies with progressive cultures strive to keep in touch with each other, whether on friendly or hostile terms; and the surest way to cultural stagnation is through a policy of isolation.

## D. THE DECLINING PERCENTAGE OF INDIVIDUAL KNOWLEDGE, AND ITS COROLLARIES

As the human ability to take advantage of a steadily mounting number of natural resources continues, the sum total or stockpile of knowledge available in a progressive society becomes too great for any one person to encompass. So there comes into play **the law of declining percentage of individual knowledge** (Fig. 104B). In order to get an understanding of how this law works we must imagine a stage when every human male knew all there was for men to know, and every female knew all that pertained to the members of her sex.

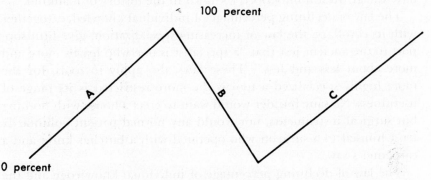

Fig. 104. Three interconnected laws of culture growth. A. The law of increasing specialization. B. The law of declining percentage of individual knowledge. C. The law of necessary cooperation.

Such a completely unspecialized level probably existed at the very dawn of cultural evolution, and at that time each individual may be said to have had 100 per cent of all the knowledge available to his sex. For contrast we have but to consider the present state of affairs in our own society. What man or woman among us knows how to raise and prepare all the food that he eats, fashion all the utensils and dishes needed for cooking and serving, make all the garments to be worn, build one's own house, cure his ailments, and build and service his own radio, television set, refrigerator, and automobile? Far from knowing how to do all these things for ourselves we rely on numerous others to do most of them for us. And to the extent that this is the case we exemplify the law of declining percentage of individual knowledge. It must be admitted that in our society and culture one person, no matter how brilliant he may be, can have only a small fraction of the total knowledge to be found among all of us.

Whenever such a stage is reached in any society the only way that its culture can be kept going is by a process of compartmentalization, which means that its stockpile of knowledge is divided up, with particular subgroups or specialists assuming responsibility for particular fractions of the total. Wherever the law of declining percentage of individual knowledge goes into effect it is invariably accompanied by a **law of increasing specialization** (Fig. 104 A). Once more, it is archeology that supplies the necessary proof. Neolithic communities always have more classes of specialists than those of the Old Stone Age; Metal Age societies have even more; and modern social units have the greatest numbers ever known in the history of mankind.

The law of declining percentage of individual knowledge, together with its corollary, the law of increasing specialization, give firm support to the ancient jest that "a specialist is one who learns more and more about less and less." These laws also apply to tools, for the more highly specialized a tool is the more restricted is its range of usefulness. No sane builder would want to erect a house with nothing but surgical instruments, nor would any normal patient voluntarily trust himself to a surgeon who operated with a butcher knife and a carpenter's saw.

The law of declining percentage of individual knowledge and the accompanying law of increasing specialization bring into action still another trend that may be described as **the law of necessary coopera-**

tion (Fig. 104 C). To prevent a very complex culture from collapsing each individual participant must be assured of the cooperation of specialists who can fill in the gaps of his own knowledge. Where each person knows only a tiny percentage of his total culture he cannot possibly insist on complete independence. All economic systems serve to illustrate various aspects of the law of necessary cooperation. At the very least they must include buyers who are willing to exchange something with sellers. Where complex methods of manufacturing are concerned other forms of necessary cooperation come into being. Planners and designers of intricate objects are economically of little worth unless there are ordinary workers who can carry out their ideas. Were it not for a high degree of cooperation between its planning staff and its labor force every modern industrial plant would have to close its doors. Similarly, managements and workers may oppose each other on many counts, but neither group could long maintain itself without the help of the other.

So essential is mutual interdependence that it may not be left to chance. Hence social regulations designed to further the law of necessary cooperation are found in every advanced culture. We could no more maintain our way of life with a Paleolithic form of social organization than we could keep up our industrial production with no more than Old Stone Age implements, techniques, and raw materials. Any society that fails to pay full attention to the law of necessary cooperation is bound to find its culture getting out of balance and veering toward disintegration.

## E. OF TIME AND THE CONSERVATION OF HUMAN MUSCULAR ENERGY

Neither the expanding utilization of natural resources nor the increase of specialization that underlie much of the growth of culture is a random matter. Consciously or not, each of these trends was developed in the interests of greater efficiency. No matter in how many ways efficiency may be defined and evaluated in other terms, it can always be measured with reference to material culture by standards of time consumption and the expenditure of **human muscular energy.**[5] Throughout the march of culture an implement that could perform

---

[5] As another instance of a labor-saving device, the letters H.M.E. will be used for the phrase, **human muscular energy.**

a given task in less time than its predecessor would, in the course of events, always displace the earlier tool. This is equivalent to saying that insofar as two instruments could do the same task mankind has invariably selected the one that accorded with **the law of time conservation** (Fig. 105A).

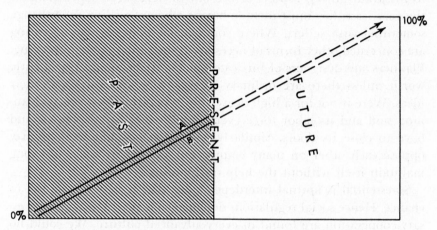

Fig. 105. The twin laws of time (A) and human muscular energy conservation (B).

More dramatic still is the law of H.M.E. conservation (Fig. 105B). This is one of the most clearly demonstrable and most surely predictable of all the laws of culture growth that can be derived from archeological evidence. Whether one is dealing with a progression of cutting implements from stone knives to steel blades; or a succession of weapons from clubs and fist-axes to spears, bows and arrows, revolvers, machine guns, and atom bombs; or with the evolution of means of transportation from foot, to horse, to automobile, to airplane; the same principle applies. The primary determinant for the acceptance of any new, material trait is the recognition, explicit or implicit, of the fact that more can be accomplished if mechanical efficiency is increased and H.M.E. decreased. Once again is the conclusion driven home that we demand effectiveness in our cultural implements rather than in our biological structures.

Even when analysis is restricted to a single technological device like an automobile the law of H.M.E. conservation may be seen to operate constantly and consistently. The first automobiles manufactured had to be cranked by hand, at a considerable cost in H.M.E.

Today, they begin with the push of a finger on a starter. Shifting gears manually, which was once the universal practice, is now almost obsolete. Tires that had to be laboriously blown up on hand pumps are rapidly and effortlessly filled with air by the use of readily available pressure pumps. Even car windows that had to be raised or lowered by turning a handle can presently be operated by touching a button.

In combination the laws of time and H.M.E. conservation work with unfailing certainty. One may be positive that no invention will succeed if its use calls for an additional outlay of time and human effort. With equal assurance one can forecast that a time and energy-saving device has an excellent chance of ultimate acceptance. No shrewd business man can be persuaded to finance the production of an item that goes against this trend. As a matter of fact a new product may not look or taste as nice as something it is trying to replace, but if it saves time and energy it stands a good chance of succeeding. Any manufacturer of prepared foods or "mixes" can vouch for the truth of this statement. So much importance does mankind attach to the laws of time and H.M.E. conservation that objects conforming to these principles are likely to be widely purchased even if their cost in money is high. The ultimate test is the efficiency of the finished artifact and not the price or the amount of labor involved in its production.

## F. THE INTEGRATED PATTERN OF CULTURE GROWTH

There is much still to be learned about the laws of culture growth that are implicit in the findings of archeology. Very few anthropologists have begun to think in terms of basic trends and to attempt to formulate their workings into laws. Fewer still have tried to fit observed trends and laws into an integrated pattern. Just the same it is encouraging to know that a start can be made along the lines set forth in this chapter.

Man became a human being, entirely different from all other animals, when he began to contrive and rely upon non-genetically inherited and extrabiologic factors. At the outset progress in this direction was slow and early hominid life was predominantly biological, but as millenia succeeded each other there was a marked increase of reliance on culture and a consequent playing down of dependence on biology. This attitude furthered the preference of *Homo sapiens* for brain over brawn and made possible an important shrinkage of non-biological differences between the sexes. Still, reliance on culture would have remained woefully restricted if man had not learned to make continually greater use of natural resources. As this aspect of human activity gained momentum a point was reached wherein the stockpile of a society's knowledge became too great for any one individual to handle, and classes of specialists arose as custodians of particular fractions of the whole. Then, to prevent its total culture from fragmenting into unconnected bits, each social unit found ways to enforce cooperation among its various members.

As one charts the laws based on past movements of culture one major objective stands out—and that is in the nature of a joint trend devoted to the conservation of time and H.M.E. What mankind does with the saved energy and time is not always clear. Some of it is doubtless used in the production of works of art; some is absorbed by amusements and sports; and some is converted to nervous or mental activities. Not all of it is necessarily utilized in ways that are officially sanctioned by a particular society; but whether individuals approve or disapprove there seems to be no way known of reversing the dual trend. Ever since *Homo sapiens* started to decrease his reliance on biology in favor of culture, and to direct his efforts to the conservation of time and energy, he has continued to press toward these goals with very little deviation.

### Selected References

Clark, J. Grahame D., "Archeological Theories and Interpretation: Old World," *Anthropology Today* (A. L. Kroeber, ed.), Chicago, 1953, pp. 343-360.

Herskovits, Melville J., *Man and His Works,* New York, 1948, chap. 7.

Linton, Ralph, *The Study of Man,* New York, 1936.

Steward, Julian H., "Cultural Causality and Law: A Trial Formulation, etc.," *American Anthropologist,* Vol. 51, 1949, pp. 1-27.

———, "Evolution and Process," *Anthropology Today* (A. L. Kroeber, ed.), Chicago, 1953, pp. 313-326.

White, Leslie A., "Energy and the Evolution of Culture," *American Anthropologist,* Vol. 45, 1943, pp. 335-356.

Zipf, George K., *Human Behavior and the Principle of Least Effort,* Cambridge, 1949.

# Biocultural Behavior

# CHAPTER 19

# The Ethnological Approach to Culture

## A. BASIC CONCEPTS AND DEFINITIONS

Physical anthropologists concentrate their efforts on the study of man's biological characteristics; and archeologists deal with the origin and growth of universal and local manifestations of past cultures; but the interplay of living people with cultural phenomena is the principal concern of ethnologists.[1] With the rare exception of hermits and the like human beings live in groups or societies, each of which has a distinctive set of extrabiological, symbolic values, that regulates the conduct of its members.

There is no mathematically precise way of defining a society, but in general it may be said to consist of a group of individuals of both sexes, who reside in one locality, recognize the same administrative authority, speak a mutually intelligible language, practice a similar way of life, and interact or cooperate for the attainment of common goals. On each score a considerable amount of variation is possible. Using the people of the United States as an example, one might question whether they constitute a society. One might justifiably ask whether residents of northern Maine really follow the same way of life as the inhabitants of southern California around Hollywood, or whether the folk in Delaware truly interact with those in Idaho for

[1] Throughout Part Three ethnologist will be used to describe one who works either in ethnology or ethnography. Similarly, no distinction will be made between an ethnologist and a cultural or social anthropologist. Some shades of difference might be brought out by the use of separate terms, but there is too much overlap to warrant keeping them apart.

329

the attainment of common goals. Only in times of great events like national elections or wars are we conscious of any important degree of cooperation among all the citizens of the United States.

Fortunately, many of the doubts that plague students of large and complex communities are less grave in the case of those who deal with so-called primitive societies, and ethnologists have traditionally worked with the latter. Primitive is also a difficult term to define, but anthropologists agree that it should not be taken to mean inadequate, immature, deficient, savage, or backward. Perhaps the best way to sense the anthropological concept of primitive is to equate it with nonliterate,[2] that is, with societies whose cultures do not include regular use of a written language.

Primitive societies differ from others in several essential regards. The differences need not be caused by an absence of writing, but on the whole it has been found that each nonliterate society occupies only a limited range of territory, whose boundaries are well-known and rarely transgressed. Within the territorial limits outsiders are rarely met, and the size of the group is so small that constant interaction with total strangers, so prominent a feature of our own lives, is rarely necessary. Living together with a restricted number of people whom one knows fairly well makes cooperation for the achievement of common goals comparatively easy. Furthermore, a primitive community is likely to have a relatively uniform language and religion, and a fairly homogeneous way of life. Rarely will it show great linguistic differences, allegiance to conflicting religious systems, or profound variations of symbolic values.

Ethnologists who occupy themselves with primitive societies are spared many of the complications that confront students of literate social units of great size. Their aim is to discover and record the basic mode of behavior that makes up a group's design for living together. For convenience this design may be called a pattern of culture. It does not take much experience to realize that even within a small, nonliterate, relatively homogeneous society, more than one culture pattern must prevail. As an irreducible minimum, it stands to reason that one is unlikely to find an identical way of life prescribed for males and females; and it is hardly to be expected that a

---

2 It is essential not to confuse nonliterate with illiterate. The latter refers to people who cannot read or write in a society whose other members can. Nonliterate refers to a culture none of whose bearers can read or write.

single design guides the conduct of infants and adults. There is also little cause for surprise if one finds varying patterns being followed by those of markedly divergent social backgrounds, greatly advanced age, or widely different occupations.

Granted that every society has a number of differing designs for living, what is an ethnologist to describe? Shall he report a great number of culture patterns, each of which applies only to a segment of society; or shall he present a single, overall pattern that may not be representative of all concerned? Anthropologists usually get around the dilemma by reporting in detail the commonest pattern of culture that applies to normal adults of either sex, and by indicating whatever significant variations customarily apply to others.

Before going further a serious student of anthropology must here memorize two fundamental axioms of the science of man. Every society seeks to perpetuate itself biologically through the birth of offspring to its members; and every society strives to continue its pattern of culture endlessly by teaching infants to know and accept its way of life. Sexual reproduction is a social as well as an individual concern, and the establishment of long-lasting cultural traditions is not a private matter. No society willingly looks forward either to biological or cultural extinction.

## B. ETHNOLOGICAL FIELD METHODS

Unlike many other scientists, an ethnologist cannot bring his subjects into a laboratory. Instead, he must go to visit them wherever they may happen to reside. This may be inconvenient, but it has the advantage of giving him a chance to study a people's manner of living in its customary setting. Whenever possible, one should select for investigation a primitive society whose culture gives promise of throwing light on some particular problem of social science. Before departing for the field an ethnologist should familiarize himself with whatever has already been written about the group and region he is going to study.

When cultural anthropology was in its infancy the matter of making contact with a primitive folk was often a serious problem. Virtually all of the investigators were Caucasoids of the Jewish or Christian faiths from Europe or America who were strange, and sometimes terrifying, to the people they wanted to observe. Conditions are much easier at present. There is hardly a tribe [3] left that has not become known to some government official, military officer, missionary, traveler, teacher, trader, or former ethnologist. Moreover, practically all primitive groups now number among their members some individuals who have received training at a school using a European tongue. Intermediaries and interpreters are therefore customarily available and, in some cases, published materials contain linguistic information by means of which it is possible to learn in advance a good deal about a language whose speakers have no means of writing.

Equipped with a background based on his reading and training, and aided by local residents who deal with the natives he intends to study, a cultural anthropologist nowadays rarely has difficulty in establishing contact with a primitive group. Whenever conditions permit he makes arrangements to live right within the community whose customs he has come to investigate. Once he has settled in a suitable place and attended to the satisfaction of his daily needs, a field worker is ready to begin the dual tasks of making himself acceptable to the point where his presence is taken for granted by his neighbors, and of noting everything that goes on about him. An anthropologist quickly senses whether his subjects distrust writing in their presence or the taking of photographs, and guides himself accordingly. No detail should be deliberately omitted from his notebooks simply because it seems trivial, for the commonplace often has greater value than the spectacular in yielding understanding.

Apart from recording all that he chances to see and hear, an ethnologist finds it wise to question selected informants on particular topics. When conducting interviews he must avoid asking leading questions and must allow subjects to wander from the point of inquiry as much as they like. Digressions frequently prove more rewarding than straightforward answers. At first a field worker must rely on interpreters, but he should take pains to learn the native language as well and as promptly as possible, so that he gradually becomes less and less dependent on what translators choose to tell him. Some cultural anthropologists supplement the data they get in interviews with answers to prepared questionnaires or standard psy-

---

[3] As used in this part of the book, tribe is synonymous with primitive society. Likewise, although a society is an aggregate of human beings, and a culture is a way of life, there is no society without a culture and no culture without a society. For this reason the two terms are sometimes used interchangeably.

chological tests. Inasmuch as these may be administered personally or by one's associates they make wide coverage possible, but not all ethnologists employ them.

Most of the anthropologists who specialize in ethnology make use of the **participant-observer** technique.[4] This means that a man seeks to share in the activities of the male natives, whereas a woman tries to take part in the daily life of her sex. A participant-observer is thus enabled to acquire much first-hand information and to learn to see things from the tribal point of view. Critics sometimes object to this approach because they fear that it makes a field worker so much a part of the very thing he is studying as to deprive him of the detachment and objectivity so essential to the scientific method. All that need be said in reply is that the danger appears greatest to those who have never tried to become participant-observers of a culture different from their own. Realistically speaking, an ethnologist is in more danger of being kept an outsider who cannot get the local viewpoint than he is of being allowed to become too thoroughly immersed in the life around him. Overcoming the biases of one's own culture is a greater challenge than the risk of going native.

At the end of a lengthy stay in the field a cultural anthropologist should have gathered a mass of detail which he must later prepare for publication as a monograph. He must, of course, systematize his material in some sort of logical arrangement, putting under a given heading all the data that seem pertinent. He must also provide whatever analyses and interpretations he can. Never should he omit contradictory items, nor pad out such gaps as may occur. Above all he must be alert to check the validity of his findings as thoroughly as he can. It is from the comparative study of many particular ways of life that ethnologists concerned with theory construct their hypotheses and attempt to merge the details of many locally functioning cultures into a grand scheme of human, cultural behavior.

## C. HOW DO YOU KNOW YOU'RE RIGHT?

Any inferences drawn from field data are bound to be wrong if the original material is faulty. Consequently, it is up to every eth-

[4] For more details regarding field methods, see the articles by J. Henry and M. E. Spiro, and B. D. Paul in A. L. Kroeber, editor, *Anthropology Today*, Chicago, 1953, pp. 417-451. Consult also, F. Kluckhohn, "The Participant-Observer Technique in Small Communities," *American Journal of Sociology*, Vol. 46, 1930, pp. 331-343.

nologist to make sure that the information he publishes is as correct as possible. There are several ways of achieving reasonable accuracy. No one of them is self-sufficient, but all together they serve to keep a worker from making gross errors.

The most common practice is for an ethnologist to question **multiple informants** on the same topic. There is no way of telling in advance whether a native is representative of his society or abnormal in some way, or whether he is truthful, willing to talk, and competent to speak on the subject under study. Accordingly, it is wise for a field investigator to question multiple informants. They should be as varied as possible, and they should be unaware of what others may already have said. If the statements of multiple informants show much agreement, one may feel fairly certain that he is getting at the truth. If there is marked disagreement one must note the fact and try to figure out what it signifies. Material obtained from a single informant is always suspect.

There is also a need for checking the **internal consistency** of one's data. If, to cite an hypothetical case, an ethnologist discovers that his informants insist that their society never indulges in violence, but finds frequent instances of assault and murder, he is faced with a marked lack of internal consistency and must seek its explanation. On one occasion, when the writer was compiling a census of the Hopi Indian pueblo of Old Oraibi in Arizona, his informants claimed at first that divorce was practically unknown among their people. Later, when their attention was tactfully drawn to much contradictory evidence they cheerfully admitted that they had been in error, and provided data that indicated as high a divorce rate as 34 percent.[5] The second set of data proved the more accurate when compared with the statements of other informants.

Another method of avoiding mistakes is to make sure that one's description of a way of life covers **the yearly round.** Many peoples practice different customs at various seasons. Ideally, a worker should stay in the field at least for a whole year, but if this is impractical he should make certain to obtain from informants full accounts of the group's behavior all through the yearly round.

The author has long been an advocate of still another device for

[5] In this case the informants may have been trying to please the ethnologist by making their culture seem to conform to the expressed standards of his own. One cannot be sure that there was any deliberate attempt to deceive.

insuring accuracy, which he calls **the divided field-trip.** Essentially this means that an ethnologist is wise to make more than a single visit to a society under study. Even if his total time in the field is limited to a few months, he would do well to leave the area for several days and to return after a lapse of time. The outstanding value of the divided field-trip is that it enables an anthropologist on his later visit to overcome some of the deficiencies of the first. On his initial arrival he might, without knowing it, have been introduced by someone whom the natives heartily disliked; he might unwittingly have dealt with unreliable informants; he might sometimes have been told deliberate untruths; his very presence might have been resented; and he might, through ignorance of local customs, have offended some members of the community. All of these faults are capable of being remedied on a return trip. Now the ethnologist may join the society without any intermediary; he knows which informants are apt to be cooperative and trustworthy, and which are better to be diplomatically avoided; few people are able to remember and repeat long after whatever deliberate misstatements they may earlier have made to an investigator; if he has previously acted properly he will find the community pleased to have him return; and he is most unlikely to give offense through ignorance of the society's symbolic values. On the whole, the advantages of the divided field-trip are so varied and numerous that they far outweigh the disadvantages of losing a few working days in the field. Besides what has already been mentioned, the divided field-trip gives an ethnologist an undisturbed chance to study his notes carefully, to discover such inconsistencies as may require further checking, to find out which topics have not been sufficiently investigated, and, in general, to lay plans based on the knowledge he has already obtained for a more adequate research program when he resumes his work.

More than anything else an ethnologist on a field-trip must never lose sight of the fact that he is a sort of guest in a society made up of sensitive human beings whose system of values is entirely different from his own. His job is to learn all he can about the other culture, not to modify or reform it. It is for him to adjust to native ways, not the other way around. Even though the period of living in a strange cultural world is temporary, all ethnologists agree that it provides an exciting and deeply rewarding experience.

Many years of ethnological research have made it clear that some subjects are best avoided at the outset. It is most unlikely that the members of any society will be willing to discuss freely with a stranger their deep-seated religious beliefs or the intimate details of their sex life. A beginner is well advised not to plunge into such matters prematurely. Information of this kind may be sought indirectly, or after an ethnologist feels that he has won the confidence of "his people." It is usually best to start one's studies with commonplace technological activities, with the collection of word lists, or with any other topic that is known to be regarded as neutral.

## D. THE GOALS OF ETHNOLOGY

Like the archeologist, the ethnologist may aim at more than one goal. He may be chiefly interested in the local design for living of a single society, or he may be more concerned with the whole range of human culture. Again, he may in either instance wish to study culture at one time period, or else he may prefer to trace the march of culture from its beginning to the present. Most ethnologists feel that whatever their approach happens to be, the broad outlines of culture growth can be understood only if one makes comparative studies of many particular cultures in all parts of the world. Thus, each ethnological investigation makes a contribution toward the understanding of culture as a whole.

What every ethnologist hopes to publish after returning from the field is a full and objective account of the prevailing pattern of culture in the society that he was visiting. Of necessity, this pattern will be a composite, made up of the ways of life of many individuals. It will also have to be a sort of average, and like all averages it will have to be carefully checked to make sure that it is truly representative of the whole society. It is best to look upon a culture pattern as a generalized abstraction. It has no more independent existence than the concept of righteousness. One can point out many examples of righteous behavior, but it is impossible to show righteousness by itself. So, too, with a pattern of culture. Many acts of cultural behavior can be shown to follow a pattern, but the pattern itself exists only as an abstract concept. Nevertheless, if ethnologists refused to organize their material into patterns, all efforts to construct theories of culture would be lost in a maze of details.

## E. THAT PERSONAL TOUCH

Sooner or later the thought is apt to arise: why could not the operator of an excellent moving picture camera and a perfect sound recorder produce a better report of a primitive culture than an ethnologist? A moment's reflection should provide part of the answer. Many people are averse to being photographed, and even if everyone were willing it would be impractical to keep the needed equipment in continuous operation for months, possibly for a year or more. Besides, many activities take place indoors, at night, during periods of bad weather, or in spots where extraneous noises may drown out what is really important. Nor would a finished sound track convey much meaning to audiences that did not understand the native language. Furthermore, one must not forget that mechanical devices can record only sights and sounds, whereas an ethnologist uses all his senses.

No instrument has yet been invented that can make discriminating selections of ethnological materials, and a trained anthropologist can certainly pick out significant items of culture better than the most proficient of cameramen. Wherever possible an ethnologist does not fail to supplement his notes with photographs, but indiscriminate picture-taking can be more harmful than helpful. Similarly, many workers take sound-recorders into the field, but once more the material to be recorded has to be carefully chosen.

Without an ethnologist to marshal facts into systematic order they remain a hopeless jumble. Coherence emerges only when similar data are fitted together according to a consistent scheme. The more clearly an ethnologist knows ahead of time the kinds of problems he intends to study and the kinds of questions he plans to ask, the more certainly will his material lend itself to adequate classification and intelligent analysis. Above all, it is the function of an ethnologist to make his data meaningful to others. No matter by what techniques he acquired his information, it is up to the cultural anthropologist to provide explanations of his field material. Only a human being can make meaningful interpretations of culture. The success of a published monograph can best be measured by the light it throws on the behavior of people in a given society, and by the extent to which its material makes possible the building of new theories pertaining to the universal workings of bicultural behavior.

## F. IN DEFENSE OF TRIBAL STUDIES

Social scientists other than anthropologists sometimes wonder why ethnologists appear to be preoccupied with primitive societies and their forms of culture. Actually, many ethnologists have begun to study modern, highly literate peoples, and they have brought to their task some of the techniques and ideas drawn from their knowledge of primitive life. This indicates that ethnology is considered to be of value in the general field of social science. The concern of ethnologists with tribal customs is anything but a curious eccentricity, for it has been shown that a grasp of primitive ways of life provides insights that lead to a better understanding of human behavior everywhere.

Primitive men and women are not second-class members of *Homo sapiens,* and their societies have patterns of culture that often parallel those of literate people. Primitive ways of life are part of the total fabric of human behavior, and must be known to those who make all of mankind the target of their studies. To be specific, all scientists try to gain knowledge of the simpler aspects of their discipline before going on to more complicated matters. No one would try to study advanced calculus without having previously learned the rudiments of elementary mathematics. So it is with the science of man. Literate, culturally heterogeneous societies, usually have such complex forms of technology and social organization that it is exceedingly difficult to get at the principles according to which they operate. Small, culturally homogeneous societies, by contrast, often function in relatively simple ways that make it easier to discover their underlying structures and the mainsprings of their actions.

There are many scholars who believe that experimentation is essential to the development of any science. According to their reasoning, studies of society can never be scientific. Ethnologists have done much to overcome this kind of criticism. Admittedly, they cannot make laboratory studies of tribal groups, but they know of so very many varied primitive societies that they can approximate the sort of experimentation that depends on the change of one variable factor at a time. The enormous diversity of nonliterate societies and cultures permits the comparative analysis of many units which may differ from each other in only one or two regards.

Studies of contemporary primitive societies are also valuable for filling gaps in the archeological record. For example, when we were dealing with the Old World's New Stone Age it was possible to describe many details of material culture, but very little could be said of human behavior. Since primitive societies whose ways of life are essentially Neolithic still exist, one can learn much from watching them in action of the probable manner in which men and women behaved in the ancient New Stone Age.

It cannot be assumed that every known group of human beings has passed through each of the earlier stages of culture delineated by archeologists. Yet, it seems certain that as a whole *Homo sapiens* did march progressively from nonliterate to literate levels. From this point of view there is much to be learned of man's cultural past by an examination of primitive societies. After all, the ultimate target of social science ought to be the behavior of mankind, and it would be a fatal error to omit from consideration those aggregates of people who happen to be primitive.

### Selected References

Bennett, John W., "The Study of Cultures: A Survey of Technique and Methodology in Field Work," *American Sociological Review,* Vol. 13, 1948, pp. 672-689.

Firth, Raymond, "Contemporary British Social Anthropology," *American Anthropologist,* Vol. 53, 1951, pp. 474-489.

Hallowell, A. Irving, "Use of Projective Techniques in the Study of Socio-Psychological Aspects of Acculturation," *Journal of Projective Techniques,* Vol. 15, 1951, pp. 27-44.

Henry, Jules, and Spiro, Melford E., "Psychological Techniques: Projective Tests in Field Work," *Anthropology Today* (A. L. Kroeber, ed.), Chicago, 1953, pp. 417-429.

Kluckhohn, Clyde, "The Place of Theory in Anthropological Studies," *Philosophy of Science,* Vol. 6, 1939, pp. 328-344.

Kluckhohn, Florence R., "The Participant-Observer Technique in Small Communities," *American Journal of Sociology,* Vol. 46, 1940, pp. 331-343.

Kroeber, Alfred L., and Kluckhohn, Clyde, "Culture," *Papers of the Peabody Museum of American Archaeology and Ethnology,* Harvard University, Vol. 47, No. 1, Cambridge, 1952.

Malinowski, Bronislaw, *Argonauts of the Western Pacific,* London, 1922, pp. 2-25.

Nadel, S. F., "The Interview Technique in Social Anthropology," *The Study of Society: Methods and Problems* (F. Bartlett *et al.,* eds.), London, 1939, pp. 317-327.
Paul, Benjamin D., "Interview Techniques and Field Relationships," *Anthropology Today* (A. L. Kroeber, ed.), Chicago, 1953, pp. 430-451.

CHAPTER 20

# Configurations of Culture

## A. SOME UNIVERSAL ATTRIBUTES OF CULTURE

Modern ethnologists are seldom content to study the culture of a primitive society as an end in itself. They prefer to regard descriptions of particular ways of life as the raw material from which may be derived laws of human conduct that may be shown to operate in all societies. So far their greatest hope of success comes from their awareness that all living men and women are biological organisms within a single species, and that they must obey the same biological dictates if they wish to maintain life and reproduce their kind. Secure in this knowledge an ethnologist is certain that regardless of which society he may be investigating he will always find a set of customs dealing with food, and others concerned with sexual relations and child-rearing. Nor is that all. No society permits its members to eat any kind of food that happens to be biologically palatable, at any time that they wish, and in any manner that they like; no social unit allows any desirous male whatsoever to have intercourse whenever and wherever he chooses with any female who happens to be biologically receptive; and no group of humans leaves the raising of offspring only to natural agencies. The strictly biological aspects of these activities are always modified by symbolic values that spell out what is right or wrong. To that extent even the most fundamental of voluntary [1] human actions are truly **biocultural.** The specific symbolic values that are associated with various bits of biological behavior vary greatly from one social unit to another, but the fact that food and sex habits are biocultural activities in all societies is a universal phenomenon.

Many years ago the statement was eloquently made that as a biological necessity food is more important than sex. Yet, except for exceedingly rare instances of full-fledged cannibalism, and with the exception of infants who are being suckled, human beings do not use one another for food. It must therefore follow that to sustain life every society's design for living together has to include means of procuring food from the external environment. For similar reasons people must obtain from the same general source whatever raw materials are needed for making houses, shelters, weapons, implements, utensils, clothes or ornaments. At the same time that man removes certain items from his physical surroundings he inevitably alters them [2] and adds other things to them, even if they be no more than body and other wastes. Hence, an ethnologist is bound to find that every culture is firmly grounded on a two-way interaction that may be expressed by the formula: **man←→environment.**

Equally universal is the concern of each society with the conception, birth and training of offspring. If these matters are not to be left entirely to biology, they will have to be performed in accordance with culturally designated rules. At the very least this means that every social unit will have as part of its culture pattern a set of symbolic values that bear on the relations of the sexes toward each other, and of adults toward infants. This feature of group life may be subsumed under the heading: **man←→man.**

A society which has worked out satisfactory relationships with its physical surroundings, and which has established suitable provisions for the birth and raising of children, must still gain for itself a feeling of assurance that it will not soon disintegrate. As long as sources of food, shelter, and raw materials continue to be plentiful,

1 Voluntary, in this context, is opposed to such involuntary actions as breathing. It does not mean subject only to one's own will.

2 This factor will vary with a society's technology. Where the latter is greatly advanced the landscape will be more drastically altered.

and insofar as there is a sufficient supply of mates for all concerned, the danger of dissolution may not loom large. But during crises, when serious shortages develop, the threat that a society may not long endure becomes grave. To counteract this potential danger every group contrives means that seek to guarantee the cohesion of its members even when some of them are ill-fed, ill-housed, or forced to stifle their sexual desires. This factor may take the form of over-riding patriotism in some instances, of religion in others, or of a combination of both. In any event, a means of welding together members of a society who may or may not be content with their way of life is another universal feature of all cultures, and may be expressed thus: **man←→supernatural.** Each of the three sets of factors will be separately treated in one of the succeeding chapters.

## B. THE SHAPE AND INTEGRATION OF A CULTURE PATTERN

Ethnology teaches us that the major features of culture neither stand by themselves nor fall into a shapeless arrangement. It may not be possible to contrive a geometric form that covers all aspects of all culture patterns, but a sense of order may be achieved if the three universal segments discussed in the preceding section are combined into a single entity, which may be pictured as a triangle (Fig. 106), in which the man←→environment interrelationships always form the base. The interactions of man←→man, and of man←→supernatural make up the other two sides, and each leg of the triangle includes many biocultural activities and values.

As one examines the **biocultural triangle** he must imagine a spring placed at each juncture where two lines meet. This will make it easier to appreciate why heavy pressure on or a marked change in the direction of any one side is bound to induce changes in the total configuration. Stated graphically a biocultural triangle may look thus △ at one stage, and like this ◁ under different circumstances. Most of the time the three main components are in equilibrium. If this is upset a period of disturbance follows, after which equilibrium may be reestablished in a new shape.

Although every feature of a society's way of life is not necessarily encompassed within the biocultural triangle, a high percentage of vital traits are always included. Ethnologists who learn to think in terms of such a configuration find that the recognition and description of all the facets of behavior that go to make up a biocultural triangle give them an objective goal to seek while making field studies anywhere. Also, the use of this device puts into concrete form the

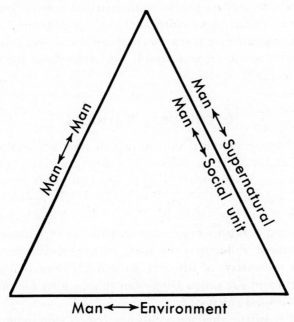

Fig. 106. A biocultural triangle. The three sides are always integrated, but do not receive equal emphasis in all societies. Some aspects of biocultural behavior are not included in the triangular configuration.

abstract concept of a pattern of culture, and makes possible point for point comparisons between the biocultural behavior of one group and that of another.

If it be true that the three principal segments of any biocultural triangle interlock, then it makes little difference at which spot an investigator starts his studies. A careful follow-up of any lead should take him all around the three sides of the figure. For instance, an ethnologist is unlikely to arouse initial resentment if he shows a friendly interest in the daily work of a potter. This cannot fail to take him well into the man←→environment aspect of the tribe's culture; after which it is but a simple step to seek information on the potter's background. Thus will be included questions about the sex, age, and relationship of the potter's teacher, the age when training began, and other attributes of man←→man conduct. Finally, it will be found that some pots are made specifically for use in sacred contexts and that design elements on others have religious significance.[3] By following up such leads an alert field worker can gain valuable information about a tribe's man←→supernatural beliefs. This demonstrates how all parts of a biocultural triangle fit together,[4] and shows how an investigator may learn much about social and religious customs even if he starts out with simple questions about the technique of pottery-making.

## C. CULTURAL EMPHASES

Besides varying in the details of which they are composed biocultural triangles, taken as units, reveal different kinds of emphases. One society may reward with prestige and honors all manifestations of strongly aggressive conduct, but another may frown upon and punish aggressors. The late Ruth Fulton Benedict selected to illustrate this point certain societies whose patterns of culture reflected strongly marked differences in basic attitudes. She described as **Apollonian** those ways of life that showed high regard for sobriety and restraint, and she called **Dionysian** those which honored intemperate and reckless behavior.[5]

Certainly it is true that some cultures have a dominant tone that seems to color the activities of all their participants. Orthodox Jewish males who lived in Eastern Europe during the late nineteenth century were Apollonian to the extent that they could achieve the most treasured honors of their communities only if they were great scholars who devoted themselves to the study of the sacred writings and their commentaries.[6] At the same period of history, far off in the Great Plains region of the United States, the Crow Indians favored Dionysian modes of action, and reserved their highest admiration and rewards for men who were daring fighters.[7]

[3] R. L. Bunzel, *The Pueblo Potter*, New York, 1929, p. 92. Pictures 1 and 2 describe prayer-meal bowls, and a design element on no. 4 is interpreted as a prayer for rain.

[4] One of the chief difficulties of the Point Four program is that it stresses the introduction of technological advances to "backward" countries, without giving sufficient consideration to the social and religious changes that are prone to follow.

[5] R. F. Benedict, *Patterns of Culture*, Penguin Books, New York, 1946.

[6] M. Zborowsky and E. Herzog, *Life is with People*, New York, 1952, pp. 74 ff. *et passim.*

[7] R. H. Lowie, *The Crow Indians*, New York, 1935, p. 215.

Since the publication of Professor Benedict's *Patterns of Culture,* other cultural anthropologists have pointed out that only a small handful of carefully selected societies are plainly dominated by a single cultural motive. Far more often, it is argued, group ways of

Fig. 107. Hopi woman grinding corn. She is rubbing a handstone against a metate. Her old-fashioned dress leaves bare the left shoulder and breast. The style of hair braiding indicates that she is a married woman.

life reveal the influence of multiple motivations. Professor Morris E. Opler has suggested that instead of having one guiding principle most cultures are organized around a number of themes.[8] Whichever may be the more accurate view, it is now fully recognized that cul-

[8] M. E. Opler, "Themes as Dynamic Forces in Culture," *American Journal of Sociology,* 1945, Vol. 51, pp. 192-206.

ture patterns show different emphases in setting up standards of approved behavior for the members of particular societies to follow.

Societies also vary in the degree to which their cultures seek to minimize the strictly biological parts of biocultural behavior. Measured in biological terms there is little difference between the functioning of a mid-Victorian female's body and that of a contemporary Hopi Indian woman. But culturally there is a profound gap. The cut of an old-fashioned Hopi dress often discloses the left breast (Fig. 107), and women openly suckle infants before either sex. Victorian women, we are told, were even reluctant to admit that they had breasts. Traditional Hopi pueblos have no toilets or outhouses of any kind, and a man cannot help but observe females in the process of elimination. Can anyone imagine a proper Victorian woman urinating or defecating in public? If one had sufficient data it would be possible to construct a trend line in which Hopi culture would appear much closer than Victorian to a biological level of behavior (Fig. 127). There is some indication that culture in general has been moving from a 100 per cent biological start in the direction of (but without being able to reach) a zero point of biology. In the absence of complete information, however, it is not possible to establish a law of cultural development based on this postulated trend.

## D. OVERT AND COVERT

Some of the difficulties involved in ethnological studies grow out of the simultaneous existence in one society of a number of different biocultural configurations. It has already been indicated that what might be correct for men may be wrong for women, and that what is fitting for adults may be unsuitable for youngsters. In homely language, it makes a big difference in any society whether a child soils itself at nine months or nine years of age. Apart from these and other variable standards based on tangible factors such as occupation, social status, and greatly advanced age, there exist what Professor Clyde Kluckhohn has discussed as **overt** and **covert** patterns of behavior.[9] By modifying his usage somewhat we may designate as overt standards those somewhat idealized notions that one consciously thinks of as typical of his culture, and which are promptly recited in response

[9] C. Kluckhohn, "Patterning as Exemplified in Navaho Culture," *Language, Culture, and Personality* (L. Spier *et al.*, eds.), Menasha, 1941, pp. 109-130.

to questions. Covert patterns may represent somewhat more realistic guides to conduct, but one is less sure to be immediately aware of them and less likely to express them readily in words. Something of the difference between them is reflected in our sayings about preaching one thing and practicing another, but when we make a contrast of this sort there is usually a hint of deceit. Such is not the case in the distinction between overt and covert with which we are dealing. One does not have to be a liar or a hypocrite to say that a given way of behaving is typical of his culture, but to act most of the time according to a different pattern. Two illustrations based on our own culture should serve to make the point clear.

Citizens of the U.S.A. will agree that in their country any person who has the price can eat whatever he wishes. Overtly there is no compulsion to prevent a wealthy man from ordering what he will in a restaurant, yet no American would ask for a breakfast of beet soup, raw oysters, and sassafras tea. Only a deeply ingrained covert pattern keeps an American from even wanting at breakfast items which, under different conditions, he might find quite palatable.

More dramatic still is another instance of contrasting attitudes. Suppose one were to ask an average American at his home if he would risk about two thousand dollars' worth of equipment, plus his own and his family's lives, merely to save a minute or two of time. The overt reply would unfailingly be in the negative, yet, any one who has observed average Americans driving cars would realize that on the road they act according to a covert pattern favoring great speed and daring, that is the opposite of their overt responses. This is the very sort of unspoken contradiction that a trained anthropologist must always be prepared to detect.

## E. THE REALITY OF CULTURE PATTERNS

Those who doubt the reality of abstract concepts may wonder if culture patterns actually exist. It can be shown that they do, even if the people most concerned with them are not aware of the fact. Let us revert to the previous example of American food habits. Suppose an eccentric individual decided that he really wanted a breakfast of beet soup, raw oysters, and sassafras tea, in what restaurant could he get them? At the opposite extreme, Americans who order fruit juice, eggs or cereal, toast, and coffee, may feel that they are expressing their personal desires, but restaurant keepers know that a pattern is being followed. Probably the most successful restaurateurs are those who most completely anticipate the patterned food habits of their patrons. What chance of success would a restaurant owner in the United States have if he catered to the unexpected whims of people who might breakfast on beet soup, raw oysters, and sassafras tea, but failed to stock fruit juices, eggs, cereals, toast, and coffee?

Storekeepers of every description realize that no matter how much Americans pride themselves on independence they actually do follow culture patterns in their buying habits. Few are the purchasers, though, who realize that they are not expressing strictly individual preferences when they buy things without obvious coercion. Yet so strong is cultural compulsion that whenever culture patterns change people usually have no recourse but to adjust their tastes to them. Many a woman who feels herself to have been best suited by a fashion that prevailed two or three years ago finds it impossible to obtain what she wants in shop after shop that carries only the latest styles. To such a person the reality of a culture pattern is no idle matter.

For those who must deal with what is called "the public," the existence of patterned behavior is a great comfort. Not only merchants but police officials would find themselves at a loss if all the residents of a city suddenly abandoned their customary patterns of conduct in order to follow purely individual dictates.

Two of the most interesting but difficult problems of social science are to determine how patterns of culture become changed, and to discover the extent to which the behavior of people is based on individual free-will or motivated by patterns of conduct that prevail in their society.

### F. MOTOR HABITS

Among the intriguing areas for studying the interplay of individual behavior and cultural conditioning is the field of **motor habits.** This phrase refers to any customarily repeated movements of parts of the body that are much alike for all members of a social unit. Motor habits may pertain to the way in which adults shake hands, roll cigarettes, take hold of the handle of a teapot, use a knife and fork, or sit on a sheepskin stretched on the ground. Gestures and facial expressions may be in the same category. To illustrate only a few of these items, all Hopi Indians roll cigarettes by moving the thumbs upward, but Navahos turn their thumbs down; all Americans pick up a teapot with the palm down, but Japanese grasp it with the palm up; and residents of India mean, "Yes," when they shake their heads halfway in the manner that Europeans use for the negative.

Motor habits are usually different for each sex in a given society. Much of the awkwardness apparent when men imitate women or vice versa, arises from the different ways in which they have learned to use their bodies. Many a burly comedian in the days when vaudeville flourished used to get his biggest laughs by pretending to crochet or to powder his nose like a lady. Some of the motor habits that distinguish the sexes are outgrowths of biology, but many are not. Biology may dictate that women only must learn all the actions that go with the nursing of babies, but there is nothing in the biology of sex that forces women to wash dishes. There are far too many educated people who fail to take account of the difference between biologically determined and culturally assigned activities (Fig. 108).

An adult who may be eager to change his accustomed way of life by adopting an entirely new culture often finds that acquisition of correct motor habits gives him more trouble than anything else. In times of war spies who could otherwise pass for enemy nationals are apt to betray themselves by mistakes in motor habits. Only those who have made a detailed study of this fascinating topic are aware of the extent to which seemingly individual body movements turn out to be standardized within the limits of particular patterns of culture.[10]

### SELECTED REFERENCES

Benedict, Ruth F., "Anthropology and the Abnormal," *Journal of General Psychology,* Vol. 10, 1934, pp. 59-80.
———, *Patterns of Culture,* Boston, 1934.
Ford, Clellan S., and Beach, Frank A., *Patterns of Sexual Behavior,* New York, 1951.
Gillin, John, *The Ways of Men,* New York, 1948, Part 4.
Kluckhohn, Clyde, "Patterning as Exemplified in Navaho Culture," *Language, Culture, and Personality* (L. Spier *et al.,* eds.), Menasha, 1941, pp. 109-130.

[10] See, for many further details, W. La Barre, "The Cultural Basis of Emotions and Gestures," *Journal of Personality,* 1947, Vol. 16, pp. 49-68.

A

B

Fig. 108. Brick carrying in two cultures. A. In India the task is assigned to women, who balance loads of bricks on their heads. B. In the United States of America men carry bricks on their shoulders, with the help of hods. Cultural differences of sexual dichotomy and motor habits are thus shown.

La Barre, Weston, "The Cultural Basis of Emotions and Gestures," *Journal of Personality,* Vol. 16, 1947, pp. 49-68.

Lowie, Robert H., *The Crow Indians,* New York, 1935.

Murdock, George P., "The Common Denominator of Cultures," *The Science of Man in the World Crisis* (R. Linton, ed.), New York, 1945, 123-142.

———, *Social Structure,* New York, 1949.

Opler, Morris E., "Themes as Dynamic Forces in Culture," *American Journal of Sociology,* Vol. 51, 1945, pp. 192-206.

Zborowski, Mark, and Herzog, Elizabeth, *Life is with People,* New York, 1952.

CHAPTER **21**

# Man's Interaction with His Environment

## A. THE STAFF OF LIFE

Man is so constituted that he cannot live and function properly unless he consumes each day an adequate amount of food and drink. This is a universal requirement with which all cultures must deal, but no two societies have exactly the same eating customs.[1] Truly has it been said that one man's meat is another man's poison. It is strange that in a matter which is so fundamentally biologic the eval-

---

[1] A good deal of information about the acquisition and preparation of foodstuffs by particular tribes may be found in R. L. Beals and H. Hoijer, *An Introduction to Anthropology,* New York, 1953, pp. 271-310; and in E. D. Chapple and C. S. Coon, *Principles of Anthropology,* New York, 1942, pp. 127-138, 142-197, *et passim.*

uation of good or bad food is very seldom if ever accomplished in any logical way. There is no society known, including our own, which has first made a thorough scientific analysis of all the nutritive elements in its environment, and then given items preference in the order that they were shown to be best suited to man's biological needs. Instead, ethnologists find everywhere the existence of food preferences based on artificial, man-made values, that have little or nothing to do with nutrition as such. A poor family of Caucasoids in the United States may bewail its inability to afford meat, but would reject a gift of plump, nutritious gophers which Navaho Indians regard as a delicacy. Even cows' milk, which is widely held to be an excellent food, was until recent years despised by Chinese, Koreans, Japanese, and other residents of the Far East. As late as 1934 the writer knew a Hopi Indian, hospitalized with an advanced case of tuberculosis, who insisted on returning to Oraibi because he was sure the attendants were trying to poison him by making him drink milk.

Symbolic values are so basic to the use of foodstuffs that as many shortages are due to scarcity of culturally approved items as are to be ascribed to the actual lack of nutriments. While World War II was being fought teams of scientists tried to persuade Allied peoples whose customary rations were in short supply to substitute other highly nourishing foods. In practically every case where the substitution failed to conform to culturally determined standards of taste and color it was strongly resisted, in spite of scientific assurances of its biological value. An interesting example of the same principle, turned about, is the practice of a soft drink company which retains an attorney who can eat various insects without harm. Whenever a suit is brought by a plaintiff claiming to have been made ill by a bug in his drink, the lawyer eats a similar specimen to disprove the claim. Apparently, juries are so impressed by this feat that they fail to consider the possibility of culturally induced damages and therefore dismiss the case.[2]

There is no substance to which arbitrary cultural values cannot be assigned. Sometimes foods come to be regarded as better suited for men or women, without reference to the actual biological differences of the sexes. Although we do not adhere rigidly to such a dis-

---

[2] On June 27, 1953, *The Ann Arbor News* carried an Associated Press dispatch describing the victory of a lawyer who ate a cockroach in court.

tinction we still recognize an unscientific tendency to associate a preference for salads with all females and a craving for thick steaks with any male. A cultural concept, unknown in our society but widespread among Indian peoples of Latin America, is the notion that foods may be hot or cold regardless of their temperature or physiological properties. One of these nonlogical classifications lists as cold such varied items as mutton, fish, maize, rice, chocolate, bread, butter, milk, sugar, and barley beer; whereas hot foods include beef, turkey, sweetpotatoes, coffee, mangoes, and chickpeas.[3] People may cling to such beliefs long after the basis for the classification has been forgotten. Ethnologists cannot explain the origin of the hot or cold concept, but they can show that it is cultural and not bio-physico-chemical. Dr. George M. Foster has tentatively traced some of these notions to the teachings of Hippocrates and Galen. They are likely to be associated with a belief that various ailments may be hot or cold. Quite often, in such cases, cures are thought to be brought about by resort to opposites, so that cold remedies and foods are used against hot illnesses, and vice versa.[4]

Foods may also be socially ranked as high or low. Sometimes this may be determined by expense which may rest on a nutritional base, as when cream costs more than milk. Just as often high class foods may be more costly but of less nutritional value, as in the case of polished and unpolished rice. Other rankings may disregard economics and biological worth altogether. Most American housewives would be ashamed to serve guests a Sunday dinner of hamburgers, onions, and other vegetables, instead of roast beef and potatoes, even though the former might be more expensive and nutritious than the latter.

There are as many variations of eating etiquette as there are food preferences. Despite the simple fact that the final aim of all feeding customs is to put food into the mouth, societies favor an incredible series of preliminary maneuvers. Most Europeans require a wide array of utensils, but inhabitants of Eastern Asia can get by with one pair of simple chopsticks. Well-mannered Hindus eat with freshly-washed hands from individual trays, but many American Indians dip into common bowls with unwashed hands. Societies may regard

[3] J. Gillin, "Moche: A Peruvian Coastal Community," *Smithsonian Institution, Institute of Social Anthropology,* No. 3, Washington, 1945, p. 54.

[4] G. M. Foster, "Relationships between Theoretical and Applied Anthropology: A Public Health Program Analysis," *Human Organization,* Vol. 11, 1952, p. 8.

postprandial belching as good form, bad, or variable. Among us babies are aided to burp; a resounding belch in polite company is a matter for apology; but in a group of masculine beer drinkers it may lead to boasting.

Extra-biologic attitudes toward food are well brought out in a consideration of prescribed forms of restraint. Societies have differing schedules for taking meals, and individuals learn to adjust their wants to cultural norms. Never, except for babies fed on demand, are the proper times for eating left entirely to the cravings of individual appetites. No matter how ravenously hungry a well-bred American may be, it would never occur to him to rush into a kitchen and begin eating before his hostess was ready to serve. Similarly, in distant Tierra del Fuego, at the southern extremity of South America, a half-starved Ona woman may be eager to pounce on a guanaco brought home from the chase by her husband, but etiquette prescribes a pause and a show of indifference before cooking operations may begin. Obviously, in all cases of this kind, symbolic, cultural values carry far more weight than the pangs of biological hunger. Much the same applies to matters of quantity. The amount that a person consumes is not always commensurate with his appetite or the needs of his body. Eating or abstaining out of politeness are very real things.

That food habits are directly connected with other aspects of the biocultural triangle may be readily shown. Eating together at celebrations like weddings always has strong sociologic implications, and so has the simplest sharing of bread. Conversely, the feeling that no party can be successful unless food is served is widespread. Perhaps a trifle less apparent, but equally common, is the use of food as a symbol of social status. The positive aspect, indulgence in luxury items that are not necessarily nutritious, is well known to all, but fewer people are aware of a negative side, conspicuous waste.[5] In our culture we look down on those who serve portions rigidly measured to the number of diners. Covertly we feel that more than exactly enough ought to be offered. A similar notion is carried to even greater extremes among the Trobriand Islanders who live near New Guinea. One of their principal staples is the cultivated yam, and on occasion farmers display heaps of yams, many of which form a sur-

[5] As here used the concept is modified from Veblen's original usage. See *The Portable Veblen*, Max Lerner, ed., New York, 1948, p. 136.

plus and will be allowed to rot. Not only is this an expression of conspicuous waste, but it is also a measure of social standing, for convention decrees that no native may pile up as many yams as does the village chief.[6]

The manner in which all three segments of a biocultural triangle are interlocked is further exemplified by the manifold religious implications of food. Practically universal are the beliefs that certain substances may fittingly be offered to supernatural powers, usually in the form of sacrifices, and that foods blessed by deities or religious officers have great extra-nutritional value for humans. Almost all cultures, too, incorporate a religious notion that certain foods are prohibited or tabued to ordinary men and women. Sometimes the prohibitions admit of no exceptions, and sometimes they apply only at particular times or under special circumstances. In our sophisticated society the existence of food tabus frequently causes embarrassment. Because of the high value ascribed to being rational and logical, many religious people in our country are reluctant to admit that they subscribe to tabus which have been aptly described as based on culturally standardized unreason. Accordingly, they make great efforts to rationalize their beliefs. Some Christians maintain that Lenten prohibitions reflect a time when it was dangerous in Spring to eat foods that had been stored from the preceding Fall. Along similar lines there are Orthodox Jews who argue that they do not eat pork because it may anciently have caused illness in hot countries. When viewed in the light of all the food tabus involved in the faiths mentioned, these explanations prove to be unsatisfactory. They do not explain why many Christians who eat meat regularly on Thursdays and Saturdays must abstain on Fridays; and they fail to throw light on the Jewish custom of allowing dairy products to be consumed immediately before meat but not after. Religious attitudes toward diet are extraordinary phenomena of culture, and need not be brought into line with biology. Their persistence into the twentieth century serves to demonstrate how consistently man gives preference, short of inducing death, to cultural rather than biological values.

6 B. Malinowski, *Argonauts of the Western Pacific*, rev. ed., London, 1932, p. 61.

## B. HOUSES AND OTHER STRUCTURES

Housing is another essential aspect of material culture that is part of man's interaction with his external surroundings. By learning to build and occupy houses man lessened the need of making biological adjustments to the weather. To the extent that habitations keep out rain, frost, wind, and direct sunlight they serve to stabilize the environmental conditions under which mankind must live. Relatively few houses are designed only to further biological needs. Features are usually added that conform to arbitrary, cultural requirements. Conspicuous waste again comes into play. All of us know that wealthy people in the United States like to build pretentious homes that are costlier and roomier than biological requirements demand. As is the case with all biocultural activities different societies may erect different kinds of dwellings even if they happen to reside in an identical setting (Fig. 109).[7] Cultural values always dictate which of a range of available materials a group will select for building, and there is no established rule that enables one to predict from the nature of a region the kinds of houses that its occupants will construct.

What is true of building materials is also true of architectural styles and household furnishings. Physical environments never compel the use of a given shape or size, although they may impose limitations on the choice of substances employed. Anthropologists can show numerous illustrations of housing practices that, in terms of logic, seem to make clever adjustments to their setting, but they can also point out examples of dwelling styles that appear to be out of keeping with their surroundings. Eskimo igloos are excellent adaptations to lands where snowfall is heavy, but the windbreaks of the Ona fail to keep out the bitter cold to which these people are subjected for many months of the year (Fig. 109B). Occasionally, specific methods of building homes or of making furniture become so thoroughly identified with particular societies that minute details of construction may be used for tracing tribal movements or contacts.

[7] On a joint reservation in Arizona the Hopi Indians occupy rectangular dwellings of stone, traditionally clustered into communal pueblos, whereas the Navaho live in individual, dome-shaped structures made of heavy timbers and earth. For further information on variations of house types, see Beals and Hoijer, *op. cit.*, 328-334; Chapple and Coon, *op. cit.*, pp. 104-110; and E. A. Hoebel, *Man in the Primitive World*, New York, 1949, pp. 115-130.

Fig. 109. American Indian structures. The snow house of the Arctic Eskimo (A) contrasts strongly with the Ona windbreak (B) of the Antarctic. In Arizona the Pueblo house (C) differs widely from the hogan (D) of the neighboring Navaho.

Structures that are meant for living quarters are found universally, but almost equally common are supplementary buildings devoted to other purposes. These, too, may vary in materials employed, methods of construction, elaboration, size, and shape. Again, like residences, they may show varying degrees of compliance with the natural environment. Man-made structures always provide evidence of the meshing of the three sides of a biocultural triangle. Professor Melville J. Herskovits has demonstrated that this concept may apply within the limits of a single dwelling,[8] and we shall discuss the subject in respect to secondary structures that are not meant for regular homes.

The clearest reflection of man's relations to his environment is to be found in the uses to which supplementary buildings are put. Commonest of all are those designed for storing surplus foods, tools and equipment, or resources to be used in manufacturing various things. Places for sheltering and feeding domesticated animals are widespread, and so, too, are working arrangements that may vary from mere covered platforms to elaborate factories. Less widely distributed, but very important on many Pacific islands, are distinct outbuildings for the preparation of meals.

As to the interactions of man to man with respect to secondary structures, the best examples are clubhouses of various kinds. Some are for the exclusive use of adult men, some are open only to members of a secret society, and others may be reserved for women. Special living quarters for unmarried warriors comprise an outstanding feature of Masai culture in East Africa, and large, communally maintained guesthouses are found regularly throughout Southeast Asia. It is often difficult to decide whether the functions of a building should be classified as social or religious. In almost all parts of the primitive world females are expected to resort periodically to menstrual lodges, but this requirement is usually connected with a supernatural fear of blood. Sudatories or sweathouses are also very common, and their use generally has socio-religious implications. The customs of the Banks Islanders in the Southwest Pacific decree that men should eat apart from women in special structures divided into small, carefully graded units; but a great deal of ceremonialism accompanies each step of the proceedings.

More clearly religious of purpose are buildings in which major

[8] M. J. Herskovits, *Man and His Works,* New York, 1948, pp. 217-220.

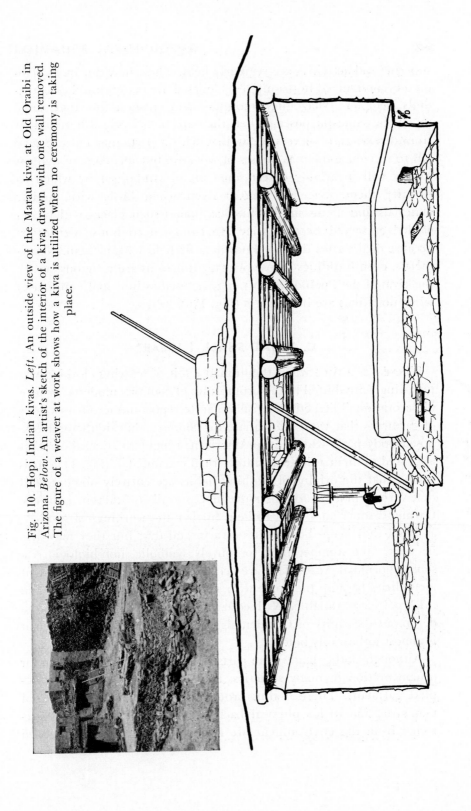

Fig. 110. Hopi Indian kivas. *Left.* An outside view of the Marau kiva at Old Oraibi in Arizona. *Below.* An artist's sketch of the interior of a kiva, drawn with one wall removed. The figure of a weaver at work shows how a kiva is utilized when no ceremony is taking place.

supernatural activities are regularly held. These may not be as elaborately constructed in primitive societies as are many churches, cathedrals, temples, synagogues, mosques, and shrines, but they serve much the same purposes. When they are not clearly differentiated from dwellings, observers unfamiliar with a particular culture may fail to recognize them as houses of worship, but members of a given society will invariably detect some bit of symbolism by which to identify them. (See Fig. 122C.) Even when built with similar materials and along similar lines as homes such places will be regarded as sacred because they are supposed to house deities or because of the rites that are known to be held within them. Nevertheless, even buildings whose primary functions are religious, as are the kivas of the Pueblo Indians, may be used as informal clubhouses when no rituals are in progress (Fig. 110).

## C. WHAT SHALL I WEAR?

There was a time when the human habit of wearing clothing was unfailingly attributed to the promptings of comfort, modesty, or love of decoration. Then ethnologists began to report numerous instances of garments that were inadequate for comfort, that deliberately exposed body parts which Euro-Americans sought to conceal, or that appeared to them as hideous rather than ornamental (Fig. 111). It is agreed that the origins of clothing habits are entirely obscure, and that various motives for their use may prevail in different cultures. Garments sometimes seem to help further the workings of biology, as when they keep their wearers warm and dry; but they may also be worn, like summer furs, for purely symbolic, non-biologic reasons. Aboriginal Australians are occasionally said to betray deficient mentalities because they may wear too little for comfort even when thick pelts are available. With equal reason these natives might wonder about the sanity of Occidentals who wear far too much when it is almost unbearably hot.

Although clothes made from parts of the human body are worn for ornamentation in many societies, they almost never serve as complete garments. There is thus brought into play another aspect of man's relation to his physical background. Plants and animals selected from the environment are counted upon to supply needed

Fig. 111. Witoto men, women, and children. The
Witoto Indians live in the tropical forests of the
Amazon. Among the women, in particular, painted
decorations take the place of clothing on festive occasions.

materials. Nor should it be forgotten that all tools used in the making of clothing likewise originate in the natural setting.

Habits of dress never fail to have sociological connotations. There is no society whose infants and adults wear identical garments, and within no culture are mature men and women expected to dress exactly alike. Differences of rank, wealth, occupation, and prestige may also be expressed in wearing apparel or ornaments. Makers of articles of clothing tend to be of one sex or the other, and many of the motor habits that distinguish males from females are associated with the making and wearing of different garbs.

Study of clothing customs always leads an investigator into the field of supernaturalism. Religious officers wear distinctive garments whenever they are performing their rites, and lay worshippers commonly put on special clothes while attending services. Quite frequently religious symbols are worn as mute prayers by laymen, and Lumholtz once described the Tarahumara Indians of Northern Mexico as being literally clothed in prayer.[9] Cultural conventions regularly prescribe gestures or motor habits connected with wearing apparel during worship, as when Christian males bare their heads and Jewish men cover them. Such usages must be classed as nonlogical, for all attempts to rationalize them prove unconvincing except to members of the faith that practices them.

## D. TECHNOLOGY

Industrial arts form a major portion of every society's material culture. Anthropologists generally study them under the heading of technology. Ingredients are so seldom drawn from the human body that the topic becomes an integral part of any effort to understand man's relations to his environment. The commonest arts and crafts, in addition to those concerned with shelter, food, and clothing, are devoted to the manufacture of household furnishings, domestic utensils (including pottery and basketry containers), agricultural implements, weapons, and means of transportation.[10] Close analyses of the materials used, working processes, correlated implements, and methods and styles of decoration provide a large body of factual data

[9] C. Lumholtz, *Unknown Mexico*, New York, 1903, p. 827.
[10] Specific details on each of these topics may be found in the previously cited works by Chapple and Coon, Beals and Hoijer, and Hoebel.

which ethnologists find of the utmost importance for making comparative studies.

Never does the technological aspect of a group's material culture stand by itself. Commonest of all sociologic connections is a division of work between men and women, ordinarily described as **sexual dichotomy**. In practice this means that each society sets aside the performance and teaching of some occupations for males and reserves others for females. When these culturally assigned activities have been in operation for a long time they come to be so intimately associated with a particular sex as to give the impression that they are biologically determined. Thus, in our society, we are inclined to think that women are better suited than men for sewing with needle and thread, baking cookies, dusting furniture, diapering babies, or nursing the sick. To whatever extent this may be true it is much more likely the result of cultural conditioning than of biological structure. This may be seen from the number of men who are professional bakers, tailors, nurses, and valets; from the great changes of female occupations, without attendant changes of body, that have taken place in the last fifty years; and from the fact that the same pursuit may be feminine in one society and masculine in another. It is not because of anatomical differences that the making of bark cloth is the work of males in African Uganda but is left to females in the Polynesian Islands of the Eastern Pacific. Except in terms of culture it would be impossible to explain why the Hopi Indian men of Northeastern Arizona weave rugs, dresses, and blankets, whereas all weaving among the nearby Navaho is done by women (Fig. 112).

Religious factors may also determine a person's occupation. Shamans who practice curing because they are thought to have received a supernatural call may be of one sex or the other in different societies. Even more to the point is the case of the Plains Indians who used to inhabit the United States just east of the Rocky Mountains. They were on the whole a warlike people whose young men were supposed to seek visions during which the spirits dictated their future careers. Every now and then a youth who was thoroughly masculine in biology would find himself ordered to do the work of a woman. The existence of such instances makes it improbable that sexual dichotomy is based on anatomical differences. Instead, they establish a strong presumption that patterns of work, except in matters directly

Fig. 112. Sexual dichotomy in patterns of work. Men are weavers among the Hopi (A), but among the neighboring Navaho, women do all the weaving (B). Wheel-made pottery (C) is almost invariably made by men in primitive societies, but hand-made pottery (D) is generally fashioned by women.

concerned with the biology of sex and reproduction, are determined on the basis of arbitrary (nonlogical), symbolic, cultural values.

## E. CULTURAL MODIFICATIONS OF ENVIRONMENT

There is a common belief that a society's physical environment remains stable except under extraordinary conditions. Actually, changes may take place under three sets of circumstances, variously associated with cultural factors. In the first place, floods, droughts, erosion, volcanic eruptions, and similar disturbances are known to bring about drastic alterations, but they are natural agencies and may operate without reference to human activities. In the second place, indiscriminate use of grazing grounds, wasteful agricultural practices, careless removal of timber or grass cover, and large-scale mining operations are some of the ways that man interacts with his environment to bring about changes, many of which may be detrimental to his future welfare. In the third place, there is a less obvious interplay by means of which some unchanging feature of the landscape may achieve a greatly altered significance through the agency of a group's level of culture.

Let us suppose that a steep mountain peak, 8000 feet high, stands midway between two communities. As long as the two settlements have no means of land travel except foot, the peak opposes a well-nigh insurmountable barrier to intercourse between them. If a road comes to be built over the mountain and animal-drawn conveyances or riding horses become available, the barrier grows less insurmountable. With the advent of power-driven vehicles the difficulties of communication dwindle still more; and for those who can use up-to-date aircraft an 8000-foot peak is no obstacle at all.

What is true of mountains likewise applies to oceans, wide streams, broad deserts, and dense forests. In each case the environmental feature may remain exactly as it was, but its functional significance will vary with different levels of culture. The ultimate effect is the same as if it were the landmark itself that had changed. That is what is really meant when people speak of the shrinking of the present globe, or when Americans refer to the dwindling of the oceans that separate them from the Old World. From a long-range point of view it is a mistake for a cultural anthropologist to treat any environment with which human beings interact as if it were static rather than dynamic.

## Selected References

Beals, Ralph L., and Hoijer, Harry, *An Introduction to Anthropology,* New York, 1953.

Chapple, Eliot D., and Coon, Carleton S., *Principles of Anthropology,* New York, 1942.

Du Bois, Cora, "Attitudes Toward Food and Hunger in Alor," *Language, Culture, and Personality* (L. Spier, *et al.,* eds.), Menasha, 1941, pp. 272-281.

Foster, George M., "Relationships Between Theoretical and Applied Anthropology: A Public Health Program Analysis," *Human Organization,* Vol. 11, 1952, pp. 5-16.

Hoebel, E. Adamson, *Man in the Primitive World,* New York, 1949.

Herskovits, Melville J., *Man and His Works,* New York, 1948, pp. 201-226.

Mead, Margaret, *Male and Female,* New York, 1949.

Morgan, Lewis H., "Houses and House Life of the American Aborigines," *Contributions to American Ethnology,* Vol. 4, Washington, 1881.

———, *Ancient Society,* New York, 1878.

Richards, Audrey I., *Hunger and Work in a Savage Tribe,* London, 1932.

# CHAPTER 22

# Man's Relations to His Fellow Men[1]

## A. HAVING A BABY

One of the axiomatic desires of every society is a wish to perpetuate itself indefinitely. Barring the restricted possibility of recruiting new members from the outside, this desire can be fulfilled only through the continuous operation of sexual reproduction. Consequently, each social unit must make adequate provision for the birth of children among its members. While every normal female, regardless of whether she is an opera singer, waitress, stenographer, or professional athlete is a potential mother, and every normal male is a potential father, no society is content to leave the bearing of offspring to chance or the powerful urgings of biology. On the other hand, societies are equally unwilling to take full advantage of biological capacities by allowing everyone to have as many children as nature allows. A balance is always struck between the full range of a group's biological potential for begetting and bearing offspring and a set of cultural restrictions on parenthood. Having babies is a biocultural phenomenon in all human societies. Popular writers sometimes make sensational references to widespread sexual promiscuity among native peoples, but ethnologists have never found a group whose culture permitted completely unregulated relations between the sexes.

What anthropologists do find is a widespread difference of moral standards. Some tribes allow a great deal of premarital license, others insist on prenuptial virginity, especially for girls. Some demand first

[1] As used by anthropologists, man is synonymous with *Homo sapiens* and includes representatives of both sexes. This has given rise to the oldest joke in the profession— a definition of anthropology as "the science of man, embracing woman."

cousins must marry, others forbid such unions. There is no uniformity of symbolic attitudes toward mating among mankind, but some features are universal. All societies distinguish sanctioned marital relations from other forms of sexual activity, all have culturally based preferences for the selection of proper mates, and all specifically forbid cohabitation between certain individuals. The commonest prohibitions, **incest** regulations, are designed to prevent intercourse between parents and their offspring, and between brothers and sisters (siblings). Ethnologists at present are not able to fully explain how incest rules arose, but they can show they are cultural rather than biological in character. Again and again, people who happen to be unaware of their relationship may be physically attracted to one another and engage in copulation, only to be overwhelmed with shame and dread if they later discover that they are close kin. If the horror of incest were truly biological, forbidden unions could scarcely take place and there would be little need of regulations to prevent them.

Marriages may be encouraged or prohibited on many grounds other than kinship. Almost anything, race, religion, economic status, degree of education, place of residence, or occupation can be used as a basis for making discriminations for or against the choice of mates. When ethnologists describe a custom that compels people to marry within a given unit they call it **endogamy;** whereas a rule that forces individuals to find spouses outside a particular group is known as **exogamy.** These terms may apply to a total society or to any of its subdivisions. Thus in the Euro-American world most marriages are **endogamous** with respect to nationality and religious affiliation, but **exogamous** in regard to the family circle.

Throughout the world wedding regulations are designed not only to direct sexual activities into culturally approved channels but also to encourage the propagation and rearing of children. The long-drawn-out helplessness of human infants is an inescapable biological fact and parents, particularly mothers, are everywhere charged with the responsibility of caring for babies at least until they can look out for themselves. If no parent is available a substitute or **surrogate** must be provided. As an Araucanian Indian from Central Chile once put it when we were discussing the use of wetnurses for an orphan, "Nohow will they let the baby starve!"

Scientists have not yet determined the proper classification of the craving for offspring. As far as an individual is concerned it may very likely be a combination of biological, psychological, and cultural elements, and in primitive societies sterile couples are particularly apt to be unhappy and to seek natural and supernatural help. But apart from any person's private desires there is also the interest of society as a whole. Among us social scientists may be gravely concerned over a falling birthrate whether they themselves are childless or parents of large families. Openly or tacitly every social unit is pleased when children are born to its members.

## B. KINSHIP SYSTEMS

As was pointed out in the preceding section, marriage regulations universally forbid certain kin from mating, and quite often prescribe the union of other relatives. Wedding rules and methods of reckoning kindred are thus seen to be closely associated. An anthropological convention divides ways of naming relatives into **descriptive** and **classificatory** categories. Descriptive systems, like ours, are supposed to use a separate term for designating each particular relative, such as one's father or mother. Classificatory arrangements never restrict the use of a term to a single individual, but unfailingly employ one term to designate a class or group of persons. Even if we grant that the two methods overlap, it is still true that Occidental societies show a strong tendency to use descriptive terminology, while primitive groups reveal a marked preference for classificatory systems.[2]

The manner in which a society identifies and labels relatives is known as its **kinship system,** and can readily be diagrammed as a sort of genealogical table (Fig. 113). Because each person is variously related to a number of people, as when I call "uncle" the selfsame man that my father calls "brother," ethnologists find it essential to present each kinship system from the viewpoint of one particular individual. This personage is labelled **EGO,** and customarily represents an average adult male.[3]

2 Professor Kroeber long ago drew attention to the fact that we group several different individuals under the designation of brother, and that as many as 32 different persons may be called cousins. See A. L. Kroeber, "Classificatory Systems of Relationships," *Journal of the Royal Anthropological Institute,* 1909, Vol. 39, pp. 77-84.

3 As a rule ethnologists present a kinship system from the standpoint of an adult man speaker, male EGO, or of a mature woman speaker, female EGO. It is seldom necessary to add further diagrams, because variant terms used by others may be discussed in the text.

People in Euro-American societies generally trace **family** kinship **bilaterally,** giving weight to the mother's and father's lines, but in a great many primitive cultures relationships are reckoned **unilaterally,** by way of one parent or the other. Where kinship is unilaterally counted through males the kinfolk make up a **patrilineal clan** or **gens,** but when it is unilaterally reckoned through females the relatives comprise a **matrilineal clan** or **sib.** A clan may therefore be defined as a group of relatives who trace their descent in one sex line from a common ancestor or ancestress. Because they are believed to be descended from the same personage, **clanmates** are likely to be regarded as brothers and sisters and are usually forbidden to intermarry. As a rule their line is supposed to have been founded at some time in the dim past when their original progenitor mated with a supernatural personage, plant, animal, object, or celestial body—usually identified as a **totem**—whose name the clan bears, and with which it feels itself intimately connected. This connection may be expressed by a symbolic design that may be used only by members of the appropriate clan, or else it may be emphasized by rituals intended to increase the numbers of the totem, or by tabus forbidding **clansfolk** to injure, kill, or eat representatives of their totem. By way of a concrete example, the members of a Rabbit clan may look upon rabbits as siblings, perform ceremonies for the multiplication of rabbits, abstain from rabbit hunts, mourn slain rabbits, and refuse to eat rabbit meat. In some cases clans may also have economic or political attributes, such as owning in common lands, houses, or rights to chieftainships.

As for clan methods of naming kindred, two principal variants are widely recognized. Patrilineal clans that have separate designations for mother's brother and father's brother, but which unite under a single term mother's brother, mother's brother's son, mother's brother's son's son, etc., are said to have the **Omaha** system (Fig. 113).

---

Fig. 113. The Omaha kinship system. In Figures 113-117 the symbol △ stands for a male; ○ for a female; and = for a marriage. The letters represent English words, so that "F" is for father; "Si" for sister; "MBW" for mother's brother's wife; "Ne" for nephew; "Ni" for niece; etc. An x designates members of EGO's own clan; and a dot indicates members of EGO's mother's clan. The Omaha system is associated with patrilineal clans or strong patrilineal emphasis. EGO's father and EGO's father's brother are merged, but EGO's mother's brother is differentiated by a separate term. EGO's mother's brother's male descendants are merged under a single term, thus over-riding generation levels.

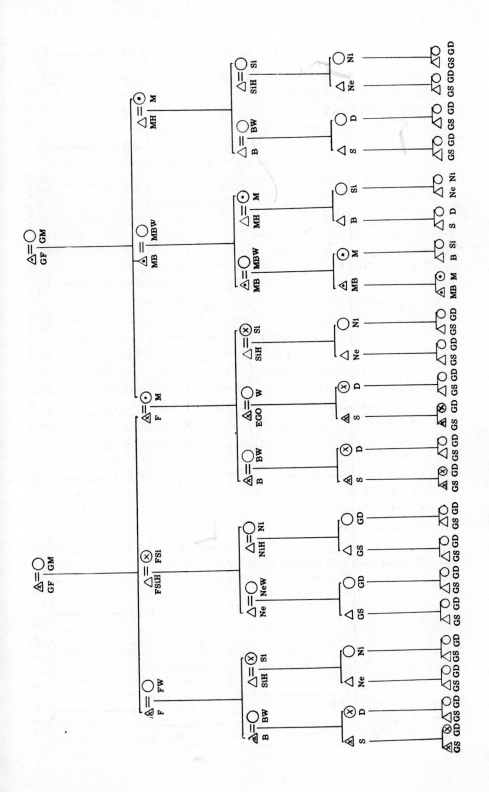

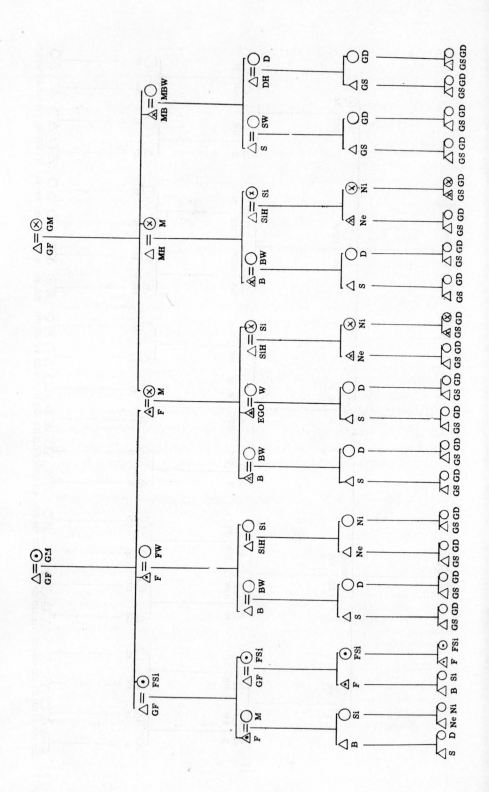

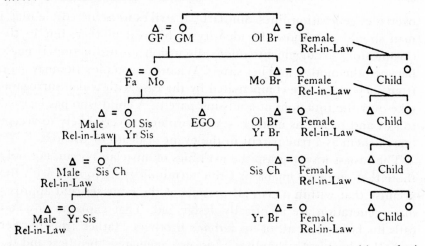

Fig. 115. A Hopi (Crow) lineage (after Eggan). The diagram shows his mother's matrilineal lineage, from the viewpoint of a male EGO. All members of EGO's own clan and lineage are connected by short, vertical lines that indicate descent ties.

Matrilineal clans that distinguish mother's sister from father's sister, but which group together the father's sister and her descendants through females (Figs. 114, 115), are said to use the **Crow** system.[4] In each of these instances, students must learn to realize, the lines that set generation levels apart are sometimes disregarded in the terminology. At least two features are common to classificatory forms of kinship nomenclature that are not found in ours. An adult EGO may find himself with a cluster of parents and grandparents, and some of them may be mere infants.

To an American ethnologist on his first field-trip it comes as a shock to have a grown-up point out a small child as his father or grandfather, but this is a logical outgrowth of any kinship system that

[4] Kinship terminology is called bifurcate-merging when some relatives are clearly set apart while others are grouped together. On this point see G. P. Murdock, "Bifurcate Merging: A Test of Five Theories," *American Anthropologist*, Vol. 49, 1947, pp. 56-68. Professor Robert H. Lowie introduced the term "bifurcate-merging" in an earlier treatment of the concept under discussion.

Fig. 114. The Crow kinship system. This is found associated with matrilineal clans or wherever a society has a strong matrilineal emphasis. EGO's father's sister is distinguished from his mother's sister, but all of EGO's father's sister's female descendants are merged in the terminology, thereby disregarding generation lines.

overrides generation lines. Similarly, it strikes us as incredible that a man should not know the identity of his real mother, but in the classificatory arrangements under discussion no distinction is made between the mother and her sisters. Whatever complexities may arise from such usages are compensated by the ease with which surrogates take over the functions of a missing parent. A child who has learned to call and regard as mothers several women is very likely to accept one of them as a true parent in the event of death or divorce.

The easiest way to grasp the workings of any clan system, not only those that employ Omaha or Crow terminology, is to start with the premise that within a clan all persons of the same sex and approximate generation are identically designated. That explains why EGO calls his father and all of his father's brothers, "father"; his mother and all of her sisters, "mother"; his own agemates, "brothers and sisters"; and their offspring, "children."

More than one system of kinship nomenclature may operate simultaneously. Men in the United States regularly apply the term, "brother," to a male sibling, a fellow member of a fraternity, and, sometimes, to a masculine co-religionist. In primitive societies **bilateral** modes of naming kin may operate side by side with **unilateral** practices. A highly important consequence is that family and clan ties may both be recognized. Where matrilineal clans are found a man very rarely joins his wife's clan at marriage. Consequently, he is of a different clan from his wife and offspring, yet his children will call him, "father," and acknowledge him as their male parent.[5] When important clan functions are being held in a matrilineal society a man may be excluded from his wife's and children's group, but in daily life he will not be treated as an outsider. The pull of bilateral, family ties, within a matrilineal clan structure was forcibly brought home to the author during a study of a village split that broke the Hopi pueblo of Old Oraibi into halves in 1906. Almost without exception family groups sided together and clan loyalties tended to be overridden.

Two other units of kindred are widely recognized by ethnologists.

---

[5] E. E. Evans-Pritchard and other ethnologists who have worked primarily in Africa have drawn attention to the existence of double descent. This implies that some alignments are made with EGO's matrilineal kin and others with his patrilineal relatives. Thus, double descent means that unilateral kin groups along male and female lines may exist side by side. For further details consult E. E. Evans-Pritchard. See also G. P. Murdock, *Social Structure,* New York, 1949, p. 50 *et passim.*

When a unilateral line is so clearly known to native informants that they can recall the genealogical connections of all who belong to it, the grouping is called a **lineage** (Fig. 115). At times a lineage is hard to differentiate from a clan, but the former lacks a distinctive name, and the latter may comprise more than one lineage. Whenever two or more named clans are grouped into a larger, usually nameless, exogamic division, the bigger grouping is known as a **phratry.** Theoretically, a phratry may arise from the segmentation of parts of an original clan, but in practice phratries function as combinations of clans.

## C. KINSHIP AND MARRIAGE

Kinship systems not only stipulate how relatives are to be labelled, but they also prescribe forms of behavior between various sets of kin. Each recognized degree of relationship carries with it a number of rights, privileges, duties, and obligations. Knowledge of these functional requirements is what gives life to the study of kinship systems, for in this way the ethnologist comes to understand how all manner of people are expected to act toward each other. Among the most important regulations affecting the behavior of kinfolk are those pertaining to marriages. Practically universal in primitive societies is the rule of exogamy that forbids clanmates to wed or to have sexual relations. Almost as common is an incest tabu directed against the mating of **parallel cousins** (offspring of two brothers or of two sisters). Such a prohibition is occasionally counterbalanced by a society's stated preference for **cross cousin** marriage, which unites the children of a brother with those of his sister. In communities where this custom prevails young cross cousins of opposite sex may be brought up with the notion that they are potential mates, and are occasionally allowed a large measure of intimacy, possibly to the extent of nonmarital intercourse. Lesser degrees of familiarity, sometimes between members of the same sex, may be formalized into **joking relationships.**[6]

6 Joking relationships refer to culturally permitted and generally standardized forms of familiarity in speech or action that prevail between particular kinds of relatives. R. H. Lowie, *Primitive Society,* New York, 1920, p. 102, expresses the opinion that joking relationships are commonest among potential mates. F. Eggan, "Arapaho and Cheyenne Kinship Systems," *Social Organization of North American Indians* (F. Eggan, ed.), Chicago, 1937, p. 76, following Tax, states that joking relationships provide psycho-

A very interesting variation of cross cousin marriage, in a clanless society, is found among the Arunta or Aranda.[7] They are Australian aborigines who once inhabited the center of their continent, and whose involved social organization affords a sharp contrast to their simple material culture. The entire tribe is divided into exogamous halves or **moieties,** each of which has two sections. If we call the moieties A and B, and their subdivisions 1 and 2, we find that the Aranda are grouped into four sections among which the following rules of marriage and descent prevail. An A-1 man must marry a B-1 woman, and the offspring become A-2 (the other half of the father's moiety). An A-2 man must marry a B-2 woman, and their children are A-1. A B-1 man must marry an A-1 wife, and their off-spring will be B-2; and a B-2 man must take an A-2 spouse, and their children will be B-1. Complicated though these arrangements may appear at first glance, they are really no more than a modifica-tion of cross cousin marriage, as may be seen from a study of Fig ure 116.

Because the Aranda use a classificatory method of reckoning kin, the rule of preferential cross cousin marriage does not unduly re-strict one's choice of mates. Each male has a whole group of fathers, any one of whose sisters' daughters he is eligible to marry; as well as a number of mothers with any of whose brothers' daughters he may wed. Among these people, too, the kinship and marriage regula-tions provide the basis for a whole network of behavioral forms. Beginning early in life an A-1 male is taught to treat all older A-2 men as his fathers, all older B-2 women as mothers, all B-1 females of his own generation as possible wives, all older A-2 women as potential mothers-in-law, and so forth. Even an Aranda stranger fits easily into the scheme as soon as his section becomes known, and violations of the code of behavior that regulates the conduct of each subgroup toward the others may be severely punished.

## D. CONSANGUINITY AND AFFINITY

Irrespective of what system of kinship nomenclature a society uses, it will be found that most of each person's relatives are connected

---

logical outlets for some of the restraints and tensions engendered by other features of a kinship system.

[7] G. P. Murdock, *Our Primitive Contemporaries,* New York, 1935, chap. 2, contains a short sketch of Aranda culture.

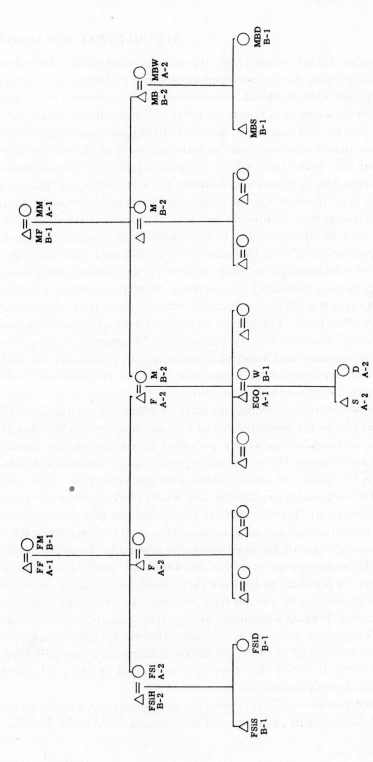

Fig. 116. Marriage pattern of the Arunta (Aranda). In this tribe an A-1 male must marry a B-1 female. If he marries either cross cousin, his mother's brother's daughter or his father's sister's daughter, he will automatically make a proper marriage.

with him by "blood" or marriage. "Blood" ties, whether they be real or fictitious, are described as **consanguineous,** and relationships through marriage are called **affinal. Consanguinity** is supposed to denote descent from a common parent or parents, but in many cases it cannot be proved and has to be assumed. Primitive people are much less likely than Euro-Americans to insist on proof of "blood" connection, and they make little effort to separate real from fictional consanguineous kin. A husband is assumed to be the father of his wife's children even if she is known to have been occasionally unfaithful. Nonetheless, primitive folk do not take the ties of "blood" lightly, nor are they indifferent to the links established through marriage. It is everywhere recognized that when two people wed they develop a new set of relationships not only between themselves but also among their respective kinfolk. This is no trivial matter, and many wedding customs express a sense of reluctance on someone's part whenever a marriage takes place. The gravity of entering into a new set of affinal relationships is one of the reasons why the blessings of a deity, also known as **supernatural sanctions,** are sought at practically all weddings. Another compelling reason for invoking religious aid is to ensure that the union will bear issue.

Primitive attitudes toward the birth of offspring are likely to be based on practical considerations as well as on emotion. Feelings of love for children are as widely prevalent as among us, but factors that we submerge or fail to recognize may be more openly expressed. There is no failure to realize that consanguineous lines are maintained by biological reproduction, and where offices or property must be transmitted to "blood" relatives the extinction of a consanguineous unit may be deplored as a tragedy. This is all the more true since the economic costs of having babies are negligible in primitive societies. It does not cost much, if anything, for medical help; it is not a serious problem to feed another mouth or to clothe an extra body; and nonliterate people have no cause to dread the expenses of education. Formal schooling hardly exists, and informal instruction is freely given as occasion warrants. Moreover, children are very often the equivalent of old-age insurance. Many an aging pair finds it comforting to realize that they have numerous progeny who will look after them as a matter of course.

The acceptance of affinal relatives is another matter, for one never knows how they will turn out and they do not have to be involuntarily accepted as do consanguineous folk. Yet, the operation of incest and exogamic regulations makes it imperative for each social division to take a chance on some outsiders when it comes to choosing spouses. A degree of unwillingness to undertake the hazards of matrimony may be expressed by individuals in the form of **ceremonial coyness,** or it may be reflected in a group's behavior. This may be inferred from the variety of ways in which two units that have once succeeded in providing each other with mates will continue to do so as long as possible. Such customs, known to all ethnologists, as having two brothers marry sisters; or the **levirate,** whereby a widow marries a brother of her late husband; or the **sororate,** which permits a man to marry a sister of his wife; or the requirement that a son must take over his deceased father's spouse or spouses; are all designed to keep going affinal bonds that have already been set up. Even cross cousin marriage may be partially interpreted in the same way, for its continuous operation results in offspring taking mates either from the mother's or the father's social unit.

A common method of preventing undue familiarity occurring between affinal relatives is to prescribe avoidance. Most widely found in primitive societies is the custom, avidly seized upon by Euro-American jokesmiths, of **mother-in-law tabu.** There is nothing amusing about a mother-in-law tabu, because its violation arouses the displeasure of one's tribesmen and may cause serious illness or death. Where the tabu is most fully interpreted, a man may neither look upon nor speak to his wife's mother. Cases are even known where a man's sickness is attributed to the fact that his father once broke the mother-in-law tabu. Similar prohibitions may be applied to other relatives by marriage.

The loss that one group sustains when a member marries is compensated as a rule by the other's payment of goods, money, or services. When it is a girl's consanguineous kindred that receive compensation it goes by the name of **bride-price,** but recompense received by the groom or his relatives is known as a **dowry.** One or two instances of true **wife capture,** in which men regularly carry off brides without prearrangement or payment are authentically reported, but more often, as in the case of so-called mock rape among the Araucanians of Chile, all details are settled in advance, the bride and her people make only a token show of resistance, and adequate compensation is later provided. Very rarely does a wedding take place in primitive society without an attendant transfer of valuable items, and in some instances marriage payments prove to be costly, and highly involved transactions.

## E. LIVING TOGETHER

As soon as a marriage has been made the newlyweds must face the problem of where they should live. Only three possibilities exist under normal conditions. A bridal pair may settle in a place that is new to each of them (**neolocal residence**); or they may go to live where the groom resides (**patrilocal residence**); or else they may settle in the vicinity of the bride's home (**matrilocal residence**). Because of the strong sentiments of attachment that a person develops for the place where he was raised and for the people among whom he grew up, the choice of habitation that every wedded pair must make is a matter of grave concern. So, too, is the distance and availability of the new site with reference to the old. Professor Ralph Linton has urged ethnographers to take pains to indicate the precise degree of isolation from a parental home that postmarital residence entails, but so far, unfortunately, his advice has seldom been followed.

Perhaps of greater significance still is the question of whether a bride and groom establish an independent household or join an already existing residential unit occupied by the parents and other relatives of either the husband or wife. When merging takes place the custom may aptly be described as forming a **unilocal residence.** Valid distinctions may thus be drawn between patrilocal and matrilocal arrangements that are either unilocal or multilocal.

The most telling aspect of unilocal habitation results when newlyweds move directly into a home where live the kin of the bride or groom. Such a proceeding cannot fail to exert a profound influence on the married pair and on any offspring that may be born to them. If the principle of unilocal residence is consistently followed in a patrilocal setting it inevitably leads to the formation after several generations of a social unit consisting of a man, his sons, grandsons, etc., together with their respective spouses and unmarried daughters. The males will form a permanent nucleus, occupying the same quarters from birth to death, bringing wives in from outside, and sending

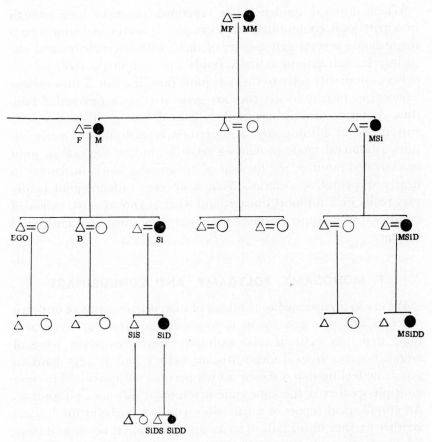

Fig. 117. Unilocal residence in a matrilocal society. The natal members of the houschold, who would normally reside under the same roof from birth to death, are shown in solid black. This alignment of relatives closely resembles that of a matrilineal lineage (Fig. 115) or a matrilineal clan (Fig. 114).

their daughters off at marriage. Where matrilocal customs prevail the same results will ensue with the sexes reversed. The exact corre-spondence of such units (Fig. 117) with patrilineal or matrilineal cians (Figs. 113, 114) was first noted many years ago. There is a good likelihood that the unilateral classification of kindred was originally based on ties of common residence rather than on bonds of con-sanguinity.[8]

8 A detailed discussion of this topic may be found in M. Titiev, "The Influence of Common Residence on the Unilateral Classification of Kindred," *American Anthro-pologist*, Vol. 45, 1943, pp. 511-530.

When unilocal residence has remained in effect long enough in a patrilocal community, for example, it serves to bring into a single home several generations of men, with their mates and off-spring. If such groups actually reside under a single roof, ethnologists customarily refer to them as **joint families;** but if they occupy adjacent or nearby houses they are generally termed **extended families.** As far as kinship terminology goes this usage, though deeply entrenched in anthropological literature, is misleading. Family implies a bilateral mode of naming relatives, but in the case of joint or extended families, the method of designating kin is unilateral in nearly all primitive societies. What is so often called a joint family may really be a **unilocal lineage,** and what is known as an extended family can sometimes be more accurately described as a **multilocal lineage.**

## F. MONOGAMY, POLYGAMY, AND CONCUBINAGE

We are so accustomed to thinking of marriage in terms of our own concepts that it is easy for us to overlook the great variety of attitudes that may exist in other cultures. Americans whose sense of morality stems from Judeo-Christian beliefs find it very hard to avoid the feeling that a society which permits an individual to have multiple spouses at the same time is somehow inferior and wanton. An ethnological report of a wife who nags her husband into taking another partner never fails to strike an American as being so incredible as to appear ludicrous. Yet, plural marriages are widespread in primitive society and there is nothing funny or shameful about them.

When a man is allowed to have multiple wives the custom is termed **polygyny,** but if a woman is permitted to have more than one husband simultaneously it is called **polyandry.** Together these customs are known as **polygamy.** Anthropologists have found polygyny to be widespread, but polyandry occurs only among the people of Tibet and in one or two other places.

As Occidentals we expect a wife to carry out at least four major functions: to conduct her husband's household affairs, gratify his sexual desires, bear and rear his children, and provide him with companionship. We find it difficult to realize that these four aspects of marriage are separable, and that it is possible for each of them to be entrusted to a different woman. Of course, many an American wife is delighted to have nurses, governesses, and servants to help her with domestic duties, but she would hardly want her husband to marry her helpers in order to make sure of retaining their services.

A man's spouses, even within a culture that freely permits polygyny, do not necessarily have equal status. Much more commonly, there is a principal wife who outranks the others and who generally has charge of running the household in which she resides. This was the case in ancient China, where a man's first wife had the greatest prestige and dominated all other females who might share her home. Since, however, the only true test of a successful marriage by Confucian standards was the birth of a male heir, a woman who failed to bear a son fully expected her mate to take secondary wives or concubines.[9] In many parts of Africa, on the other hand, a mother of many sons might still scold her husband for neglecting to marry additional wives who would relieve her of difficult household chores.

Ages before the publication of the second Kinsey report men had come to realize that the sexual desires of their wives did not always correspond to their own. According to Dr. Kinsey part of the difference may spring from biological and psychological distinctions between the sexes.[10] From this point of view it would be easy to explain why some well-to-do French women cheerfully help prepare their husbands to spend a night with a mistress. Unfortunately, this would not explain why females from other societies tend to be less cheerful under similar circumstances. Within the scope covered by the French example sexual activity can be separated from other aspects of marriage, but the phenomenon is anything but universal and its rare occurrence appears to be culturally rather than biologically conditioned. Kinsey reports notwithstanding, the biocultural implications of human sexual behavior have never been scientifically explored.

When it comes to the separation of providing feminine companionship from other wifely duties, old Japan furnishes an excellent example. Men who could afford it were expected to seek female companionship, not always including sexual indulgence, from the professional group called **geisha**. While some geisha undoubtedly

9 It would be unrealistic to think Chinese men took concubines solely for the purpose of begetting sons. Still, a child born to a concubine might by a legal fiction be taken as her own by a barren wife. The difference between a secondary wife and a concubine usually depended on the woman's social standing.

10 A. C. Kinsey et al., Sexual Behavior in the Human Female, Philadelphia and London, 1953, pp. 591-593.

granted sex favors to certain patrons, they were not as a class synonymous with prostitutes. Japanese wives were not called upon to acquire the arts of singing, instrument-playing, dancing, and making witty conversation that were the province of the geisha. And when a geisha married she no longer kept up her old skills but concentrated on meeting the requirements of a good Japanese wife.

## G. JOINING UP

Apart from the involuntary links of consanguineous relationships that await each child at birth, and different from the affinal bonds formed at marriage, there exist in primitive societies a large number of ties arising from membership in **associations.** They may be entered at different times, at various ages, in divergent ways, and for a variety of reasons. Joining may be purely voluntary or may result from social pressures that are so strong as to leave an individual no choice. Admission to associations may depend on the biological factors of sex or age; on general considerations of culture like rank, prestige, or marital status; on specific elements like occupation or the possession of a given amount of wealth; or on a combination of all three, as in the case of unmarried masculine warriors. For all their diversity associations other than the ones consisting of consanguineous or affinal relatives show two universal features. Each is exclusive in the sense that it never admits all the people of a given society, and each develops strong bonds of attachment among those who are admitted to membership. A good idea of the variety and complexity of primitive associations may be had from a brief account of several particular examples.

## 1. Masai Warriors' Groups [11]

Under aboriginal conditions the **Masai** occupied a portion of East Africa near the equator (Fig. 118). Each male, shortly after attaining puberty, was circumcised. All those who had gone through the operation in any four-year period were combined into a **warriors' group,** which acquired a distinctive name and the right to use special insignia. For an indefinite time the members lived in a special structure, away from their families, together with paramours made up of unmarried women of about their own age who had in the last four

[11] A. C. Hollis, *The Masai*, Oxford, 1905, p. xvi, *et passim*.

years been subjected to clitoridectomy, an operation that involves an incision of the clitoris. After a dozen years or so, individual members of the warriors' group would begin to leave the common habitation,

Fig. 118. Masai Warriors. Their racial type seems to fall between the extremes of the sturdy Forest Negroes and the lanky Nilotic Negroes.

marry, and settle down in the expectation of becoming tribal elders. When the last of the warriors' group had taken these steps the unit was officially dissolved, but the former members retained their distinctive name and continued to share a few common interests for life.

## 2. Crow Indian Military Societies [12]

Quite different in nearly every way were the **Lumpwoods** and **Foxes,** two **military societies** that were very popular among the **Crow Indians** who used to live in the Plains area of the United States. Each was led by elected officers who were distinguished warriors, and every spring the leaders invited about a dozen promising young men to join their organization. Membership was for life, and each society had exclusive rights to the use of a characteristic song and dance. Members lived at home and were permitted to marry, their wives sharing in a few of their public functions like feasts. From time to time each association served as a sort of police force, and feats of military daring were regularly performed for the greater glory of one's club. Fierce rivalry prevailed between Lumpwoods and Foxes, and once a year each side paraded in public whatever mistresses it had made among the wives of the rival outfit. Convention forbade a cuckolded husband from punishing his spouse or betraying anger, but a faithless woman soon found herself abandoned both by her lover and her mate. Membership in the Crow military societies was so greatly coveted, that if a man died his family brought pressure to have him replaced by a relative.

## 3. Banks Islands Sukwe [13]

On the **Banks Islands** of the Western Pacific every man sought to join the **Sukwe** society. Admission might be had at any age upon payment of a fee of shell money to those who already belonged. The Sukwe met in a clubhouse of its own in each village, and the structure functioned as a combined recreation hall, dining room, and dormitory for men only (Fig. 119). Sukwe buildings were carefully partitioned into graded sections; no man dared enter a higher portion than his own on pain of death. Members of each unit prepared and

[12] R. H. Lowie, *The Crow Indians,* New York, 1935.
[13] W. H. R. Rivers, *The History of Melanesian Society,* Cambridge, 1914, Vol. I, p. 61 ff.

ate meals together, and it was every man's ambition to get into the highest branches of Sukwe. Since heavy payments had to be made for each advance very few natives got to the very top, and those who

Fig. 119. Sukwe meeting house on the Banks Islands. Known as a gamal, the interior of this house is partitioned into carefully graded units, one for the use of members of each degree in the Sukwe society.

did were held in the greatest esteem. For a man to be out of the Sukwe altogether was a social disgrace, and even those who remained in the lowest grades for life were regarded as failures.

## 4. The Hopi Indian Marau Society [14]

As the three examples already summarized indicate, a majority of associations in primitive societies are designed for men, but women's groups are not unknown. Among the **Hopi Indians** of Northeastern Arizona every town or pueblo has its populace divided into secret orders, each of which is responsible for conducting an important ceremony for the good of the tribe. Many of these associations have lapsed, but a few remain active. At the village of Old Oraibi there used to be three feminine associations, of which the most popular was the **Marau**. Admission was entirely voluntary and without cost, and was almost never denied when requested. Despite the ease with which it might be joined the Marau was a highly regarded aggrega-

14 H. R. Voth, "The Oraibi Marau Ceremony," *Field Columbian Museum, Anthropological Series*, Vol. 11, No. 1, Chicago, 1912.

tion of females. It had its own kiva at Old Oraibi, carried out its
own initiations, performed secret rites for the promotion of rainfall,
good crops, health, and fertility, and annually staged a public dance
in distinctive costume (Fig. 120). In the eyes of the Hopi the Marau

Fig. 120. The public performance of all Hopi women's associations take circular
form.

observances were a regular part of the ceremonial cycle, and the
prayers of the women were as greatly prized as those of the men.

Additional associations are well known and a full account of their
operations would reveal a bewildering profusion of eligibility requirements for members, underlying motives, forms of initiation,
and methods of operation. Because participation is so very seldom
limited to a single group of kin, membership in associations cannot
help but create bonds that cut across ties of relationship and serve to
knit firmly together many unrelated members of a society. Some
associations carry on strictly practical activities, but even then they
usually bring a splash of color and excitement into the lives of their

community. People everywhere seem to enjoy opportunities to get away from their customary surroundings and routine duties, to learn secrets not shared by their fellows, to perform strange actions and rituals, and to wear elaborate costumes that differ greatly from conventional garb (Fig. 121).

A                                                          B

Fig. 121. A. Ona men, painted for a dance. B. Hopi men, in the costume of Buffalo dancers.

## H. LAW AND ORDER

Primitive societies are not anarchical even though they may lack formal bodies for making and enforcing laws. By definition nonliterate peoples cannot have written judicial codes, and it is most unusual to find them with clear-cut legislative and executive bodies. Nevertheless, their standards of conduct are usually known to all and punishment for offenses committed is not rare. One of the objectives

of an ethnological field-trip is to figure out from the observed behavior of a tribe whatever legal principles it seems to follow.

Law enforcement implies a degree of social compulsion that makes
an individual regulate his personal conduct to comply with the
norms of his group. It is as though each society said to its members,
"Conform, or be punished." Beyond the acceptance of this universal
concept there is no agreement on what constitutes a violation of
proper conduct or on the punishment to be inflicted. The cultures
of some societies permit and even encourage forms of behavior that
other groups may severely condemn. A distinction may be drawn
between political controls that rely on police or other formal enforcement agencies and social controls that are effective only because
of traditional usages as expressed in public opinion or reaction. Perhaps the most widespread of all legal attitudes are concerned with
the sanctity of property rights and human life. Property may be
intangible, like the privilege of using a specific design or tune; it
may have such real value as would a well-made spear; or its worth
may be completely symbolic, as in the case of shell money. Whether
property is tangible or not, whether it be individually or collectively
held, whether it is zealously guarded or freely loaned, make little
difference. Under all conditions there is present a concept of ownership, and violations of proprietary rights are punishable.

If we accept the axiom that no society likes to face biological
extinction, it follows that there will always be laws to prevent the
killing of people, especially if they are still capable of parenthood.
Distinctions may be drawn between abortion, infanticide, suicide,
murder, and various degrees of manslaughter, and some acts may
be condoned while others are not. A small percentage of tribes allow
the killing of certain babies, the very aged, or the hopelessly sick,
but most societies regret the loss of a member under any circumstances. In our society the safest tool for a killer to use seems to be
an automobile. If an intoxicated man shoots several people he may
be charged with murder and executed if found guilty; but if a
drunken driver kills an equal number of people he may be found
guilty of involuntary manslaughter and sentenced to a relatively
light prison term.[15] Other societies may make different discrimina-

---

[15] The *Detroit Free Press,* October 20, 1950, p. 12, carried a story of a youth who, while
drunk, drove through a red light and crashed into a car, killing two people and one of
his own passengers. He was convicted of "involuntary manslaughter."

tions. A man who kills an adulterous wife caught in the act may not be charged with any offense, but if he is thought guilty of having bewitched a woman he may be put to death.

There is no universal touchstone, either, for evaluating how severe the same form of punishment will be considered by peoples of different cultures. Cutting off the nose of a culprit might be regarded as unbelievably brutal in one society and as moderate in another. A slap across the face would humiliate and infuriate an adult male in the United States, but would have been taken in stride by a recruit in the Imperial Army of Japan. We might view social ostracism as light punishment for a serious offense, but primitive groups are inclined to consider rejection by one's fellows as a fate worse than death.

Responsibility for carrying out retribution seems to follow a definite trend when one compares various social systems. Where cultures are relatively simple the matter of inflicting punishment on offenders is likely to be left to the kinfolk of those who were injured, but in societies and cultures of greater development and complexity the administration of justice is left more and more to impersonal agencies and non-relatives.

Methods of evaluating evidence and determining guilt are also highly variable. They may range from a tendency to regard as guilty anyone against whom an accusation is brought to very elaborate procedures for weighing evidence, and even for the punishment of those who bear false witness. A favorite device is to subject a suspect, and, once in a while, his accuser as well, to an **ordeal.** Much as they may differ in details, all ordeals are based on the setting up of a trial or contest situation in which victory is always supposed to go to the innocent. Whether the test consists of immersion in water, grasping a white-hot iron, drinking poison, swallowing a hard crust, or trial by combat, the underlying idea seems to be that an incorruptible supernatural power will always make its decision clear by allowing the guilty party to suffer defeat. That mortals might frame the ordeal situation in order to favor or condemn a particular party is an idea that could be entertained only by an unbeliever.

Whatever particular attributes they may have, all legal systems are meant to help hold a society together and to maintain its accustomed way of life. In this regard obedience to law and patriotism fuse into a single concept. Hunger does not justify the theft of food, and sexual craving does not excuse rape. The law-abiding citizen puts his social responsibilities above his personal desires, and so does the patriotic individual. In the same connection, the highest legal authority in most primitive societies is vested in the head-man or chief, who is also the tribe's political leader. When so much power is lodged in a single personage he is likely to be equated with a deity, and the notion of divine rulers is exceedingly common. Analysis of this aspect of man's relations to man in a primitive society regularly leads an investigator into the study of man's dealings with the supernatural, for orderly, lawful, patriotic, and religious activities are constantly blended.

## I. MAN'S RELATIONS TO MAN, REVIEWED AND ELABORATED

Man's interactions with his fellows cover a host of topics, but they fall into a systematic arrangement if they are viewed in the light of the twin axioms that all societies seek to maintain themselves and their cultures indefinitely. Sexual reproduction is the only way, directly or indirectly, of continuously replenishing the supply of human beings that constitute a social unit, and on this point biological factors cannot be disregarded. Females, and females only, are capable of conceiving, bearing, and suckling children, and every society encourages them to have offspring under regulated conditions. There are other prime features of feminine biology, not previously mentioned, that also enter into the formation of social regulations. Women are so constituted, since their primary reproductive activity is to receive semen, that they are capable of having sexual relations without desire; and they can continue to have intercourse almost continuously. Men can do neither. Because of the former all legal systems recognize that rape and criminal assault can be committed only against women; and on account of the latter only a female can be an ordinary prostitute.

Except for a few such instances, social regulations are unlikely to be based on genuine considerations of biology, and some biocultural rules may even give the appearance of running counter to biology. There is no doubt that men everywhere are incapable of bearing offspring, but in societies that practice the **couvade** they may go through the forms of lying-in. Men are unquestionably stronger of physique than most women, but in many cultural situations a powerful male may be afraid even to glance at his mother-in-law. It is entirely likely that on the Banks Islands some wives dominate their husbands at home, but they would not dare to follow them into a men's clubhouse. On the whole, symbolic, cultural determinants play a greater part than biological factors in establishing what roles the sexes should play in any society.

Cultural considerations also affect the recognition and naming of kinfolk. Every anthropologist realizes that consanguinty may be assigned as well as inherited. A Toda baby in Southern India accepts as its father whatever man ritually presents its mother with a bow, regardless of whose genes it actually carries. Until modern times the Chinese regarded all people who had the same surname as bloodkin and forbade them to marry even if no trace of genealogical connection could be established. On the other hand we must not forget that wherever unilateral systems of kinship nomenclature were in force, even blood relatives as close as one's father or mother might be left out of a clan reckoning.

Each society must strike a balance between encouraging bonds of cohesion to develop among some of its members and preventing tightly-knit groups from giving up their allegiance to the social whole. Bodies of close relatives are particularly apt to form self-contained and self-sufficient cliques that may declare themselves independent of the rest of their society. As a rule, exogamic regulations and membership in scattered associations are enough to overcome the dangers of wholesale segmentation. Individuals, too, must occasionally be held in line. This can ordinarily be accomplished through legal restrictions and appeals to patriotism. Where such measures prove insufficient recourse may still be had to supernatural practices that emphasize the formation of strong sentiments of attachment to one's natal society.

### SELECTED REFERENCES

Fortes, Meyer, *The Web of Kinship among the Tallensi,* London, 1949.
Hoebel, E. Adamson, "Law and Anthropology," *Virginia Law Review,* Vol. 32, 1946, pp. 836-854.
Hollis, A. C., *The Masai,* Oxford, 1905.
Kroeber, Alfred L., *The Nature of Culture,* Chicago, 1952, section 2.

Lévi-Strauss, Claude, "The Social and Psychological Aspects of Chieftain-
    ship in a Primitive Tribe: The Nambikuara," *Transactions, New
    York Academy of Sciences,* series II, Vol. 7, 1944, pp. 16-32.
———, "Social Structure," *Anthropology Today* (A. L. Kroeber, ed.), Chi-
    cago, 1953, pp. 524-553.
Lowie, Robert H., *Primitive Society,* New York, 1925, chap. 10.
Morgan, Lewis H., "Systems of Consanguinity and Affinity of the Human
    Family," *Smithsonian Institution, Contributions to Knowledge,* Vol.
    17, No. 218, Washington, 1870.
Murdock, George P., *Social Structure,* New York, 1949.
Radcliffe-Brown, A. R., "The Social Organization of Australian Tribes,"
    Oceania, Vol. 1, 1930.
Rivers, W. H. R., *The History of Melanesian Society,* Cambridge, Eng-
    land, 1914, Vol. 1, pp. 60-79.
Titiev, Mischa, "The Influence of Common Residence on the Unilateral
    Classification of Kindred," *American Anthropologist,* Vol. 45, 1943,
    pp. 511-529.
———, "Old Oraibi," *Papers of the Peabody Museum of American Archae-
    ology and Ethnology,* Harvard University, Vol. 22, 1944.
Voth, Harry R., "The Oraibi Marau Ceremony," *Field Columbian Mu-
    seum, Anthropological Series,* Vol. 11, No. 1, Chicago, 1912.

CHAPTER 23

# Man and the Supernatural[1]

## A. THE LEAST COMMON DENOMINATOR

From time to time in the preceding chapters references have been made to religious activity as a segment of the biocultural triangle that schematizes the greater part of every society's design for living together. Religion is such a vast and emotionally laden subject that it may mean all sorts of different things to different people. Ethnologists have found it so difficult to establish a satisfactory all-embracing definition that they have gone to the other extreme. In keeping with a suggestion originally proposed by E. B. Tylor, they have tended to work with a **minimum definition** that provides the least common denominator of elements to be found in all manifestations of religion. By reducing Tylor's proposal to its barest essentials we arrive at a minimum definition of religion as "a belief in the supernatural." Of itself the term, "belief," implies an element of faith, a willingness to accept something without tangible demonstration or proof; and when "belief" is applied to the supernatural it signifies the acceptance of an order of things that cannot, as far as is known, be grasped by man's senses or any extension thereof. When we describe something as supernatural, then, we mean that we believe it can never be made manifest to human taste, touch, smell, sight or hearing, even with the aid of devices like powerful telescopes or

1 This subject is broad enough to warrant an entire book. Since a single chapter cannot cover the whole field, it is only fair to the reader to explain the basis on which topics were chosen for inclusion. The guiding principle has been to bring out the sociocultural implications of the supernatural. Omitted from consideration are such important features as individual feelings of pleasure or comfort that worshipers may derive from religious practices.

sound amplifiers. To believe wholeheartedly in the existence of anything that cannot and may never be grasped by one's senses forms
the very core of religion. Beliefs of this sort, which need have no
bio-physico-chemical reality whatsoever, comprise the quintessence of
algebraic mentality which can deal with abstract symbolic values as
readily as if they had objective reality.

Actually, no religion fails to go far beyond the two elements in
the minimum definition, but every society builds its religious super-
structure on the same least common denominator. Since supernatural
concepts have no material existence and may differ widely from culture to culture, there is no way that an ethnologist in the field can
recognize, before they are pointed out to him, the objects to which
an unstudied tribe ascribes religious significance. It may take a long
time before people confide their beliefs to an investigator, and in the
meantime he must be very circumspect lest he unintentionally dam-
age or pollute something that may turn out to be holy in the minds
of the natives.

## B. SACRED, PROFANE, AND THE CONCEPT OF MANA

As an anthropologist gains the confidence of a tribe and begins to
learn their innermost system of symbolic values, he comes to realize
that they divide their world into **sacred** and **profane** categories.
Certain objects, places, words, and people will be classed as sacred,
whereas seemingly identical items will be treated as secular or profane. The only difference will be one of native belief. An example
from the Christian religion might deal with the distinction between
a font of holy water and a similar basin of plain water. Through the
use of none of his senses or scientific apparatus could an outsider,
even if he were a specialist in qualitative chemistry, detect any difference in the two liquids, yet no true Christian would dream of
using them indiscriminately.

The particular component of supernaturalism that distinguishes
the sacred from the profane may be described as **mana.** Mana can
best be understood as a powerful force, beyond the understanding
or control of ordinary folk, that has an unlimited capacity for getting things done. Within itself mana is amoral and neutral in the
sense that it is neither automatically good nor bad, and that it is
indifferent as to whether its accomplishments are considered bene-

ficial or harmful to individuals or societies. In this respect it is exactly like electricity which cares not at all if it is used to kill a person or to run a refrigerator. Because it can with equal facility do good or harm in the eyes of men, mana is always regarded as potentially dangerous. However, again like electricity, it is subject to a measure of control, and some people in every society learn to handle it safely, usually through training but sometimes by inspiration. All others must avoid unauthorized contacts with mana in any form.

A splendid example of how the power of mana may work is to be found in the Old Testament.[2] Uzzah, a cart driver, was transporting the sacred Ark of the Covenant from one place to another. The road was rough, and at one point Uzzah reached out to steady the Ark with his hand, whereupon he was stricken dead. No matter how good his intentions may have been, Uzzah was not authorized to touch so mana-charged an object, and his impulsive action cost him his life. Yes, the power of mana can destroy as well as aid mankind, and that is why efforts must be made to keep it under control. To safeguard the lay public sacred things may be plainly marked with symbols that serve to identify them and to act as warnings, they may be kept hidden in secret places, or they may be subjected to **tabu**, which has the effect of keeping unqualified people at a safe distance. A tabu is a restraining order, a prohibition backed up by the threat of supernatural punishment for any violation.

To sum up the material so far presented in this chapter, a society may ascribe supernatural value to anything that seems to have an inexplicable capacity for getting successful results. This capacity is thought to be a kind of mysterious power called mana, which may be assigned to a weapon with which a warrior dispatches many enemies, to a stone that is believed to have brought rain, to a person of high rank whose commands win obedience, to anything worn by a mighty personage, or to whatever has been in contact with something already thought to have been endowed with mana. For mana is transferable and can be handed on by touch or inheritance. Everything that is endowed with mana is sacred, all else is profane.

So great, continuously active, and amoral is the force of mana supposed to be, that it can be exceedingly dangerous if uncontrolled. It may even cause sickness or death to befall those who handle it

---

2 *Old Testament*, Samuel II, 6:3-8. Mana was first described, with very little variation from the way it is here used, in R. H. Codrington, *The Melanesians*, Oxford, 1891, ch. 12.

B

C

A

D

without proper authority or training. To protect the general public from harm everything in the world of the sacred is usually proclaimed tabu, which has the practical effect of warning laymen to keep away or suffer the consequences.

## C. PRIESTS, SHAMANS, WITCHES, CHIEFS, AND GODS

If the power of mana is too dangerous to be left uncontrolled, ways must be found of directing it into beneficial channels. This can be done only if some persons become qualified to deal with the supernatural and succeed in setting up techniques for getting it to work in man's favor. Individuals who specialize in dealing with the world of the sacred are to be found in all societies, and are known as **shamans, medicinemen,** or **priests.**[3] As a rule, shamans or medicinemen are considered to have personal supernatural powers, particularly for curing disease, and they may perform no regularly scheduled rites, practicing their special skills only at the request of those who desire their services. Another category of practitioners who deal with the supernatural consists of **witches.** Those who engage in **witchcraft** are most often feared because they are reputed to exert their extraordinary abilities for anti-social purposes, causing to befall illness, death, bad weather, crop failure, and similar catastrophes. Priests are not necessarily thought to be born with personal supernatural power, but they may be considered to owe their efficiency to training for the performance of regularly recurrent ceremonies. Instances are not unknown in which the same person may be regarded as capable of acting either as shaman, witch, or priest, presumably because of a mutual ability to manipulate supernatural forces. Because of their supposed power, witches may be dreaded but left unharmed; and

[3] There is enough resemblance in the characteristics of shamans, medicinemen and priests to justify their designation by a single term. It is hardly necessary to point out that "priest" is being used to denote anyone qualified to deal with the supernatural, and not in the sense of a particular kind of Christian clergyman.

Fig. 122. Medicinemen, High Priest and God. A. Witoto shaman. His costume marks him apart from the ordinary Witoto men in Fig. 111. B. Navaho medicine man. He is emerging from a sweat lodge where he was trying to effect a cure by singing over a patient. C. Sacred tipi of the Omaha Indians. Its distinctive nature is evidenced by the white color and the symbols of vegetation. D. Reverence for Hirohito. Japan has a high literacy rate, but before World War II, the people reverenced their emperor as a combined ruler, high priest, and living god.

when things go inexplicably wrong priests are liable to be accused of witchcraft.

Except in a limited number of tribes priests are distinguished from laymen by the clothes they wear (Fig. 122 A), the tasks they perform, the objects they handle, the tabus they observe, and the codes of conduct that they follow with particular respect to food and sex habits. Because their duties must bring them into close touch with things supernatural, all priests acquire an aura of sanctity, and are themselves held to become charged with mana. The same applies to their costumes and whatever they may use in the performance of their sacerdotal activities.

Members of nonliterate societies do not, as a rule, differentiate one kind of extremely great power from another. Some tribal leaders, or **chiefs,** exert so little control over their subjects as to be scarcely distinguishable from their fellows. Others have so much authority that they may be considered to have as much mana as priests. Their persons, habitations, and belongings are equally likely to be thought sacred and to be subject to tabu. To a commoner it makes no difference if the power to regulate, disrupt, or terminate his life is derived from a supernatural or political source. Anyone who wields great authority over others will be looked upon with much the same awe and respect as a supernatural personage. The tendency to equate sacred and political power is particularly strong in societies where the chief actually has priestly functions. Instances of this kind are far from rare. At Old Oraibi the village Chief is automatically leader of the town's most important religious observance, the Soyal. Throughout the Pacific islands of Polynesia countless chiefs serve as priests, and similar examples can be cited from any large area on the globe. Speaking broadly, it is only in recent times and in restricted portions of the Euro-American world that a sharp distinction has been drawn between chiefs and priests, or between "church" and "state."

Not only are powerful chiefs frequently equated with priests, but they may even be identified with **gods.** In minimum but basic terms a god may be defined as a supernatural personage heavily endowed with mana. The tie between strong chiefs and gods seems to rest on the assumption that the soul of a person who exerted great power while alive will retain his mana in the other world. Because it is to the advantage of the surviving members of the society to have their late chief's power exerted on their behalf, his soul may be called upon for help by his former subjects. For this important task the dead chief's successor is commonly thought to be best suited. Wherever such customs are practiced a succession is set up whereby a chief acts as a priest while alive, and becomes converted to a god when he has died. These customs also help to explain why some chiefs are so likely to be regarded as future gods that they may be reverenced as divine even while they are still alive (Fig. 122D).

## D. RITES OF PASSAGE

As was said earlier, belief in the supernatural provides the basic foundation of religion, but no society stops short at that point. Rituals are always developed that are intended to win the favor of the supernatural in support of man's enterprises. Some peoples believe that help must be granted whenever a correct approach is made by qualified experts, but others think that supernatural forces can never be coerced and must be allowed to act as they please.[4] In either case every social unit makes some effort to get supernatural help, especially in times of crisis. This does not mean that the members of any tribe place all their reliance on sacred aids. Within the limits of their knowledge and abilities people always try to gain their ends by using all the tangible resources at their disposal, but if these prove to be inadequate calls may be made for supernatural assistance. Varying proportions of natural and supernatural means may be used in combination, but seldom is one technique employed in a primitive society to the total exclusion of the other. Never does a nonliterate farmer pray for a good crop without bothering to work in his fields. No more would a baseball player in the United States rely on a lucky token to get him a homerun without swinging as hard as he could on a pitch that he liked. The more uncertain the satisfactory outcome of a critical situation may be, the more likely are religious elements to be combined with other methods of achieving a happy solution.

About fifty years ago Van Gennep made the astute observation

---

[4] Some anthropologists seek to differentiate magic from religion on the grounds that the former has a much greater element of compulsion. The deeper one goes in the study of such supposed distinctions, the more insignificant they become. In this book anything based on a belief in the supernatural is classed as religious, and no effort is made to separate magic from religion.

that primitive peoples regard a life cycle as a journey from one stage of existence to another. Each individual normally passes through the phases of birth, puberty, marriage, and death. These represent, according to Van Gennep, critical points of human existence which require supernatural help if a person is to make a safe transition from one stage to the next. Van Gennep termed these religious practices **rites of passage,** and in one guise or another they may be found in all societies.[5]

Birth and infancy are universally believed to be full of hazards for a mother and child and, to a lesser extent, to other relatives and the community at large. Fears of childbirth, blood shedding, infant mortality, and of evil spirits that may enter weak or immature bodies are variously expressed. Protective countermeasures are everywhere to be found. They may exhibit more concern for physical rather than spiritual dangers, or the other way around, but in most cases the means of protection will show a blend of natural and supernatural elements. There is a commonly held notion that primitive women give birth without physical difficulty, but rarely can it be proved that they bear children any more easily than literate women. Cultural conventions may encourage loud outcries during labor or may insist on stoic silence, but the biological mechanisms of parturition are everywhere much alike.

Only a few exceptional societies attempt to treat the delivery and rearing of infants as phenomena that do not require supernatural intervention. Even so, let it be noted, modern obstetricians and pediatricians who rely exclusively on scientific techniques still have the same objectives as primitive shamans who resort to a great deal of supernaturalism. This touches on only one of many overlaps between medicine and religion. The belief that "Cleanliness is next to Godliness" is far from dead, and in the New Testament the sick are advised to go for help to the elders of the church.[6]

Contemporary psychologists and psychiatrists are agreed that puberty and adolescence are critical periods and full of problems. Primitive peoples long ago realized that the transition from childhood to adulthood was exceedingly difficult, and in countless ways they besought supernatural assistance. Rites of passage concerned

<hr />

[5] A. Van Gennep, *Les Rites de Passage,* Paris, 1909.

[6] *New Testament,* James, V: 14. "Is any sick among you? Let him call for the elders of the church; and let them pray over him, anointing him with oil in the name of the Lord."

with this stage frequently take the form of a **tribal initiation,** whose underlying intent is to emphasize the transfer of youngsters to adult status. Quite often, the transition is dramatized by "killing" the initiate as a child and having him "re-born" as an adult. These ceremonies signalize the end of one phase of an individual's existence and the start of a new one.

Marriage presents a different set of problems. Foremost of these are the dangers involved in blood-letting, wherever female virginity is demanded of brides; reluctance to admit an outsider to intimate relationships with a group of consanguineous kin; fear that the wedded couple may fail to have offspring; and concern over a young couple's fitness to rear whatever children they may have. No sure method of guaranteeing the soundness of marriages is known anywhere, and it should cause no surprise that primitive societies look upon weddings as critical transition points which benefit from supernatural help for their safe passage.[7] Hardly ever does one find a society that completely dispenses with religious sanctions at marriage, and equally rare are societies that do not allow divorce to function as a sort of safety-valve for allowing the escape of tensions arising from marriages that have failed.

Of all the rites of passage those that occur most regularly in primitive societies are concerned with death. Here is an inevitable source of recurring crises, for no tribe is complacent about losing members, yet none can prevent their loss. There are several major aspects to the social problems raised by death. Strenuous efforts, both biological and supernatural, are made to keep a person from dying; religious rites are performed to encourage the soul of the deceased to depart, without undue delay, for the other world; steps involving supernatural practices are taken to ensure the soul of the departed of a satisfactory existence in the afterlife; and mourning customs call for increased solidarity among the survivors. So highly regarded are religious efforts to attain these ends that death rituals tend to be retained even by people who profess to be atheistic or agnostic.

All social groups have an ambivalent attitude toward the dead. They may, as has just been said, seek in every conceivable way to prevent an individual from dying, and they may bitterly mourn his

7 Not all societies recognize the validity of civil marriages. People in the United States who are not deeply religious are nevertheless apt to plan church weddings or their equivalent.

BIOCULTURAL BEHAVIOR

passing when the time comes, but they may also do all they can to
dispatch the soul of the deceased and to keep it from returning to
the land of the living, except on specifically authorized occasions.
Spirits of the dead are universally regarded with a mixture of love
and fear.

## E. GROUP RITUALS AND CEREMONIAL CALENDARS

Just as important as rites of passage that emphasize individual life
cycles and adjustments to society are tribal ceremonies that are meant
to aid a whole group's relations with its physical setting or to
strengthen the bonds of cohesion that unite all its members. There
is no need to repeat that human bodies are not self-sufficient mechanisms, and that they must get oxygen, food, water, and raw materials
from their environment. But no one can guarantee that the environment will provide enough of what is needed, or that a favorable zone
will never change. Persistent doubts constantly arise, and where
technological methods are poorly developed assurances of continuing
supplies can be had only from the world of the supernatural.

Actual deficiencies of the natural environment are always increased
by the selective effect of cultural evaluation. Many a group that finds
its food in short supply would have more than enough to eat if it
would be willing to consume everything that is edible. Some societies, it is true, occupy regions that would keep them on the verge of
starvation under any conditions, but a good number would be
better off if they broadened the base of their culturally approved
foods. Shortages from similar causes may arise in any branch of
material culture. When conventional dress goods like cotton, silk,
wool, or rayon are scarce and expensive in our society, burlap sack-
ing may be cheap and plentiful, but it is hard to imagine a young
woman going to a party in a burlap gown.

In the final analysis, it does not matter whether shortages arise
from deficiencies of nature or cultural preferences. Primitive peoples
know pitifully little about overcoming the one or changing the
other. Small wonder that they resort to elaborate ceremonies in the
hope of improving their lot. Rituals for increasing the food supply,
augmenting raw materials, controlling the weather, and warding off
natural catastrophes are universal and commonplace. Besides the
material benefits that they are supposed to bring they also serve to

assign responsibility for man's welfare to the supernatural, and by this means they draw resentments and blame away from any living member of the society. Literate folk are not the only ones whose social solidarity is increased by the concept that whatever happens is the will of God.

Supernatural aid and responsibility are also invoked whenever man's relations with his fellows prove faulty. Matters like an unequal balance of numbers between the sexes, sterility, divorce, irresponsible parenthood, hostility between neighbors, or hatred of chiefs may result in crises as serious as shortages of material goods. Some social deficiences can be remedied through human actions or change of cultural standards, but others seem to lie beyond the province of man.

No society waits until a serious crisis has actually arisen before it performs such group rituals as it considers beneficial to its total membership. Emergency rites may be held on occasion, but most observances take place at stated times, without reference to the needs of the moment. In such cases the religious activities are regulated by a **ceremonial calendar.** Even nonliterate people may have ways of keeping track of the year's progress. Simplest of all are means of watching each day's sunrise, following the sun's north-south movements, and noting the solstices or turning points that occur annually around June 21 and December 21 (Fig. 123). Groups that live by farming in northern latitudes are particularly anxious to make sure that the sun starts northward after the winter solstice, thus bringing

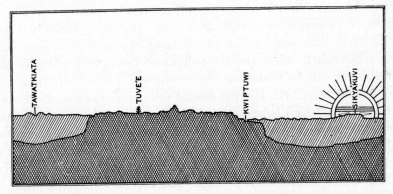

Fig. 123. Oraibi's sun calendar. Watchers of the eastern skyline at Oraibi used to keep track of the sun's annual movements by noting the points at which it rose at daybreak.

longer days and the warmth of spring and summer, without which agriculture must fail.[8] Winter solstice ceremonies frequently mark the end of one year and the beginning of the next. Various ways may be used to express the ideas of a termination followed by a fresh start. They may range from the making of resolutions and the cancellation of old debts, to thoroughgoing housecleaning, and enactments of death and rebirth. Sometimes, too, efforts are made to help the sun gain in strength after the winter solstice. Such rites often take the form of **new fire** ceremonies, during which fresh fires are kindled, whose growing light and heat symbolize the sun's progress toward the summer season.

Religious calendars are never limited solely to the recognition and celebration of the solstices. Rites may be performed at any season, particularly when work is slack, but only in well-integrated, actively functioning societies are annual ceremonies systematically held. Time and again have ethnologists found it to be true that when a tribe is neglecting its ceremonial calendar it is also giving up its old way of life. Failure to maintain established religious practices and failure to keep up a traditional pattern of culture are directly interconnected.

## F. PRIMITIVE RELIGION AS A SOCIAL FORCE

Whatever other purposes it may serve, a belief in identical supernatural forces always helps to bind tightly together the inhabitants of a primitive community. The disunity so plainly visible in literate, heterogeneous groups, whose people adhere to various creeds, is unknown in nonliterate tribes. Not every primitive individual participates to the same degree in religious exercises, nor does each person necessarily show the same depth of conviction. Skeptics and unbelievers may be found anywhere, but under truly primitive conditions one never finds friction among followers of two or more competing faiths. Social cohesion is also strengthened by the previously noted use of supernaturalism to relieve powerful chiefs and other tribal leaders of blame when things go wrong. From every point of view religion turns out to be a strong binding force in primitive societies. Nor should it be thought that its effectiveness is unrecog-

[8] In the southern hemisphere, or in other parts of the world, different calendrical points may be important. Onsets of rainy or dry seasons, equinoxes, or other phenomena may be more crucial than the solstices.

nized in literate cultures. Professor Miner has recently written with respect to Mohammedanism that its sacred text, the Koran, explicitly aims to achieve political unity through common religion.[9]

A tendency to ascribe supernatural qualities to patriotic observances is evident in all nonliterate groups, and is not entirely missing from so sophisticated a culture as ours. We speak of the flag as sacred, and men as reverently bare their heads before it as they do in church. There is not much point to debating whether precisely the same shades of meaning are to be attached to the attitudes of people in the presence of national or religious symbols. They may be regarded as alike as long as they are described in the same terms, give rise to similar forms of behavior, and serve the same end of strengthening a social unit's sentiments of attachment to the group as a whole. When the idea of regarding as supernatural whatever emblem represents a society is combined with the notion that a chief is a supernatural personage, it becomes clear that primitive peoples are held together by the twin ties of religious and political allegiance (Fig. 131A), p. 453.

Death represents the greatest threat to social cohesion and to the desire of each tribe to prolong its collective existence indefinitely. Since there is no material method of preventing death's inroads, recourse to supernatural agencies is the only way to soften or neutralize its impact. That is why the notion of another world, where the souls of the dead live on after the fashion of life on earth, is so common. It amounts to saying that a deceased person, even if his body is no longer present, is still a member of his society. Very often tribes go still further by claiming that spirits of the dead have greater mana than their owners had in the flesh, and by performing rituals to win the favorable use of that extra supernatural power. Insofar as a society's dead, in broad terms, are the forebears of the living, a sort of generalized ancestor worship comes into play. This is not the same thing as the particularized veneration of specific ancestors that prevailed in China and other Oriental countries, but different though they are the two systems of belief have a common base.

In brief, religion may well be disruptive in a heterogeneous society containing groups of adherents to various faiths, but in a homogeneous community it acts as a strong, unifying force. It strengthens

[9] H. M. Miner, *The Primitive City of Timbuctoo,* Princeton, 1953, p. 72.

the allegiance of individuals to their tribe, functions to overcome dissatisfactions arising from defects in man's relations to his environment, smooths over many rough spots in man's dealings with his fellows, and helps to negate the unsettling effects of death. What appeals to patriotism alone try to accomplish in Euro-American societies, a combination of patriotism and religion seeks to bring about in nonliterate cultures. It is with the help of deeply held beliefs in the supernatural that primitive groups seek to keep in line the hungry, poorly housed, badly clad, and sexually starved. No matter where ethnologists may look, they find religious activities employed to bolster the weak links in any tribe's social organization.

## G. SUPERNATURALISM VERSUS SCIENCE

Cultural progress is inevitably associated with an increase of knowledge. Nonliterate folk, by and large, have far less knowledge at their disposal than do literate people. This is equivalent to saying that the former are more ignorant. Ignorance is not to be confused with stupidity. Some men and women who are basically quick to learn and apply new bits of information may be ignorant of many reputed facts, and others who are slow to learn may have much factual knowledge. In other words, primitive people are ignorant because they do not know many facts, but some of them may nevertheless be surprisingly clever.

Much of what literate folk know is organized under the heading of science. As it is to be interpreted in the present context, the essence of science is an understanding of tangible causes and their effects. A society that has a great deal of knowledge in this respect has a choice of two ways of explaining phenomena, whereas a primitive group has only one choice. As an illustration, suppose a plot of ground which has yielded good crops year in and year out suddenly fails to grow anything although external conditions appear to be unchanged. Primitive farmers, presumably lacking all scientific knowledge of plant and soil diseases, would have no choice but to regard the event as supernaturally caused and to resort for help to prayer and exorcism. A modern farmer, under the same circumstances, would have two courses of action. He might call on an agricultural specialist, or he might resort to religion.

Simple knowledge of cause and effect relationships may not in itself lead to greater reliance on science than on supernaturalism. What is much more likely to prove effective is based on the **law of controlled causation.** Whenever men are able to demonstrate that they can produce stated effects by manipulating their causes, the phenomena with which they deal move from the realm of religion to the realm of science. Thus, as more facts become scientifically known the law of controlled causation covers more cases and man's reliance on the supernatural shrinks. This is only another way of saying that as the amount of knowledge in a society goes up, there is a proportionate diminution of its dependence on supernaturalism (Fig. 124). To test the validity of this hypothesis one has only to note

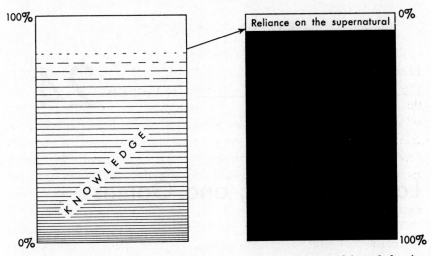

Fig. 124. Knowledge and supernaturalism. As the percentage of knowledge increases within a society, its reliance on the supernatural diminishes proportionately.

that genuine reliance on the supernatural remains strongest in sophisticated societies in precisely those areas, like the question of life after death, where the law of controlled causation cannot be said to operate.

### SELECTED REFERENCES

Codrington, R. H., *The Melanesians: Studies in Their Anthropology and Folklore,* Oxford, 1891.
Durkheim, Émile, *The Elementary Forms of the Religious Life,* Glencoe, Illinois, 1947.

Goode, William J., *Religion Among the Primitives,* Glencoe, Illinois, 1951.
Howells, William W., *The Heathens,* New York, 1948.
Miner, Horace M., *The Primitive City of Timbuctoo,* Princeton, 1953.
Titiev, Mischa, "Notes on Hopi Witchcraft," *Papers of the Michigan Academy of Science, Arts, and Letters,* Vol. 28, 1943, pp. 549-557.
Tylor, Edward B., *Primitive Culture,* Boston, 1874.
Van Gennep, Arnold, *Les Rites de Passage,* Paris, 1909.
Wagley, Charles, *Amazon Town,* New York, 1953, chap. 7.
Wallis, Wilson D., *Religion in Primitive Society,* New York, 1939.

CHAPTER 24

# Language, Arts, and Games

## A. THE ROLE OF LANGUAGE IN CULTURE

This chapter is meant to drive home the lesson that a biocultural triangle does not encompass all the essential aspects of a society's way of living together. Foremost of the facets so far omitted is language. The basic importance of human speech for the development and continuation of any pattern of culture need not be questioned. Symbolic values can best be expressed through linguistic utterances, and no other way is known for teaching children to accept and follow a particular form of culture. Only when they are put into words do abstractions of any kind acquire a sort of reality, so that it would be impossible to teach the essentials of a system of supernatural beliefs without the use of language. For instance, Christianity could not be taught without reference to words like faith, soul, God and Heaven.

Every human society has a language and a culture. The two are completely interdependent. Some scholars would go so far as to say that language and culture are one and the same, but for practical purposes it is better to admit their close ties but to treat them as separate. After all, language deals only with forms of behavior that can be verbalized, but culture is also concerned with numerous activities, like motor habits, that may never be expressed in words nor accompanied by speech. There need be nothing verbal about tipping one's hat, yet it may be an important act of culture and may convey as subtle a symbolic meaning as any word.

That human beings who possess algebraic mentalities are the only animals capable of assigning arbitrary values to vocal utterances has already been pointed out (p. 158). But once man acquired that capacity he seems never to have improved on it. One language is as good as another for conveying meaning, and in this sense it can be flatly stated that there is no such thing as an inferior language. On the basis of their experiences with many societies and cultures ethnologists find it impossible to rate languages as better or worse, or more or less effective.

Language is so integral to culture that a group of anthropological specialists devote themselves almost exclusively to its study. As is true of ethnologists, they most often deal with nonliterate peoples. At first the analysis and interpretation of primitive tongues was attempted by scholars who had been trained to deal with the written languages that make up the great Indo-European family. Some of these men attempted to do field work, but they usually took along grammatical tables of declensions and conjugations based on their knowledge of Indo-European forms. Into these previously prepared diagrams they tried to force whatever native languages they were studying, and anything that could not be fitted in was marked missing or deficient. None of the pioneer students of primitive speech was aware of the now obvious fact that each culture had its own vocabulary and grammar for expressing its ideas. In the footsteps of men like Boas, Sapir, and Bloomfield, anthropologically trained linguists in the United States began to go into the field without prejudice and to seek to understand native tongues only in terms of what they heard and saw.

## B. LINGUISTIC ANALYSIS [1]

Vocal utterances to which a social group may assign symbolic meanings cover a wide range of possibilities. Sounds that strike speakers of English as clicks, hisses, snorts, gulps, or whines may be just as conventional for speaking other languages as are the consonants and vowels familiar to us. The only requirements for what is called **articulate speech** are that the sounds to which values are to be attached must be distinct, with a beginning and end that can be recognized, and that they must be capable of almost exact repetition by all who speak the same language. Students of primitive tongues require first a means of noting down whatever sounds they hear in articulate speech. Only after a language has been recorded in writing can it later be systematically analyzed and compared with other tongues that natives use orally. Obviously, the English alphabet is not equipped to render accurately the many sounds that human beings can make with their vocal apparatus. Before linguistic analysis could proceed, therefore, it was necessary to develop an all-embracing system of notation by means of which any articulate utterance could be transcribed.

All languages consist of sounds whose production, orderly arrangement, and combination serve to convey definite meanings. Every tongue that is spoken uses only a fraction of all the vocal noises that men can make. Each language, then, has a structure, consisting of a finite number of distinctive sounds to which its speakers attach meaning, and the smallest identifiable unit of sound is called a **phoneme.** English examples are *th* in *something,* or *b* in *banker.* Phonemes rarely stand alone, but are combined with other minimum units of sound in fixed patterns, of which the smallest element that has meaning is called a **morpheme.** When an indivisible morpheme can stand by itself and carry the significance of a word, it is called **free.** Monosyllables in English are usually **free morphemes,** as in the case of words like *fish* or *book.* When a morpheme conveys no meaning as long as it is by itself, it is called **bound.** Examples of **bound morphemes** include the *ly* of *lovely,* and the *er* of *driver.*

Sounds that frequently recur in a language fall into characteristic sequences or patterns that may be quite rigid. Thus, the *ng* of *clang*

---

[1] This section owes much to the treatment of language in Beals and Hoijer, *op. cit.,* chapter 17.

never starts a word in English, the *h* of *hollow* never ends one, and the sound *r* may follow initial *p* as in *pray*, but *p* can never follow initial *r*. Speech arrangements are learned early in life, and adult speakers adjusted to a single language find it very difficult to learn a new one. Both the production of sounds and their position in words or morphemes are equally fixed in each culture. This explains why people who habitually use a sound in one place, let us say initially, may have trouble in using virtually the same sound in a different position, let us say finally. Study of a language's sound system is known as **phonology.**

Besides studying sounds and their order of occurrence in morphemes or words, linguists are also concerned with their arrangement into meaningful phrases and sentences. **Syntax** or **grammar** is now the goal. Again, each language has a set of fixed rules. If word order is an important grammatical device it means one thing to say "dog bites man," and quite another to say "man bites dog." Pitch or intonation changes are equally effective for conveying different meanings, as we realize when we say, in level tones, "Oh, yes"; or, with rising pitch, "Oh, yes?" Differences of accent also produce a variety of meanings. School children in recent years have teased their parents to say "What am I doing?" with the stress on a different word each time. When an unwary adult obliges with, "Whát am I doing?" "What ám I doing?" "What am Í doing?" and "What am I doíng?" the child retorts, "Making a fool of yourself!"

There are many other ways of changing the meanings of words and sentences. Well known is **phonetic modification,** whereby *woman* is singular and *women* is plural. Also widely used are **reduplications,** so that when the Saramacca Bush-Negroes say, *hesi,* it means "to go fast," but when they say, *hesihesi,* it means "speed." [2] Frequently employed, too, are the devices of adding prefixes, infixes (the addition of an element into the middle of a word), and suffixes. No language uses one method to the total exclusion of the others, and linguists are alert to describe all the ways in which speakers of a specific tongue achieve variations of meaning.

A number of goals are sought by anthropologically trained linguists. They are anxious to record accurately as many primitive

---

2 This example is taken from M. J. Herskovits, *op. cit.,* p. 449.

languages as possible; they try to analyze the sounds, arrangements, and grammatical changes by which a variety of meanings may be communicated; they seek to show in how many details a language may reflect the environmental or cultural setting of its speakers; they attempt to demonstrate the historic changes brought about in a language by internal factors or external processes such as borrowing; and they are interested in fitting related tongues into larger and larger units.

Those who habitually converse with one another form a **speech community,** but within the same speech community differences may exist between the usages of infants and adults, men and women, occupational groups, residents of different parts of a large area, or on the basis of training and education. If these variations, most often known as **dialects,** do not prevent all or most of the members of a society from understanding one another, the speakers of the various dialects may still be said to form a single speech community, and this is usually the case with primitive tribes. Only within extremely large and heterogeneous social units is one likely to find speakers of dialects or languages that are not mutually intelligible.

A complete language, including its structured use of phonemes, methods of uttering sounds, vocabulary, and grammar, is so complex that it is unlikely to have been independently invented more than once. Accordingly, when linguists find two separate peoples speaking similar or identical tongues, they feel justified in assuming that at an earlier period of history the two groups had lived together. Even if every fact about the settlement of the United States and Canada were lost, linguists would postulate from their speech resemblances that the Caucasoid settlers of North America had once been in close contact with the English. Linguistic analysis, taken by itself, might not reveal which group had remained in its homeland, and which had traveled to other regions, but the fact of an earlier connection could be established beyond dispute.

Not very long ago it used to be taken for granted that a person's thoughts dictated his choice of words. Some modern linguists are of the opinion that the reverse may be true. The late Benjamin Whorf once stated flatly that an accepted pattern of word usage is often prior to certain forms of thinking and behavior.[3] This parallels

[3] B. L. Whorf, "The Relation of Habitual Thought and Behavior to Language," *Language, Culture, and Personality* (L. Spier *et al.*, eds.), Menasha, 1941, p. 75.

Kluckhohn's assertion that every language influences what its speakers see, feel, think, and talk about.[4]

Wonder is sometimes expressed because no international language has ever been a success. The failure is not due to any lack of technical skill on the part of linguists. What is often overlooked is the patent fact that no language exists apart from a society and its culture. Every tongue reflects the cultural background of its speakers and gives an indication of how they interpret their universe. Speakers of Eskimo have a great number of words describing snow under varying conditions; and Arabic is reported to have several thousand different words pertaining to camels and their equipment. A language functions, therefore, to channel human experiences into particular forms. Paradoxically, we express our thoughts in words, but our words help to shape our thoughts. Not until there is a universal culture by which all the world lives is there much chance for an international language to succeed.

According to a recent estimate by Professor Harry Hoijer, the most widespread family of languages is the Indo-European. It includes Germanic, Slavic, Romance, Greek, Indo-Iranian and others, and taking all its branches together it is spoken by some 900 million inhabitants of Europe and Asia. Within these continents another 43 million folk speak languages of the Turkic, Mongolian, and Tungus families. Southern India has about 58 million speakers of Dravidian tongues, and East Asia has 450 million Sino-Tibetan speakers, of whom 400 million use Chinese tongues. East Asia also includes approximately 23 million users of Korean, and well over 80 million Japanese speakers.

Africa has relatively small numbers who speak historically important Semitic and Hamitic tongues, but there are some 50 million each who speak Sudanic, just south of the Sahara, and Bantu further south. The islands of the southern basin of the Pacific Ocean (Oceania), are dominated by tribes belonging to one large linguistic family called Malayo-Polynesian. It is used by nearly 45 million natives, and includes the speech of all aborigines except the inhabitants of New Guinea and Australia. In contrast to Oceania's uniformity is the situation in the New World, which apparently shows the greatest linguistic diversity on earth. A few million pre-Columbian American Indians spoke tongues pertaining to well over 80 distinct

4 C. Kluckhohn, *Mirror for Man,* New York, 1949, p. 166.

families, each of which was unrelated in any manner to the others, and none of which had any connection with the languages of the Old World. Anthropologists may be forgiven if they smile a bit knowingly when people ask, "What is *the* Indian word for . . . ?"

Malinowski and others have drawn attention to the great power that is inherent in words. Cases are known where words have been equated with the very things for which they stand. This is particularly common in the use of names in primitive societies. To possess a person's name is equivalent to possessing the person. That explains why real names are often hidden and nicknames substituted. There are even cases of name concealment between spouses, until they have been married long enough to trust each other's good intentions. Names of the dead are often tabu, and it is most unusual for the names of deities to be freely revealed. "Thou shalt not take the name of the Lord . . . in vain," is a commandment of universal distribution. Either in primitive or literate societies the principle is much the same and rests on the identification of an object or person with its name.

## C. VERBAL ARTS

Speech forms are used primarily for communicating ideas from a speaker to his auditors. Most utterances in daily life are directed to some practical end, but it is perfectly possible to use language only for conveying or heightening emotions. Story-telling combines the two purposes, for it may be used to impart lessons at the same time that it arouses pleasure. Few primitive peoples look lightly upon story-telling. There may be restrictions on who is permitted to tell tales, as well as on the time, place, subject-matter and listeners. Simple stories are told in what we would describe as prose, and are subject to a minimum of restrictions. Tales that are well known and often repeated throughout a speech community, together with popular sayings, proverbs, and riddles make up its **folklore.** Attempts have been made to distinguish various kinds of tales on the basis of their subject-matter, but it is impossible to make clearcut distinctions. As a rule of thumb stories may be classified as **myths** if they deal primarily with supernatural characters or events, and as **legends** if they are devoted to historic or supposedly historic happenings. There are so many narratives that blend the two characteristics that anthropologists have just about given up the effort to separate myths from legends.

Folklore [5] is not without practical significance. It often mirrors a tribe's culture, past or present, and affords clues to migrations and contacts with other peoples. Many stories reassert the moral values of a society, and some tales are specifically used to provide instruction. Of universal distribution are narratives that seek to describe the origin and nature of the universe, to account for the characteristics of familiar animals and other aspects of the environment, to explain the beginnings of life and death, and to picture the otherworld and what goes on there. Two common features of folklore help to strengthen the solidarity of a society. Death is dismissed as unimportant, arising from some trivial error; and the less favored are given opportunities to blow off steam without harm to the social fabric, by laughing at stories in which the high and mighty suffer failure or discomfiture.

Because each language imposes a rigid limitation on the number of vocal sounds to which meanings are attached, and because each tongue likewise delimits the way in which sounds are to be combined, the order in which they must be stated, and the stress and intonation with which they are to be expressed, every prose utterance cannot fail but repeat some of its elements over and over again. Repetition of sounds forms the basis of alliteration, vowel harmony, and rhyme; and ordered recurrences of stress make up rhythmic patterns. When these aspects of speech, singly or together, are deliberately emphasized **poetry** results. Its use is found in all cultures, and it has been noted that it always increases the emotional impact of a statement on its hearers. Furthermore, both rhyme and rhythm, as they are employed in poetry, make remembrance and memorization easier on account of their repetitive qualities. All of these factors help to explain why **prayer** so frequently resembles poetry. There is commonly a covert belief that a prayer formula which is supposed to have gained supernatural help in the past will lose its effectiveness if it is changed in any way. That is why the language of prayer is so much more conservative than everyday talk. It is because poetry has the power to arouse emotion at the same time that it makes for

---

[5] The narratives that comprise folklore are the product, characteristically, of unknown or anonymous authors. This topic is fully discussed in S. Thompson, *The Folk Tale*, New York, 1946.

easier memorizing and exact repetition that it so often becomes the vehicle of prayer.

Very closely allied to poetry is the production of vocal music or **song.** In each case the same bio-physico-chemical mechanisms are employed. It is easy enough to say that song is poetry with the addition of melody, but it is extremely hard to explain what melody is. Cultural conditioning, which may rest on entirely arbitrary values, plays so great a part in this context that what strikes some people as a pleasant succession of sounds may appear to others as harsh and disturbing. Nevertheless, the intimate relation of song to poetry has been recognized at least for many centuries, and it has been firmly established that in ancient times much poetry, both secular and sacred, was meant to be sung.

There is also a close connection between language and **drama,** insofar as the latter contains characters who are supposed to say, recite, or sing something in a fixed sequence. Like poetry and song drama serves to arouse and heighten an audience's emotions; and like folklore it can be used effectively to drive home lessons that reflect a tribe's cultural beliefs. Drama can also give concrete expression to intangible ideas, such as having a player impersonate Lust or Greed. Religionists early realized how effective a device this was for representing supernatural concepts, especially to nonliterate, or illiterate spectators, and it is no accident that the modern English drama grew out of sacred, theatrical performances. In primitive societies a high proportion of religious ceremonies prove to be clever dramatizations of myths.

## D. NONVERBAL ARTS

As far back as the Old Stone Age craftsmen sometimes took pains to perfect an implement in ways that could not possibly improve its practical effectiveness. Modern examples of the same sort of thing would include decorated chairs that are no more comfortable for sitting than plain ones, ornamental garments that add nothing to the wearer's "creature comforts," carved musical instruments that may not sound as well as their uncarved parallels, and pearl-handled revolvers that may or may not shoot straight. For want of a better way of explaining this phenomenon many scholars refer to an esthetic urge or drive. Whether or not human beings actually possess such a drive toward art the fact remains that great numbers of them go to considerable lengths to embellish things for non-practical purposes, or to purchase artistic products. Whatever their basic motives may turn out to be, such activities are always related to a pleasurable emotion. Either the workman takes delight in what he is doing, or the user enjoys the non-essential elements, or mere spectators find pleasure in the contemplation of something artistic. It is also possible, as our expression "Art for art's sake," implies, to make esthetic things that have no reference whatsoever to practical considerations. On the whole, primitive peoples are unlikely to separate art from utility. Anything capable of arousing emotion can be put to use, without exception, in the exercise of religion.

**Instrumental music** comes closest to the structure of the verbal arts. Its aim is to produce particular sounds, in a fixed order, and in accord with a definite pattern of stress, intonation, and rhythm. A society may as readily affix meanings to musical utterances as to words. We learn to regard some products of instrumental music as sad and others as happy, and we are inclined to think of marching soldiers when we hear what we interpret to be a martial air, or of brides when we listen to the strains of a wedding march. As in the case of vocal expressions, no two social units need to ascribe identical meanings to the same sounds, hence what one group regards as mournful another may interpret as gay.

Instrumental music is less often played for its own sake in primitive societies than it is used to accompany singing or **dancing.** Once again there is a close connection with verbal arts. Dancing has been aptly described as "poetry in motion," and its essence consists of rhythmic movements of the body or some of its parts. As modern choreographers know so well, dancing can also be used to tell a story. When it is combined with instrumental music, dancing has a powerful emotional effect on performers and spectators alike. It can induce trance, mass-hypnotism, ecstasy, or frenzy. Primitive religions make such great use of dancing that the terms dance and ritual are often used synonymously. Early Christianity relied much on dancing, but in recent years a number of sects have frowned on the use either of instrumental music or dancing.

Something might well be said here of the famed **Kachina** dances of the Hopi Indians. They are essentially religious performances, but they incorporate a great many esthetic elements. In Hopi belief a

Fig. 125. Hopi Kachina dancer. The Jemez (Hümis) Kachina costume pictured is a favorite type for the Homegoing (Niman) dance, which ends the open season for Kachina performances in midsummer. However, this costume is not obligatory for the Homegoing dance. It may be worn, in addition to many other styles, on other occasions.

RED

YELLOW

TURQUOISE

GREEN

Kachina is a friendly spirit, capable of bringing rain and other benefits to the tribe. Long ago the Kachinas were supposed to have lived on earth, but enemies killed them off. To gain their aid Hopi men impersonate the Kachinas and dress in elaborate costumes, gaily painted, and featured by a large, colorful mask that completely hides the face and head of the wearer, and comes to rest on his shoulders (Fig. 125). In advance of a public performance the dancers resort to kivas to prepare their costumes, learn a newly composed cycle of songs, and practice the appropriate steps and gestures. On the scheduled day, they appear in the village plaza and sing and dance, with intervals of rest interspersed, from daybreak to sunset. Occasionally, they are accompanied by a drummer or by performers who scrape an animal shoulderblade (scapula) rhythmically against a notched stick that rests on an inverted gourd. Kachina dances are highly esteemed by participants and observers alike, both for their religious values and their artistic appeal.

**Painting, carving,** and **sculpture** belong in a different category, and are often termed, "Graphic and plastic arts." [6] They may be realistic or representational, or else they may be abstract or conventionalized. Sometimes they stand by themselves; more often they are connected with utilitarian or religious practices (Fig. 126). Their manner of production and the uses to which they might be put have always intrigued anthropologists, but in recent years attention has been focused on the relation of the artist to his society and culture. Answers are being sought to such questions as: Does the impulse to make a work of art arise spontaneously, or does it have to be acquired? Is artistic ability inherited or received through training? Is there an unlimited freedom of scope to artistic formulations, or is each artist forced to work within broad limits set by the nature of his medium and the cultural concepts of his society? None of these questions can be settled fully, and some cannot even be partially answered. This much is known. Natives can and do distinguish what they consider good art from bad, great differences of individual ability are recognized, and the vast bulk of artistic output conforms in general to the established forms and techniques that prevail in the culture of a given society. Rare, indeed, is the individual genius who can transcend the cultural limitations imposed upon him.

6 Details and illustrations of this subject are fully treated in M. J. Herskovits, *op. cit.,* pp. 378-413.

Fig. 126. Navaho sand painting. A medicine man is teaching an apprentice how to make a sand painting by sprinkling grains of colored sand on a neutral background. Figures so constructed represent gods and cosmic symbols, which are part of the elaborate curing rites that comprise the essence of Navaho religion.

## E. LET'S PLAY GAMES

Professor Kroeber has defined play as wasteful but pleasurable bodily activity.[7] By "wasteful" he means presumably that play is not directed to the satisfaction of any of the biological imperatives. He finds playfulness most fully developed among mammals, and he attributes to the rechanneling of play impulses a great many human actions that culminate in esthetic and intellectual products. Kroeber's viewpoint is very interesting and may explain why games and amusements are universal features of all human societies. Among men play is inevitably a biocultural rather than a strictly biological activity. Human bodies may perform all the requisite actions, but cultures determine how the bodies shall be used and what the rules of any game shall be.

Anthropologists like to distinguish between **games of chance** and **games of skill**. As with the question of his esthetic urge, the nature

[7] A. L. Kroeber, *Anthropology*, New York, 1948, pp. 28-29.

of man's interest in gambling has never been settled. A novice in the study of ethnology is usually amazed to discover how varied and widespread games of chance are in primitive societies. Card games, dice games, guessing games, and lotteries occur in a tremendous profusion of forms, and the stakes may be exceedingly high. In many tribes an excited player may gamble away not only valuable property, but even a beloved wife or child. Men have gambled themselves and their families into slavery, yet no society seems to profit from their misery and games of chance continue to be played throughout the world.

Games of skill may also provide a basis for gambling, but this is not always the case. Various motives may underlie the playing of games of skill. A few are for sheer intellectual pleasure, others are little more than physical pastimes, many involve competition and an effort to outdo one's rivals, some serve the avowed purposes of training exercises for war, and not a few have religious motivations.

Games of skill that test only intellectual prowess fall into classes closely resembling checkers or chess. These are allied to others, like backgammon, which combine skill with chance. In such games counters are moved across a board not according to individual decisions but as determined by throws of dice. E. B. Tylor, late in the last century, found that games of this type had worldwide distribution, and his studies led him to conclude that their presence in America gave evidence of diffusion from Asia,[8] but Kroeber has more recently cast doubt on Tylor's conclusion.[9]

Most games of skill depend on the strenuous yet well controlled use of the body. Essentially, this is what modern athletes call, "Good form." Here again do we meet the advantages of man's ability to look ahead and to anticipate future rewards for difficult actions that yield no results at the moment. All athletes are aware of the drudgery of practice periods during which good form is acquired, but few players dare to rely on natural talents to the extent of forgoing training sessions. As games of skill become more highly organized, the amount of effort devoted to preliminary training increases.

One of the best known games of skill in primitive societies is hockey (chueca), as played by the Araucanian Indians of Chile. This

[8] Tylor's studies are conveniently summarized in A. L. Kroeber and T. T. Waterman, *Source Book in Anthropology*, New York, 1931, pp. 388-397.

[9] A. L. Kroeber, *op. cit.*, p. 551.

tribe was among the last big ones in the New World to be pacified
by Caucasoïds, and until a few decades ago its entire culture was
geared to war. As long as active fighting prevailed, the Araucanians
frankly looked upon hockey as a training exercise for war, and the
terms for hockey player and warrior were used interchangeably, but
since their pacification the natives play chiefly for sport and wager-
ing. The game resembles field hockey as played by teams of women
in Euro-American countries, but it is a rough and tumble masculine sport among the Araucanians. It calls for speed, stamina, daring,
and good coordination, qualities whose usefulness in war is self-
evident.[10]

## F. SUPERNATURALISM IN GAMES

Stewart Culin, an outstanding specialist in the study of games, has
unequivocally stated that many games which appear on the surface
to be played only for gain, exercise, or amusement, are also performed as sacred rites for pleasing the gods. They may be played in
the hope of winning favors from the supernatural world; or else for
such specific purposes as driving away evil, averting sickness, producing rain, and aiding the reproduction of plants, animals, and
human beings.[11] Games have undergone so many changes and rein-
terpretations in historic times, that a modern reader may doubt the
truth of Culin's analysis, although everyone rather vaguely associates
superstition with gamblers and athletes. The best link between the
playing of games and religious practices seems to depend on the
element of the unknown. When we are at a loss to understand why
something unexpected happens in sports or gambling, we are apt
to attribute it to "luck," but primitive peoples are much more likely
to assign such events to supernatural forces. From this point of view
it is simple to see why all games of chance should have religious implications. The connection with games of skill may be less clear,
until we realize that in them, too, the outcome is never known in
advance, and wherever the law of controlled causation cannot be
applied recourse is had to the supernatural.

Games of chance are closely related to ordeals, in the sense that

10 M. Titiev, "Araucanian Culture in Transition," *Occasional Contributions from
the Museum of Anthropology*, Ann Arbor, No. 15, 1951, pp. 125-128.

11 S. Culin, "Games of the North American Indians," *Annual Report, Bureau of
American Ethnology*, No. 24, Washington, 1907.

the winner is supposedly determined by some extra-human or super-natural agency. That is why difficult decisions may be left to a throw of dice, the cutting of cards, the drawing of lots, the toss of a coin, or a similar activity. Counting out procedures, if truly left to chance, belong in the same category. Needless to say, literate individuals who indulge in such practices may have no awareness of the supernatural implications of what they are doing, and may even resent any inter-pretation along religious lines. Not everyone is willing to equate be-lief in luck with faith in the supernatural.

Games of skill frequently show religious motivations. Several North American Indian tribes used to play a type of hockey or shinny in which the ball was stuffed with seeds. The idea was that if the ball were quickly burst and the seeds widely scattered, the gods would send early and bountiful harvests. Throughout many parts of the world games organized like a tug-of-war are used to induce super-natural powers to send favors such as sunshine in the direction indi-cated by the winners. Among the Hopi Indians a swift runner carrying water automatically represents a prayer for rain to come speedily.

Performers who strive for victory in games very commonly seek supernatural additions to their skill. Everything from a favorite gar-ment to a lucky coin or a rabbit's foot may be used to supplement one's own ability. Paraphernalia that are thought to be full of mana because they were used with success in the past may be used to the exclusion of all similar items. Sporting circles are full of talk about "lucky bats," "lucky shoes," "lucky racquets," "lucky fishing-rods," and so forth. Many players also resort to bits of private ritual, such as always repeating a set formula in a crisis, or always touching sec-ond base with the left foot as one comes in from the field.

The reliance which primitive peoples may put on supernatural decisions as expressed in the results of games should not be depre-ciated. Early in September 1906, the Hopi pueblo of Old Oraibi found itself so badly divided over many questions, including the acceptance of "white" schooling, that it was agreed to separate the two factions permanently. To decide which should leave their tradi-tional home, a line was traced on the ground and the sides faced each other, with the understanding that those who were pushed across would be the losers and would have to leave. In the ensuing "push-fest" the Conservatives who opposed the new schools lost, whereupon their leader yielded to his fate and led his followers to a vacant site where they founded the village of Hotevilla.[12] Here were about 400 individuals who, with their ancestors, had lived at Oraibi for centuries, but who left their old homes without further argument because their gods had made known their wills through a kind of game.

## SELECTED REFERENCES

Bloomfield, Leonard, *Language*, New York, 1933.

Boas, Franz, (ed.), "Handbook of American Indian Languages," *Bureau of American Ethnology*, Bulletin No. 40, Washington, 1911.

———, *Primitive Art*, Oslo, 1929.

Culin, Stewart, "Games of the North American Indians," *Bureau of American Ethnology*, Annual Report, No. 24, Washington, 1907.

Hoijer, Harry, "Relation of Language to Culture," *Anthropology Today* (A. L. Kroeber, ed.), Chicago, 1953, pp. 554-573.

Kluckhohn, Clyde, "Myths and Rituals: A General Theory," *Harvard Theological Review*, Vol. 35, 1942, pp. 45-79.

Sapir, Edward, *Language*, New York, 1921.

Thompson, Stith, *The Folk Tale*, New York, 1946.

———, "Advances in Folklore Studies," *Anthropology Today* (A. L. Kroeber, ed.), Chicago, 1953, pp. 587-596.

Titiev, Mischa, "The Religion of the Hopi Indians," *Forgotten Religions*, (V. Ferm, ed.), New York, 1949, pp. 364-378.

———, "Araucanian Culture in Transition," *Occasional Contributions from the Museum of Anthropology*, No. 15, Ann Arbor, 1951.

Voegelin, Charles F., and Harris, Zellig, "Linguistics in Ethnology," *Southwestern Journal of Anthropology*, Vol. 1, 1945, pp. 455-465.

Whorf, Benjamin L., "Four Articles on Metalinguistics," *Foreign Service Institute, Department of State*, Washington, 1949.

———, "The Relation of Habitual Thought and Behavior to Language," *Language, Culture, and Personality* (L. Spier, *et al.*, eds.), Menasha, 1941, pp. 75-93.

[12] M. Titiev, "Old Oraibi: a Study of the Hopi Indians of Third Mesa," *Papers of the Peabody Museum of American Archaeology and Ethnology*, Harvard University, Cambridge, Vol. 22, No. 1, 1944, p. 86 ff.

# CHAPTER 25

# The Individual and His Culture

## A. GROWING UP IN A CULTURE

Not so long ago it became apparent that something vital was missing from the traditional studies of culture. Progress was being made in the identification of laws of culture growth, sharper analyses of cultural processes were being formulated, and there was an increasing understanding of cultural configurations and integrations, but little attention was being paid to the impact of culture on the personalities of specific persons. Today there is an increasing tendency to avoid treating culture as though it existed in a vacuum, and to stress the impact that cultures exert on the personalities of the people who grow up in them. Studies of culture and personality require detailed investigations of identified individuals. A host of modern anthropologists, including practically all whose names are best known to the general public, devote their efforts to the interplay between individual behavior and the cultures of the societies in which they live. Professor Kluckhohn has neatly characterized this aspect of the science of man as devoted to the person-in-a-culture.

Researches into personality formation owe much to the hypotheses so convincingly advanced by **Freud.** Among the cardinal points of **Freudian** theory are the concept of infantile sexuality, which seeks gratification from the moment of birth, and the notion that feelings of love, hate, anger, repression, and frustration which are experienced in early life may be buried for years before expressing themselves overtly in ways that may not reveal their true causes. These features of Freudian doctrine have led investigators to devote much attention to child-rearing customs and, since toilet training and weaning are widely interpreted to induce frustration in babies, great stress is laid on studying these practices in varied societies. A few extremists have read far more meaning than the majority of anthropologists consider justified into toilet training and swaddling habits

For determining what grievances, resentments, hatreds, delights, or loves an individual may carry below the level of his conscious thoughts and attitudes, some anthropologists have begun to favor the use of **projective tests.** These fall into two groups. One type asks a subject to perform tasks, like drawing a man or a horse, wherein the things that he emphasizes or omits may provide clues to his innermost traits of personality. The other kind confronts a person with a series of vaguely-defined pictures, based on inkblots or deliberately ambiguous sketches, which the subject is asked to explain or interpret in any way that he pleases.[1] Answers obtained from projective tests of this sort have been found to reveal many things that lie below the threshold of consciousness. A growing number of ethnologists now give projective tests in the field. Sometimes they turn the results over for analysis to third parties and in a surprising number of cases, psychologists unfamiliar with the subjects concerned have made diagnoses of personality that closely agree with the independently formed judgments of the field workers.

Some psychologists and psychologically oriented anthropologists go so far as to try to explain the nature of culture itself as a reflection of individual personality traits. There was a time, for example, when the emphasis on war that characterizes numerous societies, was attributed to the workings of a "death instinct" in the populace. Most modern scholars are reluctant to make such assumptions, and the origins of cultural emphases are usually left unexplained. Contemporary anthropologists are content to agree that each newly born child, or **neonate,** is faced with a pre-existent society and culture to which it must learn to adjust itself. Put another way, it amounts to saying that every baby must learn to conform to its society's established patterns for group living. What is called **learning theory** is thus involved, and to this vital subject many research workers have turned their attention. A common interest in learning theory is only one

[1] Best known of the tests based on indefinite pictures is Murray's Thematic Apperception Test (T A T). Standardized ink blots are used in the Rorschach tests. A handy treatment of the entire subject may be found in H. H. and G. L. Anderson, *An Introduction to Projective Techniques,* New York, 1951.

of several fruitful links between anthropologists and psychologists.

Another area of joint activity concerns an awareness that the psychological potentials of a human being can be realized only if he has the chance of interacting with other representatives of *Homo sapiens*, that is, if an infant is raised in a society. Otherwise, a child cannot develop into a normal adult. It must have contacts with older people, who stand in definite relationships to it, who will attend to its physical needs, and who will teach it the systems of values that are essential ingredients of their patterns of culture. Such responsibilities are conventionally entrusted to parents or their surrogates, but other kin, friends of the family, neighbors, playmates, and religious or political officers always supplement parental teachings. Through the combined efforts of all concerned the sum total of cultural concepts in his society is brought home to a neonate, and he becomes aware of the forms of behavior which he is expected to acquire. As he grows older a child absorbs more of the culture of his group. He learns that he can relax in the presence of certain individuals but must be on his best behavior with others, that some particular persons will readily feed him on request, while others may not, and so forth. In the course of time the youngster will become an adult and a parent, whereupon he will transmit to his children much of what he learned in infancy. Some temporary changes in a culture pattern may be brought about through individual stubbornness or nonconformity; and long-continued group resistance (like a feminist movement) may lead to permanent modifications; but on the whole people transmit to their offspring the same pattern of culture that they learned as children. In the sense that it is something which can be handed on from one generation to the next, a culture pattern may be said to have an existence of its own. Before studies of culture and personality can be successful, they must be preceded by a thorough knowledge of the culture within which a subject has been reared.

## B. THE PROCESS OF ENCULTURATION

Although there are a great many definitions of culture it is pretty well agreed that the term includes those objects or tools, attitudes, and forms of behavior whose use under given conditions is sanctioned by the members of a particular society. It is also axiomatic that cultural values cannot be transmitted through biological inheritance, so that each child must start to learn the culture of its group after it has been born. In any study of neonatal development an anthropologist must begin with the assumption that a child is born with a fairly adequate biological organism but without a shred of culture. From the first moment of its birth, however, a human baby begins to feel the impact of culture, in the way it is received from its mother's body, the mode in which its umbilical cord is cut and tied, the fashion in which it is washed and handled, and the manner in which it is swaddled or clothed. Every one of these activities is culturally conditioned, and the neonate's first experience with culture is entirely passive. At the exact start of its postnatal life a newly born infant can react only biologically, but shortly after it begins to behave bioculturally, and as it matures it will find itself playing down the purely biological aspects of its conduct and stressing cultural values. It is as though a child began postnatal life as a 100-percent biological mechanism and thereafter tried to reduce its biological conduct to a hypothetical vanishing point (Fig. 127). In reality, of course, biological activities can never be totally eliminated from human behavior.

For the process of adjusting individual responses ever increasingly to a society's patterns of culture, Professor Herskovits has chosen the fitting name, **enculturation**.[2] Enculturation may be regarded as the system by which each society molds the biological organization of its neonates to a set of pre-existing cultural norms. During a child's earliest years the process continues to impinge on an organism that is chiefly passive, and is concerned with such fundamental habits as eating, sleeping, and eliminating. A neonate's experiences during this period are thought to be of particular significance in the formation of its adult personality.

If it be granted that a baby's initial activities in postnatal life must necessarily be biological, it follows that many of its earliest experiences with the process of enculturation will be restrictive or frustrating. No matter how eager societies and their cultures may be to satisfy infantile demands there is no group of human beings that drops everything instantaneously to feed a child at the first sign of hunger; or allows it absolutely unlimited freedom of muscular movement; or everlastingly permits it to excrete when and where it will. Sooner or later each child must learn to eat, move, and eliminate in

2 M. J. Herskovits, *Man and His Works,* New York, 1948, pp. 40-41 *et passim.*

accord with the culturally determined set of rights and wrongs that prevails in its society. As it learns to conform, every baby must experience restricting checks on its biological behavior. No doubt neonates differ in the degree to which they can tolerate restriction, but no

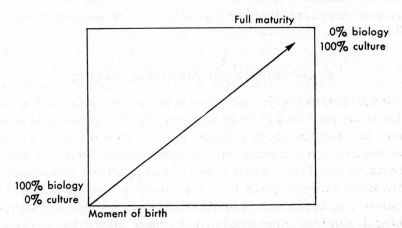

Fig. 127. The progress of enculturation. No human being ever reaches the extreme point in the upper right corner, but all neonates follow the indicated trend line as they go from birth to maturity.

human infant can completely avoid developing some feelings of displeasure or hostility as it reacts to enculturation. There is an assumption that a child reared under easy-going conditions that restrict very few of its activities, cater to its wants, and permit toilet training and weaning to occur without signs of adult impatience or distaste, will grow into a well-adjusted adult. Unfortunately, there has been little proof of the truth of this assumption. On the contrary, it is known that the Navaho, who are brought up in a highly permissive atmosphere, show as many adult maladjustments as do grown-ups in other societies. Plainly, the influence of child training on mature personalities is a subject that is not yet entirely understood.

Most of the requirements of enculturation are patterned similarly for all normal children of comparable age, sex, and social background. Such demands are regularly repeated, and can be predicted without much difficulty by any observer who is well acquainted with a particular culture. We know that girls in our society will be taught not to reveal their thighs when wearing street dress, and we anticipate that boys will show an interest in athletics. But, apart from patterned regularities, children may be exposed to unexpected conditions to which they must nevertheless adjust, as when an American youth is injured so severely that he can neither play nor watch sporting events. Random experiences place a severe strain on the formation of individual personalities, yet the demands of cultural conformity are such that something approximating normal adjustment is required despite all handicaps.

## C. INTERIORIZING CULTURAL VALUES

As a baby grows up in any society it begins to learn that much of what it was permitted to do as an infant it is not allowed to do at a somewhat later date. Such teachings take the form of negative statements directed to a youngster by older people. "Don't do this," "Don't be naughty," "You mustn't," is what a child hears repeatedly. Consciously or not, a baby finds itself recurrently put into a hostility-fraught situation, wherein it will gain rewards for yielding to the demands of grown-ups, but will arouse adult displeasure if it persists in following its own dictates; and adult displeasure, it soon learns from experience, leads to punishment in one form or another. Yet an infant will not be happy if it is constantly prevented from doing what it wishes. Psychologists have found that the only way out of the dilemma is for a child to identify its views with those of the more powerful grown-ups, until it gradually acquires the feeling of *wanting* to do what they feel it *ought* to do. When this stage has been reached the instances of frank hostility diminish and the youngster may be said to have **interiorized** the cultural values of its society. Much of the earlier antagonism may persist in the subconscious levels of personality, but on the surface conformity without compulsion seems to prevail. Studies of personality formation, as well as analyses of the interplay between individuals and their cultures, must take into account the process of **value interiorization.**

A number of psychologists believe that the process starts with the experience of birth. They hold that the first month of a baby's postnatal life is for the most part directed to an effort to re-establish its fetal equilibrium. Some societies, for which the term, **fetusphilic,** has been proposed,[3] attempt to make the transition from prenatal life easier by reproducing the physical conditions of life in the womb.

[3] S. Bernfeld, *The Psychology of the Infant,* New York, 1929, p. 7.

They give a neonate warm baths and wrap it in soft garments. Other societies, which may be called **fetusphobic,** act in opposite fashion by dousing a child with cold water and wrapping it tightly or harshly. These variations of neonatal treatment reflect some of a society's standards and affect the infant's degree of anxiety. How different value interiorization must be under such contrasting conditions!

Interiorization is most successful when an individual carries out its precepts without conscious thought. If the welfare of a society depends on promptness, it would never be enough for each person to have to remind himself periodically that he must be on time. Only when everyone concerned has so completely interiorized the value of promptness that he no longer has to think about it can promptness be taken for granted by the society as a whole. This type of thoroughgoing interiorization provides the only guarantee that a pattern of culture is functioning properly.

Because the processes of enculturation and value interiorization go on simultaneously or nearly so, they are sometimes regarded as one and the same. They are not, however, alike. During its enculturation a baby remains passive and has no option but to allow itself to become enwrapped, as it were, in its society's culture. Interiorization is an active process, and an infant has a small degree of choice with respect to the selection of the items it will interiorize, as well as to the method, time, and order in which interiorizing will take place. A crude analogy may help to illustrate the essential difference between the two processes. A neonate may be likened to a child with a cent in a candy-store. The money represents its limited facility for coping with culture. When the storekeeper, who stands for parents or adults in a society, puts out a few bits of penny candy (cultural traits), it is he who makes the choice of what to offer, and his actions correspond roughly to enculturation. He may even go so far as to push one particular piece forward, which the little purchaser is very likely to choose. When the child makes its selection and actively takes the candy into itself by sucking, chewing, or gulping, it is as though it were interiorizing an item of culture.

To drop the analogy, we seem to have arrived at a pair of universal laws governing the interplay of an individual and his culture. Each society insists that its neonates must adjust themselves to the pattern of culture which begins to enfold them as soon as they have been born (Fig. 127); value interiorization is one of the major mechanisms by which every baby makes the compulsory adjustment. Within the limits of even a single society and its culture the process of interiorization is complex and multidimensional. It appears to be compounded from at least three sets of variables which probably differ for each infant. The first variable is biological, for it cannot be assumed that each neonate begins life with exactly the same inborn equipment. Experiments with very young children have proved that they react differently to stimuli that are precisely alike. The second variable is sociological, for every additional child that is born to a family occupies a different place in respect to its siblings, and confronts its parents at different stages of their age and experience. The third variable is cultural, inasmuch as no design for group living remains static forever. Hence, what a first child learned to regard as wrong, a later child may well be taught to accept as proper.

This discussion should also help to explain why a pattern of culture may, in theory, be treated as something that has an existence independent of the people who are its carriers. Patterns of culture are transmitted from one generation to another quite apart from the life and death of particular persons. They can also be more or less completely accepted and interiorized in various ways by different people. Finally, the laws which govern their origins and changes need not necessarily take into account the wishes or desires of the individuals whose conduct they help to regulate. How subtly a culture pattern that flourishes without individual control can affect behavior is strikingly brought out by the studies of Dr. Gesell. The maturational sequences of an infant's biological development which were carefully worked out in his clinic at Yale University,[4] and which were assumed at first to be universal, were later found to be partly biocultural and to have their best application to children of middle-class parents in New Haven.

Early in the book the point was made that a human baby-to-be can exercise no choice over the genetic factors that it will receive from its parents at the moment of conception. This situation was contrasted with an infant's post-natal acquisition of culture over which, in theory, it can exercise a measure of control. Theoretically, a growing child can accept, modify, or reject any trait of culture whatsoever. Why, then, do people so seldom fail to accept the values of their cul-

[4] A. Gesell, *Embryology of Behavior*, New York, 1945.

ture, even if many items are uncongenial or distasteful? The answer revolves around a few basic points. In the first place enculturation begins at so early an age that a baby must be a passive recipient, without much capacity for active agreement or disagreement. In the second place, it is impossible during the early stages of life to reject a culture without repudiating parents, kinfolk, and other members of the society on whom one's welfare depends, and from whom one is learning the only way of life in his range of experience. In the third place, it is neither easy nor quick for an individual to learn a pattern of culture thoroughly. We know that if we were asked to name an informant who could properly explain our culture to an outsider, we would suggest not a young child, nor an adolescent, but a mature person of twenty-five years or older. This is equivalent to saying implicitly that we think it takes at least a quarter of a century to learn a single manner of living. Even if it be granted that a second way might be learned more rapidly, it would still be extremely difficult for an adult who had been brought up in one fashion to learn flawlessly the requirements of speaking a new language, forming new motor habits, adopting new eating habits and preferences, and accepting a new set of outlooks on life, including a new political allegiance and the practice of a new religion. The sheer difficulty of learning another culture pattern intimately is enough to discourage all but a small number of people from forsaking the way of life that they learned as children. Finally, it will be found that each society rewards with high status and prestige those who learn to abide by its system of culture values. It thereby offers a measure of compensation for some of the difficulties that an individual may undergo when he adjusts his body build or temperament to cultural requirements.

## D. INDIVIDUAL TEMPERAMENT AND PATTERNS OF CULTURE

In all investigations of enculturation and interiorization there is a question that stands forth prominently. What does each child bring into the world with which it must confront its society's culture? No matter what reply is made, one fact seems indisputable. Whatever equipment a neonate has when it leaves its mother's womb is biological in character and has been genetically inherited from its parents. If any influences penetrated to the developing embryo between its conception and the moment of its birth, they must first have been translated into bio-physico-chemical elements within the body of the mother. Present knowledge provides no exceptions to the rule that a newly born baby is a 100 percent biological organism.

Thanks to the complexities of human reproduction the likelihood is slim that any two offspring, always excepting identical twins, will have precisely the same genetic composition. To this extent it may be argued that no two neonates face the world with exactly the same inborn equipment. Even if they found themselves in absolutely similar societies and cultures, which is impossible in practice, they would still react in different ways. Yet, each would seek air, food, warmth, dryness and stability; each would respond to some stimuli by crying, and to others by falling asleep; and each would digest food and excrete waste matter in fairly predictable ways. In the most minimum and essential aspects of its biological activities, therefore, each infant somehow reaches an equilibrium between its unique nature and the conformity of biological behavior that applies to its entire species. As it grows older another kind of balance will have to be struck, this time between the child's inherited biological character and the culture pattern to which it must mold itself. By the time it has reached biological maturity each youngster will have learned to conform reasonably well to the standards set by its culture, but each will have paid a different price in terms of suppressions and repressions. Cultural conformity is a hard taskmaster, and has been known to exact high fees in the shape of warped personalities.

Individual personality is the product of an inherited biological character modified by the demands of culture. Variations in people may result either from the effects of a similar pattern of culture on different biological organisms, or else from the impact of essentially dissimilar ways of life on reasonably similar biological entities. The possibilities inherent in these situations may be illustrated by combining some of Sheldon's notions with some of Benedict's. According to Sheldon, people of the **mesomorphic** type, who are muscular and sturdily built, are **somatotonic** of temperament and like physical exercise, show a love of daring and boldness, seem indifferent to pain, and are assertive and aggressive, especially when under the influence of alcohol. These temperamental characteristics agree quite well with Benedict's portrayal of **Dionysian** patterns of culture, which honor aggression and reckless conduct in men.

Almost exactly opposite are the personality traits of those whom Sheldon calls **ectomorphic**. They are thin and fragile in anatomical structure and have **cerebrotonic** dispositions. Their actions are restrained, they are inhibited in dealing with others, hypersensitive to pain, and resist alcohol and other drugs. On the whole their temperaments are in accord with Benedict's account of **Apollonian** culture, which rewards self-restraint and sobriety.

If a male of mesomorphic biological build and somatotonic temperament happens to be born into a society with a Dionysian sort of culture, he will conform easily, without conflict and with little cause for psychological maladjustment. Similarly, an ectomorph who is cerebrotonic can be expected to adjust smoothly to the requirements of an Apollonian way of life. But youngsters of all kinds are born into every sort of society, which means that somatotonics will find it hard to suit themselves to Apollonian patterns, and that cerebrotonics will suffer where Dionysian standards prevail.

The use of Sheldon's and Benedict's terminology does not mean that the author accepts their teachings without reservation. He firmly believes that there is a grain of truth contained in their analyses, and that some peoples and cultures can be found that conform to their descriptions. At the same time he is convinced that what they have brought out applies best to extreme cases and has less application to the majority of individuals and patterns of culture, which tend to be mixed rather than purely of one type or the other.[5] These extremes have been used only to bring the main issues into sharp focus. What psychological price do individuals strongly given to one kind of behavior pay when they force themselves to conform to a way of life that is not congenial to their innate temperaments? How many maladjusted and neurotic individuals in any society result from the unspoken insistence that everyone, regardless of his inborn biologically determined disposition, must regulate his conduct in agreement with predetermined cultural norms, which he may find uncongenial, but over which he can exercise little or no control? These are fundamental questions to which all social scientists would do well to direct their attention.

A program ought to be undertaken to discover exactly what hap-

[5] Several technical details also stand in the way of the author's full acceptance of either Sheldon's or Benedict's viewpoints. Discussion of these details, however, seems out of place in an elementary textbook. For example, the American Pueblo Indians are inclined to be Apollonian in culture, but they are not ectomorphic in body build.

pens to a neonate's inherited biological system as a child starts to modify it in keeping with the requirements of his culture (see Fig. 127). Now it is conventional to say that cultural restrictions induce feelings of frustration in babies, who cry because they are helpless to do what they would like. Professor Norman R. F. Maier, a psychologist, suggests a contrasting interpretation. He defines frustration as "behavior without a goal," [6] and he asks whether such crying might not be a "problem-solving technique." Perhaps Professor Maier is right. It is just as likely that infants cry deliberately for the purpose of being taken out of an unpleasant situation, as that they weep only to express resentment and helplessness. Answers to vital questions of this sort will never be found as long as students of personality and culture continue to start with personality structures that are fully or reasonably well formed, and then try to deduce the kind of childhood training that a subject may have had. Such a deductive method puts investigators of personality on the level of medical research before the causes of most diseases were well known. In those days workers could not recognize an ailment until it was well advanced, which made cures exceedingly difficult and preventive medicine impossible. Only if they reverse their approach and begin to examine inductively the mechanisms by which newly born infants adjust their inherited biological natures to prescribed standards of culture, will students of personality reach a scientific goal. By this means they may learn how personalities are formed at such an early stage that corrective measures can be applied, where necessary, before it is too late.

## E. STUDIES OF NATIONAL CHARACTER

One of the most recent outgrowths of anthropological research on problems of personality and culture has been an interest in **national character.** These studies do not restrict themselves to small, homogeneous, tribal groups, but undertake to deal with large, literate, and heterogeneous social units on the scale of the United States, or the Soviet Union. They are based on the assumption that all citizens of a modern nation are exposed to so many uniform cultural institutions, such as economic regulations or patterns of federal government, that they develop similar characteristics of personality and behavior. Efforts are made to delineate national character in terms of regulari-

[6] N. R. F. Maier, *Frustration: The Study of Behavior Without a Goal*, New York, 1949.

ties of conduct which can be predicted. It is also assumed that all members of a society who share an identifiable pattern of culture, will show similarities of intra-psychic structure. If a certain action is condemned by a given society, then all the people in the group will show shame if they perform the disapproved action. Underlying this approach is the hope of developing a new psychocultural theory that will explain how human beings embody and learn to live by the cultural norms of their society.

Proponents of national character studies, led in the United States by Dr. Margaret Mead, are confident that this is a legitimate branch of anthropology. They recognize that big societies tend to divide into sub-groups, but they claim that it is possible to reconcile the customs of the smaller divisions with the established ways of life of the larger unit. One American, they argue, is more like another American than he is like a Balinese, whether he be a New England textile worker or a Texas rancher.

As for the use of anthropologists in this type of research, it is felt that they have much that is valuable to contribute. They are acquainted with disciplined studies of small, homogeneous, primitive societies which may serve as models for analyzing large nations; they are accustomed to integrating the various aspects of culture into one whole structure; they have been schooled to discount their personal biases and prejudices; and they are acquainted with so many cultures as to make possible valid comparisons. At the same time, it is realized that a solitary observer who may be competent to make a single-handed study of a small community, might be unable to handle all the complexities of a nation-state. For this reason teams of investigators are recommended, at least one of whom should be thoroughly acquainted with anthropological concepts and techniques. The anthropologists' research tools are supposedly transferable from use in studies of small tribes to investigations of large nations.

As in the case of all personality and culture studies, thorough knowledge of culture patterns ought to be acquired before research on personality formation is begun. Whether born into a tribe or modern nation, an individual must mold his individual character to the pre-existing standards of his culture. Child-training practices are basic to an understanding of personality formation, but they may also provide clues to a society's system of values. Plots of popular films and novels, autobiographical accounts, and large-scale projective tests may also throw much light on national emphases. Ultimately, it is likely to be found that while all cultures are individually unique when viewed singly, they are apt to reveal many similarities when examined on a comparative basis. Once we reach an understanding of the universal elements that exist in all cultures, we shall have arrived at a better grasp of the biocultural behavior of all mankind.

## SELECTED REFERENCES

Benedict, Ruth F., "Psychological Types in the Cultures of the Southwest," *Proceedings, Twenty-Third International Congress of Americanists,* 1928, pp. 572-581.

Dennis, Wayne, "The Socialization of the Hopi Child," *Language, Culture, and Personality* (L. Spier, et al., eds.), Menasha, 1941, pp. 259-271.

Gillin, John, *The Ways of Men,* New York, 1948, Section 5.

Gorer, Geoffrey, "Themes in Japanese Culture," *Transactions of the New York Academy of Sciences,* Series 2, Vol. 5, 1943, pp. 106-124.

Hallowell, A. Irving, "Culture, Personality, and Society," *Anthropology Today* (A. L. Kroeber, ed.), Chicago, 1953, pp. 597-620.

Haring, Douglas G., (ed.), *Personal Character and Cultural Milieu,* Syracuse, 1948.

Hilgard, Ernest R., and Marquis, Donald G., *Conditioning and Learning,* New York, 1940.

Hutt, Max L., et al., "Social Values and Personality Development," *The Journal of Social Issues,* Vol. 5, No. 4, 1949.

Kardiner, Abram, *The Psychological Frontiers of Society,* New York, 1945.

Kluckhohn, Clyde, and Murray, Henry A., (eds.), *Personality in Nature, Society, and Culture,* New York, 1948.

Linton, Ralph, *The Cultural Background of Personality,* New York, 1945.

Mead, Margaret, "The Implications of Culture Change for Personality Development," *American Journal of Orthopsychiatry,* Vol. 17, 1947, pp. 633-646.

———, "National Character," *Anthropology Today* (A. L. Kroeber, ed.), Chicago, 1953, pp. 642-667.

Newcomb, Theodore M., and Hartley, Eugene L., (eds.), *Readings in Social Psychology,* New York, 1947.

Sapir, Edward, "The Contribution of Psychiatry to an Understanding of

Behavior in Society," *American Journal of Sociology*, Vol. 42, 1937, pp. 862-870.

Sheldon, William H., and Stevens, S. S., *The Varieties of Temperament*, New York, 1942.

CHAPTER 26

# Some Aspects of Biocultural Behavior in the United States

## A. PREAMBLE

Until about thirty years ago, anthropologists in America [1] were neither expected nor trained to concern themselves with large, literate societies, including their own. It then dawned upon some scholars that ethnologists working with nonliterate tribes had developed techniques that might successfully be applied wherever groups of human beings habitually lived together. First in the field was Dr. Robert Lynd who, with his wife, Helen, and a small staff, undertook an intensive study of the city of Muncie, Indiana, in 1924. Professionally, Dr. Lynd was classed as a sociologist, but his methods combined features of sociology with cultural anthropology. The Lynds resided in the community under observation, participated in its life, conducted interviews, distributed questionnaires, analyzed newspapers, and examined census data. Throughout their stay they tried to maintain the same objectivity that a cultural anthropologist seeks

[1] For the sake of convenience America and the United States will be used interchangeably in this chapter.

to achieve while he is living with a primitive tribe. When the results were published,[2] they created a furor that soon led others to enter the promising new field which the late Clark Wissler called, "the social anthropology of contemporary life." Within a period of less than three decades a great number of books have been published on various phases of life in contemporary America.

Only a few years after the appearance of *Middletown,* a very interesting group of studies was being sponsored at Harvard University. Dr. Elton Mayo, who had worked at the Fatigue Institute in England during World War I, and who had become convinced of the biocultural nature of weariness, organized a research project that was carried out at the Hawthorne plant of the Western Electric Company, near Chicago. The investigations were conducted jointly by representatives of the firm and members of the Harvard School of Business Administration. One of their immediate objectives was to study the output of six girls who assembled telephone relays in a small room. Production increased as physical improvements were made in working conditions. Toward the end of the period of experimentation the working conditions were returned to the original level, yet there was no attendant drop in the number of relays assembled. Analysis revealed that the girls had been organized into a team, whose pride in their work continued to make them exert themselves even when they were no longer pampered with physical comforts.[3] Other studies supported the conclusion that working teams are social units, with integrated and cohesive elements and systems of values, such as exist in any society.

Dr. Mayo also exerted much influence on the career of W. Lloyd Warner, who had recently returned to Harvard from a long ethnological sojourn among Australian aborigines. Professor Warner was led to apply anthropological techniques to American society. With a large staff to assist him, he undertook an exhaustive study of a typical New England community in Massachusetts. The results were published in a number of volumes under the general title of "The Yankee City Series" after Professor Warner had transferred to the University of Chicago. They represent the most intensive analysis ever

[2] R. S. and H. M. Lynd, *Middletown: A Study of Contemporary American Culture,* New York, 1929.

[3] This experiment was fully described in F. Roethlisberger and W. J. Dickson, *Management and the Worker,* Cambridge, 1940. It had a profound effect on labor-management relations in many industries.

made of an American city and its patterns of culture. It is impossible to single out the most important contribution resulting from this project, but one of its most telling consequences was the convincing proof that social classes really exist in America, despite assertions of democracy and the belief that all men are equal. Warner and his associates found six classes in Yankee City, two Lower, two Middle, and two Upper. These were clearcut in terms of occupation, place of residence, degree of prestige, and membership in clubs and other associations. No one factor was all-important as a determinant of one's class. Doctors, for example, ranged from Lower Middle to Upper Upper, but the negative fact that money of itself was not decisive for membership in a social class was thoroughly demonstrated, and came as a shock to many social scientists.

Since the early 1930's a great many anthropologists have devoted themselves to investigations of American and other literate communities. Some worked alone but most worked with colleagues from other disciplines. Some have reported on an entire city; others have devoted themselves to sub-groups; and some have continued to deal with organizations of workers. Out of their combined efforts has emerged a more accurate picture of America's social organization, and a better grasp than had previously existed of its patterns of culture. A large number of fine studies are now available, but we shall not try to review all their findings.[4]

## B. HUMAN ENGINEERING

Soon after the application of ethnological techniques to nonprimitive societies had been demonstrated, anthropology was drawn into the arena of practical affairs. During the 1930's the Commissioner of Indian Affairs, Mr. John Collier, began to rely increasingly on anthropologists to help him revise the workings of his Bureau. Somewhat belatedly, this established a rough parallel to the British program of providing training in anthropology for colonial administrators. By the time that the United States entered World War II late in 1941, a good number of anthropologists had had some experience in dealing with practical problems as they applied to

[4] Only two works will be cited here, but they contain many references to other studies. See C. Kluckhohn, *Mirror for Man,* New York, 1949, chap. 9, and W. L. Warner, *American Life,* Chicago, 1953.

primitive peoples. When the United States forces, during the Asiatic phases of the war, were brought into contact with strange tribes in remote places, it did not take long to discover that the Americans who were most likely to have had previous experience in the regions concerned were a handful of ethnologists. Their knowledge of these spots, and their experience with natives and their patterns of culture, were widely drawn upon by various government agencies. Within the United States other anthropologists were called upon, particularly by the War Relocation Authority, to help with programs that concerned the removal of Japanese inhabitants from the Pacific coast, and the administration of various relocation centers.[5]

At about the time that these activities were going on, other anthropologists were beginning to apply their knowledge to civilian affairs, particularly in the field of industrial relations. Spearheaded by Dr. Eliot D. Chapple, much was done to supplement and expand the findings that had been made at the Hawthorne plant; and Chapple's scheme of analyzing social situations by determining which person initiates action whenever there is contact among individuals, was made part of the conceptual framework.[6] Chapple states that his basic assumption for an understanding of human relations in industry is that attitudes, emotional reactions, and productivity are functions of the interactional situation, which represents the interplay of personality and culture. Improvements are made either by putting people with personality problems into different interactional systems, or else by changing some aspect of the culture pattern within which a person works. Dr. Chapple's approach is based on his awareness that workers in a large industrial plant form a social unit with its own system of values, coupled with the knowledge that changes in one segment of a biocultural triangle are likely to bring about alterations in the other parts. He thus finds it possible to introduce material innovations, such as modifying a layout, with the intention of causing subtle changes in an individual's personal relations, usually without the subject's knowing what has happened.

Another group of anthropologists, more directly under Professor

[5] For an important work on this subject, see A. H. Leighton, *The Governing of Men*, Princeton, 1946.

[6] A good summary and review of anthropological techniques for studying industrial relations is to be found in E. D. Chapple, "Applied Anthropology in Industry," *Anthropology Today* (A. L. Kroeber, ed.), Chicago, 1953, pp. 819-831. Dr. Chapple uses a machine, the Interaction Chronograph, which provides accurate statistical data.

Warner's leadership, has entered the field of industrial relations, chiefly in the Chicago area. They do not use Dr. Chapple's methods, but they also base their work on anthropological concepts of social and cultural structure. Much of what they do is related to psychological techniques of interviewing and counseling. Large industrial concerns have found the services of various kinds of applied anthropologists to be so valuable that members of this branch of the profession earn higher salaries than their academic colleagues. Instead of continuing to discuss their efforts we shall attempt, in the remainder of this chapter, to fit the broad outlines of America's culture into the sort of biocultural configuration that was used in the analysis of nonliterate societies.

## C. MAN AND ENVIRONMENT IN THE UNITED STATES [7]

As one looks at the American scene from the standpoint of an anthropologist, it becomes self-evident that a distinction must be drawn between rural and urban conditions. While the countryside has made little change, comparatively speaking, in the natural environment, the city has almost completely altered its original physical setting. Urban dwellers live almost entirely within a man-made environment, and so much has the landscape been modified that city folk are incapable of raising their own food or securing at first hand the raw materials for the erection of buildings and the manufacture of garments, utensils, and similar products. Willy-nilly, each city's populace must depend for vital supplies of all sorts on rural sources beyond its limits, and the larger the city the bigger will be the district required to service it.

Because of the greater density of urban populations, the amount of their total knowledge is much greater than can be found within a rural area of comparable size. This means that a higher degree of specialization must exist in the cities, and that some country residents will be drawn cityward whenever they require the services of specialists or feel the desire to learn a specialty. Some specialists will inevitably concentrate on arts and entertainments, which will exert another magnetic pull toward the city. Others will make improve-

[7] Much that will be said about culture in the United States applies to other Euro-American countries whose ways of life are generally comparable to those of the United States.

ments in housing and various material traits, which will prove attractive to Americans whose cultural values stress physical comforts and the use of devices that conserve time and human muscular energy. City dwellers, cut off from direct contact with the natural environment, must purchase raw materials and vital necessities, so that a pattern of exchanging work for money has to be formed. Interest in the accumulation of money is another compelling motive of American culture, despite Professor Warner's findings in Yankee City, so that rural folk who want to increase their dollar earnings find themselves attracted to large cities.

America's population trend toward urbanization cannot be understood only as an aspect of material culture. Enormous changes of social organization have always accompanied the technological advances made or enjoyed by city dwellers. To ensure and facilitate the necessary cooperation without which hordes of specialists cannot possibly exist, each city devotes much effort to social legislation, making rules to protect the property which specialists produce, and trying to strike a balance between the cost of goods and the wages of workers. City life provides more possibilities than rural residence for social mobility, and one of the strongest cultural motivations in America is the desire of parents to have their offspring do better than themselves. Coupled with this attitude is the lack of compulsion for children to take up the same occupations as their elders. If youngsters are to get ahead of their parents, they must be encouraged to follow pursuits that hold forth the promise of greater prestige, larger money rewards, or both. Cities offer better opportunities of this nature than do rural communities, where most people are farmers and a child has little alternative but to follow in the footsteps of the parent of his sex.

One of the most telling social effects of a city environment has been the decreasing reliance on kin, and the corresponding increase of dependence on strangers. This becomes most noteworthy after a child has begun to go to school. Thereafter, he will receive less and less of his education and training from kindred; and he will also depend on nonrelatives to prepare his food, make his garments, protect his property, punish his transgressions, provide him with transportation, and afford him the pleasures of recreation. Residence in an urban setting rarely makes possible a concentration of kinfolk in one place and, regardless of our folk sayings about blood being thicker than water, a distant relative who is seldom seen plays little effective part in one's life. One learns to rely far more on friends who are close at hand than on far-off kindred. Whether in a primitive tribe or in an American city, nearness of residence provides a potential substitute for ties of kinship. A person who lives in the country, or a native in a nonliterate community, rarely has dealings with strangers, whereas an adult city dweller spends much of his waking time in their presence.

The intimate connection of technology with social affairs was brought home to the writer with startling clarity in the off-hand remark of a friend. "We worry about solving our present difficulties," he said, "and we haven't even settled the social problems of the cotton gin." If this statement is carefully analyzed it reveals a train of ideas that runs something as follows. The cotton gin was invented just prior to 1800. Before that time, the difficulties of clearing seeds out of cotton were so great that it was pointless to raise vast crops and, consequently, there was little need of great numbers of farmhands. With the invention of the cotton gin the conditions were reversed. Seeds could be quickly picked out, profits grew with the size of a yield, and there was a persistent demand for cheap labor. To meet this demand Negro slaves were imported, and it is an historic fact that virtually all American Negroes are descended from ancestors who were brought to the United States between the time of the cotton gin's invention and the beginning of the Civil War. Insofar as race problems in this country concern Negroes they may be traced back in history to the cotton gin. This shows what grave social consequences may result from the introduction of a single, helpful technological item.

## D. MAN'S DEALINGS WITH MAN IN AMERICA

Although many vital aspects of man's relations to man in the United States are directly connected with matters of technology and urbanization, there are other features of social organization that are only indirectly concerned with material culture. One of these deals with the changing status of an individual when he weds. Between birth and marriage, a child is a member of a social unit (Fig. 128A), which has been named **the family of orientation.** On the assumption that EGO'S parents remain alive, and that he has one brother and one sister, we find him establishing reciprocal ties of privilege and obligation with his father, mother, brother and sister. Each tie involves a different set of rights and duties; and EGO finds his position subordinate to his parents, but approximately equal to his siblings. When EGO weds, and ultimately begets a son and a daughter, he assumes a new status in **a family of procreation** (Fig. 128 B). Within this group

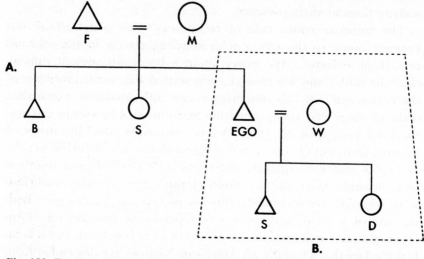

Fig. 128. Families of orientation and procreation. While EGO is unwed, he resides in his family of orientation (A), where he is equal to his siblings but subordinate to his parents. When, at marriage, he shifts to his family of procreation (B), he becomes dominant over his children.

he holds the dominant position, although he has important responsibilities toward his wife and children.[8] Such a shift of status takes place quite commonly in all human societies, but in the United States unhappiness may result from the distaste of newlyweds for living with relatives, as well as from a lack of fixed standards of conduct. Suppose EGO'S father were sick and old. While EGO lived in his family of orientation he would be expected, as soon as he was mature enough, to help support his father. But if the father were still living when EGO married, what then? He is obligated to look after his wife and children, he is probably living away from his natal home, and he may not be earning enough to continue paying for his father's care. Most Americans would agree that a husband's first

8 W. L. Warner, *American Life*, Chicago, 1953, pp. 81-83.

duty is toward his family of procreation, but they would also agree that it is not right to neglect a sick and aged parent. Not all societies permit conflicts of this kind to arise. In Japan, a man's obligations to his father are paramount and remain fixed. A filial son would neither feel upset nor arouse social criticism merely because he favored a parent over his wife and children.

America also faces problems that never arise among primitive groups. Thanks to the splendid advances of medical science, the average life span has been sizably increased. Yet, this worthy accomplishment has created grave and unsolved questions with respect to the place of elderly people in our society. Illogically we are making a successful scientific effort to produce, for the first time in human history, a large body of oldsters, but sociologically we do not know what to do with them (Fig. 129). Geriatrics, a branch of social science

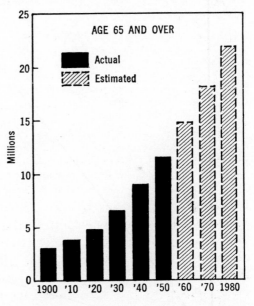

Fig. 129. Increase of older people in the United States. Actual figures are indicated by solid columns; projections into the future are shown in the stippled columns.

devoted to matters of aging and the aged, has been making vigorous strides toward an understanding of the problem, but has not yet made much progress in solving it. Technological advances have also speeded the cultural equality of the sexes. Now that women are enabled to do nearly anything nonbiological that men can do, our educational system fluctuates between training girls for business careers or for motherhood and domestic tasks. Children, as well as old people and housewives, are differently regarded in the United States, particularly in its cities, than they are in primitive societies. No realist would care to deny that children in America are often unwanted, neglected, or rejected, perhaps because the parents do not care to assume the expense and responsibility of rearing offspring who will yield little in return as soon as they can move away or get married. Among tribal groups the phenomenon of rejected children is a rare occurrence; and even where infanticide is completely sanctioned, a parent may make great efforts to have a baby adopted rather than put it to death.

An important weakness of American social structure is an outgrowth of teachings whose intent is to deny the biological characteristics of man. Whenever arbitrary cultural values differ widely

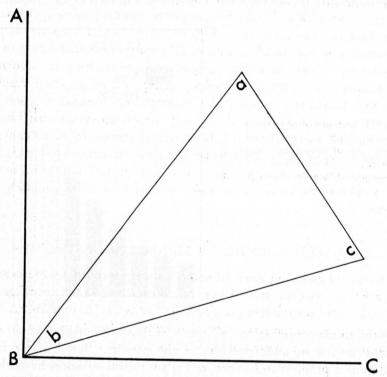

Fig. 130. Biocultural unconformity. The heavy lines are for the biological forces that underlie human behavior and the light lines represent cultural responses. Trouble spots arise whenever ab diverges from AB, or when bc is too far removed from BC. The further the gap between them, the greater is the likelihood of trouble.

from the realities of biology (Fig. 130), they create potential trouble spots. Boys and girls reach physical maturity when they are about 15 years old, yet the average age at marriage is over 20. There is thus a gap of five or six years, much more in numerous instances, when young people are biologically capable of having sexual relations but are culturally forbidden to indulge. During the very years when potency and desire are at their height, our society has not a single culturally approved outlet. Even the most cursory glance at statistics of crime and delinquency will show that the age group 15-20 gives more than its share of trouble. As long as we refuse to bring our patterns of culture into closer conformity with biological imperatives, we shall be unable to remedy many defects in our social system.

Related to the foregoing problem is our reluctance to face squarely up to the distinction between biological and cultural parenthood. Every normal adult knows how to beget a baby, but comparatively few men and women know how to bring up a child properly. Many a person who had little trouble in achieving motherhood or fatherhood finds himself at a loss when it comes to training an offspring to fit into the culture pattern of his society. Yet we persist in assuming that all parents are suited for raising their youngsters. There is a curious contradiction in the current American system that insists on teaching the biological facts of sexual reproduction (which requires a minimum of knowledge and skill) to prospective parents, but which tends to take for granted the cultural implications of parenthood that require a great deal of highly specialized knowledge and skill.

## E. AMERICAN SCIENCE, RELIGION, AND PATRIOTISM

Every student of modern American culture is struck by the lack of reliance on religion. Even where the number of steady churchgoers is high, there is a tendency to attribute the fact to various causes, but not to a deep-rooted conviction that help can be obtained from the supernatural. Unquestionably, a good part of the reason for this situation lies in the high development of science. Where controlled causation by human beings can be demonstrated there is not much need to seek supernatural assistance. With few exceptions scientists of one sort or another, rather than priests, are called upon for help when people fall ill, crops fail, animals sicken, or mentalities break down. True reliance on religion is most manifest in fields like international tensions where scientists are, at present, most helpless. Until recent years man had little prospect of regulating the weather, and prayers for relief from bad conditions were his only recourse. Today the picture in America is changing. Science is still uncertain about methods of producing rain or sunshine, but one does not have to be very bold to predict that in the near future the regulation of rainfall will move into the sphere of controlled causation, and when it does man's reliance on the supernatural will decrease still further. A preview of this situation has already been given. Tribes in the Southwestern United States, whose men formerly prayed and danced for rain, no longer hold these ceremonies now that they can get ample water by turning a faucet. Emotional and other satisfactions may continue to be sought from religious exercises, but in practical matters the rise of scientific knowledge will unfailingly result in a shrinking reliance on supernaturalism.

Another interesting aspect of religion in America is its close connection with patriotism. Two types of loyalty are to be found within this country. Either Americans belong to a tightly-bound international religion which takes precedence, in some matters, over national allegiance (Fig. 131 B); or else they maintain national loyalties despite differing religious faiths (Fig. 131 C). Neither of these situations provides as much cohesion as the double ties of patriotic and religious unity (Fig. 131 A), that are characteristic of tribal groupings. Interestingly enough, the modern totalitarian nations featuring Nazism, Fascism, or Communism have all tried to duplicate the twice-bound structures of primitive societies (Fig. 131A) by merging political loyalty with state worship, and by trying to deify the head of the state. The United States, having made separation of church and state a cardinal point of its Constitution, cannot, even if it would, revert to the primitive condition. Unable to use both religion and patriotism for holding American society together, we have tried to double the ties of loyalty (Fig. 131 D) in an effort to achieve the same effect. That is why in times of crisis, when the threat of social disintegration looms large, Americans increase the demands for effective patriotism by calling for more and more tokens of loyalty, through enforced oaths, investigations, exclusion of foreigners, and pledges of allegiance.

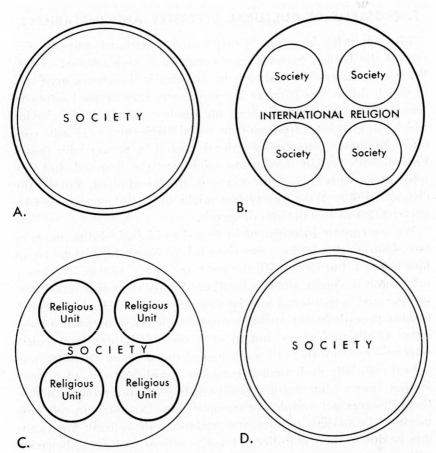

Fig. 131. Social and religious bonds. The light lines stand for the limits of social, national, or loyalty bonds; the dark ones for adherence to a common religion. A. The primitive condition. In nonliterate societies ties of religion tend to coincide with and reinforce the social bonds that hold members of a society together. The pattern so formed is structurally firmer than (B) or (C). B. Varying social units within a single, international religion. This represents the situation of those who adhere to a common faith but have differing political loyalties, as is true of French Catholics, American Catholics, Italian Catholics, Irish Catholics, and many others. C. Differing religions within a single social structure. A good example would include American Catholics, American Protestants, American Jews, and American Moslems. D. Double ties of loyalty. At present the Constitution prevents the United States from establishing a national religion. In times of crisis efforts are made to achieve the solidarity of A by doubling the patriotic bonds of loyalty that hold a national group together.

## F. PROBLEMS OF CULTURAL DIVERSITY AND INSTABILITY

Like any other large and widely scattered national unit, the citizens of the United States do not comprise a homogeneous society. What complicates the situation in America is the inconsistent way in which differences from an assumed norm may be used either to reward or punish. Yet, there is no absolute standard of behavior which can guarantee freedom from social displeasure to all who conform. In upper class circles around Boston, a person who speaks English with Italian intonations might well be despised, but one who speaks with an English accent might be admired. But in any class of Middle West society fun might be poked at anyone who affected British mannerisms of speech.

We are equally inconsistent in regard to biological differences of race. Caucasoids who have one-sixteenth of Negro blood may try to hide the fact, but those with the same amount of Indian blood may brag about it. Again, where a small percentage of Indian blood may be esteemed, a half-breed may be stigmatized. A similar lack of uniformity prevails in our attitudes toward religion. America is a Protestant Christian country, but in some districts Baptists are greatly respected and in others they are looked down upon. Divorces, too, are differentially evaluated. Among the Amish any talk of divorce arouses horror, but among Hollywood's top entertainers two or three divorces per couple are commonplace. No one can tell how much of the anxiety, tension, and restlessness of so many Americans may be due to their inability to know exactly what kind of behavior will win them the favor of their fellow-men.

Lack of consistent cultural values may lead to very tragic consequences. Throughout most aspects of American life there runs a current of emphasis on speed. "Time is of the essence," the lawyers say; and our children are frequently admonished to hurry up, and not to waste time. Industrialists build automobiles capable of going faster and faster, and communities compete in building roads suitable for greater speeds. Yet, overtly, we are reluctant to admit that high speeds are responsible for so many traffic fatalities. Recently, a bright young woman who had survived the crash of a speeding car that had killed some of her companions, was asked by a judge why she had consented to go on what was sure to be a wild ride. "I like speed," she replied simply. No doubt the judge was so shocked that he failed to give the young woman credit for being honestly consistent.

Another outstanding problem of American society, related to the lack of fixed standards, is the rapidity with which cultural values change. A social sub-group which has adjusted itself to one set of cultural values is disorganized and bewildered during any period of transition. Children of immigrants, who reject the ideas of right and wrong that their parents brought from a foreign country, are apt to feel uneasy until they have absorbed the values of American culture. Much the same applies to the native-born. When the Lynds visited Muncie during the boom years of the mid-1920's, they found the populace firmly believing in the traditional American values of rewards for hard work, the difficulty of keeping a good man down, and the notion that anyone who really wanted to work could find a job. About ten years later, when the Lynds came back to Muncie in a time of economic depression, they found the populace upset and in a state of transition.[9] They were in the process of being forced to give up their old system of values, but they were not yet ready to accept a new set of principles. So, the Lynds found such incongruities as people standing in line to cash government checks on which their very lives depended, yet cursing the government for sponsoring work projects.

Equalization of women's status has also led to a change of values. Not many generations ago, an American woman was not supposed to have a career outside the home, nor to receive much formal schooling. In keeping with the situation high value was attached to being a good mother and housekeeper. Women took pride in keeping their children neat and their houses spic and span, and got much pleasure from being praised for their efforts. Nowadays, mechanical implements are capable of taking so much drudgery out of a housewife's duties that she is more apt to have extra time for outside work.[10] It is considered old-fashioned for a woman to have no interests outside her home and family. Social rewards go to those who play the most active parts in higher education and community affairs, or who demonstrate the greatest skill in business or politics. After all, it is hardly to be expected that a young woman with a Ph.D. degree in

[9] R. S. and H. M. Lynd, *Middletown in Transition*, New York, 1937.

[10] Reliance on servants may have been equally or even more helpfully effective in reducing a housewife's duties in times past, but mechanical appliances are much more readily available to all classes of American society than servants ever were.

astrophysics will regard keeping her children neat as her chief mission in life. The American public is not yet prepared to elect a female as President of the United States, but the number of women holding important federal offices has increased markedly in recent years; and at the last nominating convention of the Republican party a feminine candidate for President was named, albeit none too seriously. With the highest honors being won in activities outside the home, American women cannot be blamed for refusing to restrict their talents to the lowly valued tasks of keeping house and children spotlessly clean.

Transitions from one pattern of values to another are just as upsetting to individuals as they are to groups. A child who has been taught to observe one set of standards up to a given age cannot, without some difficulty, accept a different set of values on short notice. Not enough attention has been directed to this problem. We are naive if we think that an American girl who has been taught to cherish her virginity and to resist the advances of all men for twenty years or so, can without uneasiness give herself to a man one night later, simply because she has been legally married to him that day. We know too little about the control of social relationships to suggest practical remedies for removing trouble spots, but American society will continue to suffer disturbances until we do learn, at least, how to move smoothly from one group of cultural values to another. Rapidity of culture change is a striking phenomenon of the whole modern world; and all children are likely to be faced with the problem of being trained for one set of values in infancy, only to be forced to live out their adult lives by other standards.

## Selected References

Chapple, Eliot D., "Applied Anthropology in Industry," *Anthropology Today* (A. L. Kroeber, ed.), Chicago, 1953, pp. 819-831.

———, and Arensberg, Conrad M., "Measuring Human Relations: An Introduction to the Study of the Interaction of Individuals," *Genetic Psychology Monographs,* No. 22, 1940.

Davis, Allison, *et al., Deep South: A Social Anthropological Study of Caste and Class,* Chicago, 1941.

Kluckhohn, Clyde, *Mirror for Man,* New York, 1949, chap. 9.

Lynd, Robert S., and Helen M., *Middletown: A Study of American Culture,* New York, 1929.

———, *Middletown in Transition,* New York, 1937.

Mead, Margaret, *And Keep Your Powder Dry,* New York, 1942.

Roethlisberger, F. J., and Dickson, W. J., *Management and the Worker,* Cambridge, 1939.

Warner, W. L., *et al., Yankee City Series,* New Haven, 1941 ff.

———, *American Life: Dream and Reality,* Chicago, 1953.

West, James, *Plainville, U.S.A.,* New York, 1945.

CHAPTER 27

# Retrospect and Prospect

## A. A BACKWARD GLANCE AT THE SCIENCE OF MAN

Throughout the last century an impressive amount of work has been done in all branches of anthropology. When a massive stockpile of knowledge had been accumulated, an unfailing law of cultural growth went into effect and an increasing number of specialists arose. Much is to be gained from such a development, for specialists always refine existing techniques and learn to use them in a way that brings to light many previously unsuspected facts, and makes possible fresh interpretations of data and the formulation of new hypotheses and theories. Counterbalancing the advantages is the great danger of disintegration resulting from the threatened separation of parts that were once found together. As is true of so many other sciences, anthropology is faced with the possibility of fragmentation or dismemberment. Already there are archeologists and ethnologists who know little of each other's work, and physical anthropologists who cannot understand an essay on primitive linguistics. This book is based on the conviction that it is not yet too late to demonstrate that all segments of the science of man belong together and contribute to a total understanding of the human species and its behavior.

No matter from which direction one chooses to approach the study of anthropology it soon becomes apparent that the thing called culture cannot exist without mankind. No other animal can develop it, live by it, or maintain its existence by transmitting it through education from one generation to another. It is true that for purposes of certain theoretical analyses one can separate culture from its carriers, but this does not apply to the study of its origins. There is no way of understanding how culture began unless one finds out the ways in which the biology of *Homo sapiens* differs from that of other animals who are devoid of culture. And since man did not come by his body suddenly, it becomes necessary to examine the process of evolution by means of which the human form acquired its unique characteristics. Most of the biological material in this text has been included with a view to clarifying the steps by which man came to have a distinctive body, one capable of devising and continuing culture. Once that stage was reached, we find mankind dividing into a number of stocks and races, every one of which is equally capable of symbolic cultural behavior. As far as is known, *Homo sapiens,* in spite of its diversity of forms, is truly a single species within which interbreeding may take place without biologically harmful consequences. All races, whether supposedly pure or admittedly mixed, have turned their backs on exclusively biological methods of living, have designed patterns of biocultural behavior, and have shown themselves capable of absorbing one another's forms of culture.

Having brought the story of man to the point where culture begins, we next took up the record of cultural progress through time. Archeologists have been able to prove that after a painfully slow start in the Old Stone Age, there was a gradual speeding up of new developments in the Middle Stone Age, followed by rapid acceleration, which became the rule throughout the Metal Ages and has continued into our own day. Not until cultural progress had matured over many millennia did it reach a stage where it could provide mankind with an alternative to biological behavior. As cultural devices became more and more fitted for coping with life, man came to rely on them increasingly, sometimes to supplement his biology and, occasionally, to take its place. Just the same, man has had to continue obeying the biological imperatives. There have been times when men took pride in claiming that they had triumphed over their physical bodies and animal natures, but the facts reveal that throughout all stages of history people continued to breathe, eat, digest, excrete, and reproduce. However, human beings everywhere have chosen to convert these activities from biological to biocultural processes. This they did by introducing arbitrary cultural values which called for the modification of actions that have remained entirely biological among all other creatures.

While archeologists can discover a great deal about past forms of culture, they are prevented by the very nature of their objectives from learning much about the workings of biocultural behavior. To find out about this important aspect of human life it was necessary to turn to the findings of cultural anthropologists. After many facts had been gathered from primitive societies throughout the world, comparative ethnological analyses revealed that beneath a bewildering profusion of differing details a universal pattern could be discerned. In the course of time it was found that most of the features of each society's design for group living fell into a configuration that could be expressed as a triangle. It was also found that the various segments of the triangle were tightly integrated, and that the entire figure might be said to have a distinctive slant or emphasis. Once this doctrine gained acceptance, ethnologists branched out into various directions. A number continued to visit primitive societies yet unknown to science, and to describe their patterns of culture; some concentrated on the tasks of studying how cultural configurations were held together, taught, and learned; others looked into the consequences which demands for conformity to cultural values had on the personalities of individuals; and still others began to transfer ethnological techniques from the investigation of small, homogeneous, primitive tribes to large, heterogeneous, literate societies, particularly in the United States.

Much understanding of the nature of man, society, and culture has resulted from the combined efforts of anthropologists. One might think that they have attacked the problems of *Homo sapiens* and his behavior from every conceivable angle, but something remains to be said of an approach that has not yet been discussed.

## B. WHEN CULTURES MEET

Attention has already been called to the fact that in the interests of some kinds of analyses it may be legitimate to treat patterns of biocultural behavior as if they had an existence of their own. It is from this point of view that the present section is written. Cultural configurations are most distinctive when they are formed by isolated communities. As long as means of transportation and communication were poorly developed, many tribes regularly lived apart from all neighbors and established individual, localized ways of life. When facilities for transport and communication reached their present efficiency, the chances for living in isolation became less and less. At present there is hardly any society which has not felt the impact of a culture different from its own. To the process of the intermingling of cultures the name, **acculturation,** has been given,[1] and while the term can be used for the whole or partial mixture of any different ways of life, it is commonly applied to the study of the influence of a Euro-American culture on that of a nonliterate, relatively isolated group.

The most obvious approach to research in acculturation is for an observer to list the kinds and numbers of recognizably foreign objects, such as cast-iron stoves or sewing machines, to be found in a primitive society. A survey of this sort, considered by itself, has only superficial value; but it can afford a basis for studying the history of culture contacts and the nature of diffusion. Reports of acculturation gain in value as they contribute to an understanding of cultural processes. Ethnologists have begun to examine such dynamic aspects as the motives which may influence adaptation of some new items and rejection of others. They are also inquiring into the ways that strange features are modified or left intact, and how they are fitted into the native culture pattern. Other valuable results come from a study of the degree of compulsion that might have forced peoples to accept a foreign trait against their will, and from an analysis of the effects of something borrowed on persons of different sex, age, occupation, or social standing.

A few rules of general cultural behavior have already emerged from acculturational investigations, broadly considered. Unless there is a great deal of force involved, a receiving society is likely to accept

[1] M. J. Herskovits, *Acculturation*, New York, 1938.

only such items as fill a conscious need, particularly if they can be interpreted as mere modifications of existing traits. Most readily borrowed are objects of material culture, whose use will result in a great saving of time and human muscular energy. Nonliterate people are rarely articulate about their motives for borrowing, but even a simple list of Euro-American things accepted by a number of primitive groups confirms such a conclusion. Metal tools and weapons seldom fail to supplant similar implements of stone or wood, especially if their use does not require long training. Also, manufactured garments can always be counted on to replace home-made clothes. Women are more likely than men to cling to native forms of dress, and religious personages are even more conservative. For the most part, though, store-bought clothing soon becomes the rule for those who have sufficient money. The acceptance of new material traits cannot be considered apart from the degree of success with which individual natives enter into the money economy of the Euro-Americans with whom they have contact.

Non-material traits are more likely to meet with widespread resistance. Nevertheless, as was brought out in the treatment of the cotton gin, even the acceptance of a purely technological trait is likely to alter a people's social and religious structure. Realization of this fact, though usually implicit rather than explicit, lies behind the refusal of many "backward" nations to accept offers of material assistance from the United States. In the non-material realm, Euro-American forms of religion are apt to be initially rejected, although they may later be accepted through missionary and other pressures. Anthropologists have found Christianity to be surprisingly flexible. Sometimes it is deliberately molded to primitive shape by evangelists who hope by this means to gain ready converts; and sometimes it is given strange twists through the ignorance of native practitioners.

One of the areas of greatest resistance is in the field of speech. Many a people who seem to be thoroughly acculturated in other respects, continue to speak their native tongue in addition to a Euro-American language. At the present time the Araucanian Indians are practically indistinguishable from their nearby Chilean neighbors in physical appearance, dress, occupations, and the use of material objects, but every person who considers himself an Indian speaks Araucanian at home. In another part of the world the Japanese provide an outstanding example of the same phenomenon. Throughout the course of centuries they borrowed all sorts of cultural items from China. They even began their system of writing by employing Chinese characters as a basis. Still, at no time did spoken Chinese offer the slightest challenge to the continued use of Japanese speech.

As might be expected, a strong group seeks to impose its system of cultural values on a weaker one. If the difference of strength is very marked the latter cannot resist; and if the stronger society appears to be better adjusted and more prosperous, the weaker one may show eagerness to accept the other's ideas. But a value system does not exist apart from an entire configuration of culture, and it is often impossible for the imitating society to take over the complete way of life of the dominant people. There must then follow a sad period of transition, during which the weaker society continues to lose faith in its own traditional values, but lacks the means to adopt the more desirable ones. This fate befell most North American Indian tribes, and this was the situation in which the Araucanian Indians found themselves after they had been pacified and forced to live as farmers on reservations. The blow fell with unequal strength on the males. Under their former culture men normally gained prestige as warriors, and farming was left principally to women. Since their conquest Araucanian men have been badly dispirited. They can no longer win esteem on the battlefield, and their old system of values gave little masculine honor to skill in farming. Caught in a state of transition, the men incline to laziness and often take refuge in drunkenness.[2]

## C. LOOKING FORWARD

An anthropologist would be unfaithful to his convictions if he feared to look ahead and make predictions. For all that has already been accomplished in the science of man, a great deal more remains to be done. If the activities of *Homo sapiens* are to be directed to socially desirable objectives for all mankind, human behavior must be brought into the range of controlled causation. Before this can be done greater knowledge will have to be obtained in several critical areas.

[2] M. Titiev, "Araucanian Culture in Transition," *Occasional Contributions from the Museum of Anthropology*, Ann Arbor, No. 15, 1951, pp. 142-52.

Future research will have to be directed to the problem of cultural origins. If it be true that man alone is capable of symbolic behavior, what is there in his bio-physico-chemical composition that sets him apart from all other animals? At the moment we are forced to postulate that algebraic mentality is somehow a function of increased brain size. If that is so, what is the threshold below which symbolization is impossible? If other factors are involved, what are they and how do they function? And when the matter of origins has been settled, we would still like to know precisely why so many cultural values run counter to biological necessities. Why should people everywhere, in varying degree, make efforts to conceal biological activities involving excretion or sexual relations? Why should an American who has dined well feel ashamed if someone tells him he has crumbs on his lips? Why do members of many societies feel uneasy about eating in full view of others? It is simple enough to rationalize some of these attitudes, as by postulating that the odors of stale urine or fresh feces are offensive, but there is no universal agreement on what constitutes a bad smell, and numerous tribes are indifferent about handling the waste products of the human body. Navaho young women show no distaste when scraping fecal material from garments; yet they do not defecate in their living quarters; and in recent years Hopi men drank urine as medicine and used it for fixing dyes, but never did they urinate indoors after infancy.

Suppose we by-pass the question of origins and simply assume that all normal humans have the capacity to symbolize, and that all societies formulate biocultural standards for living together. We are then faced with a new set of questions which future investigators must try to answer. How does a configuration of culture acquire an emphasis, Dionysian or Apollonian, which nearly resembles the personality structures of certain kinds of individuals? What is the exact nature of the process of interiorization? What happens to a child's inherited biological structure as it learns to conform to the cultural values of its society? In other words, what price does an individual pay for adjusting to biocultural norms, particularly if they run counter to his inborn biology? Then again, basic problems await solution in respect to group behavior. Why are some aspects of a foreign culture eagerly accepted, while others are stubbornly resisted? Why are people more willing to develop the new motor habits required for the use of borrowed material objects than they are to acquire new forms of speech? More basic still would be satisfactory answers to the questions of why mankind in general has preferred cultural over biological adjustments, and why the species has consistently favored the saving of time and the conservation of human muscular energy. Partial explanations for some of these matters are already available, but a great deal that is now uncertain will have to be clarified by future research workers.

An area that is badly in need of new approaches and further work is the field of cultural dynamics. We know that there are forces making for stabilization and equilibrium, and others that bring about changes, but when it comes to understanding their natures and workings social scientists are as badly off as were students of biological evolution before there was any knowledge of genetics. A force may be described as a potential for inducing change, and every human society's way of life is subject to such pressures, yet pitifully little is known about how to control change in the realm of culture. Individuals must be prepared to accept varying sets of cultural values as they grow from infancy to adulthood and as they enter on changed marital or occupational statuses. Societies must also be ready for change now that isolation is virtually impossible. Any investigation of a society in transition ought to throw light on some characteristics of cultural dynamics. As in any study of dynamics, there should be an analysis of a balance of forces, in this case forces of sociocultural change versus forces of inertia.

Anthropologists of the future will have to concern themselves with still another aspect of dynamics, the relations of cultural to biological forces. These may most readily be seen operating in the field of man's interplay with his physical environment. The needs for oxygen, food, drink, and shelter from the elements originate as biological imperatives, but since man cannot satisfy them with the attributes of his own body, the biological needs stimulate cultural responses, and so serve as forces of culture. These forces press upon every society that seeks to survive, and express themselves in the form of particular cultural adjustments or institutions. At present too many social scientists are concerned with institutions and pay scant attention to the forces that bring them into being. It is a little like trying to understand the workings of electric light bulbs without knowing anything about electricity. Man's relations to man likewise consist of institutions, like marriage or child-raising, that may be interpreted as cultural responses to biological forces; but for the present man's dealings with the supernatural can seldom be directly connected with biology, and must be attributed largely to sociocultural pressures. Once anthropologists begin to deal with basic forces rather than institutions, they will be in a better position to formulate scientific laws on the basis of which sound predictions can be made.

## D. CONCLUSION

There are many reasons why a book of this kind should end on a note of optimism. Modern anthropology is less than a century old, has attempted to cover a diversified range of topics, and has dealt with a tremendously long span of time, but it has received professional attention from a relatively small number of scholars. Nevertheless, it has aroused great interest and has had a valuable catalytic effect on other disciplines devoted to an understanding of man. Above all, modern anthropologists have proved that it is possible for human beings to study their fellow men dispassionately, and have shown that no generalizations about mankind are valid unless the entire species is taken into account. No longer can a few men and women of a single type, from a single region, or possessed of a single way of life, be regarded as the equivalent of *Homo sapiens*.

The anthropological view of man has served to call into question the claims of all those who would glorify one stock or race at the expense of another. Biological differences among various groups of mankind have been more closely investigated by physical anthropologists than by any other scientists, and their conclusions are soundly based and positive. No race is biologically better than any other; mixture between stocks or races is not biologically harmful; there are no sure differences of mental potential; no society of humans lives on a purely biological "animal" level; and any group of mankind has the capacity to learn any other unit's patterns of biocultural behavior.

When it comes to the study of culture, anthropologists have again made some outstanding contributions. Thanks to the painstaking work of archeologists, they have been able to show the great antiquity of human efforts to develop culture, the various stages through which it has passed, and the different combinations of traits that may develop in various localities. At the same time they have provided evidence for the establishment of universal laws of culture growth that over-ride regional considerations. What archeologists dealing with extinct peoples and cultures could not do, ethnologists have undertaken. They have shown how human beings as living organisms interact with their cultures, and they have worked out the basic configurations that patterned ways of life seem to take in all societies. Some ethnologists have stressed the effects that culture patterns exert on individual personalities, and others have emphasized the ways in which culture patterns are integrated and subjected to forces of change. Ethnological techniques for the study of primitive communities and their ways of life have been found to be applicable to analyses of modern societies or such subdivisions as industrial organizations in the United States.

Finally, several aspects of cultural anthropology deserve special mention. To the analysis of culture patterns ethnologists have brought the same objective viewpoint that prevails among physical anthropologists. They insist that ways of life must be studied as wholes, wherein each part is integrated with the others. They have refused to measure primitive cultures against any preconceived notions of right and wrong, good or bad. There was a time when the anthropological insistence on relativism threatened to do away with all absolute concepts such as normality; but quite recently, on the basis of wider knowledge of universal forms of behavior, new absolute standards are being formulated. As a last word, anthropologists have found no barriers, in theory, to the establishment of a pattern of culture for human beings everywhere. Whenever the peoples of the world demand it, anthropologists will help to fashion a diversified way of life that will suit the needs of all mankind.

SELECTED REFERENCES

Beals, Ralph, "Acculturation," *Anthropology Today* (A. L. Kroeber, ed.), Chicago, 1953, pp. 621-641.
———, "Urbanism, Urbanization, and Acculturation," *American Anthropologist,* New Series, Vol. 53, 1951, pp. 1-10.
Boas, Franz, *Anthropology and Modern Life,* New York, 1932.
Herskovits, Melville J., *et al., Acculturation: The Study of Culture Contact,* New York, 1938.
Linton, Ralph, *Acculturation in Seven North American Indian Tribes,* New York, 1940.

———, "Present World Conditions in Cultural Perspective," *The Science of Man in the World Crisis* (R. Linton, ed.), New York, 1945, pp. 201-221.

Malinowski, Bronislaw, *The Dynamics of Culture Change*, New Haven, 1945.

Mead, Margaret, *The Changing Culture of an Indian Tribe*, New York, 1932.

Redfield, Robert, *A Village that Chose Progress: Chan Kom Revisited*, Chicago, 1950.

Titiev, Mischa, "Araucanian Culture in Transition," *Occasional Contributions from the Museum of Anthropology*, University of Michigan, No. 15, Ann Arbor, 1951.

# Index

# Index

EUROPE

Danube

BLACK SEA

*Troy ASIA MINOR TURKEY

GREECE

ANATOLIA

Mycenae *

CRETE

CYPRUS

MEDITERRANEAN SEA

Gt. Pyramid
* ●Cairo

SINAI

EGYPT

Nile

RE

THE EASTERN MEDITERRANEAN Z